THEORY OF FUNCTIONS

THEORY OF
FUNCTIONS

OF A

COMPLEX VARIABLE

BY

C. CARATHEODORY

PROFESSOR, UNIVERSITY OF MUNICH

TRANSLATED BY

F. STEINHARDT

VOLUME TWO

Second English Edition

CHELSEA PUBLISHING COMPANY
NEW YORK

TRANSLATOR'S PREFACE

In this translation of the second volume of Carathéodory's *Funktiontheorie*, the translator has again aimed at a faithful rendering of the original text, except for the elimination of a number of misprints and minor errors.

For the reader who may have bypassed the chapter on Inversion Geometry in Volume I on a first reading, or in the customary first course on Complex Variables, it will be advantageous to study that chapter before going too far in the present volume.

F. Steinhardt

EDITOR'S PREFACE

As has already been mentioned in the preface to the first volume, the author of this book lived to see the whole work through the press, so that the text of neither volume required any changes or additions by the editor that might otherwise have been needed. The division of the work into two volumes was ascribed, in the above-mentioned preface, to certain extraneous reasons; nevertheless, we might add here that the second volume, being devoted to carrying the subject on further, is in part devoted to more recent results and problems—to some, in fact, that owe a good measure of their exposition and development to Carathéodory himself; the present volume requires, correspondingly, somewhat more from the reader than does the first. In keeping with the character of the whole work, the second volume stresses the geometric point of view even more than does the first. Considerations of a Weierstrassian cast are absent.

The present volume contains Parts Six and Seven of the entire work. The first of these two parts is devoted to the foundations of Geometric Function Theory, its three chapters dealing with bounded functions and with conformal mapping. Among the topics treated here, we mention G. Pick's beautiful interpretation of Schwarz's Lemma and a rather detailed account of the theory of the angular derivative. For the important theorem of Fatou on the boundary values of bounded functions, Carathéodory has chosen his own proof, which dates back to the year 1912.

After a brief study of the elementary mappings, the exposition of the theory of conformal mapping begins with the Riemann Mapping Theorem, which is the core of the whole theory. The author gives a proof that applies right off to bounded regions of any connectivity, proving the existence of the mapping function by means of a well-known iteration method. He then proceeds on the basis of this central theorem to study the group of congruence transformations. For reasons given by the author in his preface (see Vol. I, p. viii), no systematic account is given of the theory of the universal covering surface nor of the general theory of Riemann surfaces. The same goes for the general theory of uniformization. However, the student is shown the construction of a specific covering surface, and he acquires an important tool for uniformization theory in studying the sections that deal with the simultaneous mapping of nested annular regions. The mapping of the frontier is treated in detail, but Carathéodory does not include here the more complicated investigations of the frontier, nor his theory of prime ends. The proof of the Schwarz

Reflection Principle is given under quite general conditions and nonetheless remains very simple; the boundary values are only assumed to be real, not necessarily continuous.

The four chapters of the seventh and last part deal with the triangle functions and Picard's theorems. A solid foundation for the study of these functions requires some elementary facts about functions of several variables and differential equations. These facts are derived in the first chapter. This is followed by a detailed exposition of the hypergeometric differential equation. There are tables summarizing all of the fundamental solutions of this equation and giving the exceptional cases as well as the connecting formulas. This provides the student with all of the analytic tools required for the mapping of circular-arc triangles. The third chapter gives a geometric study of certain special cases, namely of the Schwarz triangle nets and the modular configuration. The fourth chapter gives the most important theorems on the exceptional values of meromorphic functions. Carathéodory begins this chapter with Landau's theorem, deriving from it the theorems of Picard and Schottky. Some more recent results on the essential singularities of meromorphic functions form the conclusion of the work.

Munich, May 1950

L. Weigand

CONTENTS

Part Six

FOUNDATIONS OF GEOMETRIC FUNCTION THEORY

Part Seven
THE TRIANGLE FUNCTIONS AND PICARD'S THEOREM

FOUNDATIONS OF GEOMETRIC
FUNCTION THEORY

CHAPTER ONE

BOUNDED FUNCTIONS

Functions of Bound One (§ 281)

281. Let $f(z)$ be a regular analytic function defined in some bounded region G. If $|f(z)| \leqq 1$ holds true at every point of this region, we shall say that $f(z)$ is a *function of bound one in G*. For $f(z)$ to be of bound one in G, it is necessary and sufficient that the moduli of all of the boundary values of $f(z)$ in G be less than or equal to unity.

We shall prove the following result, which is due to Lindelöf: If $f(z)$ is known to be bounded in G, then to conclude that $f(z)$ is of bound one in G it suffices to establish the above condition at all but a finite number of points $\zeta_1, \ldots, \zeta_p$ of the frontier of G.

To prove this, we first note that if ϱ stands for the diameter of the region G, then the functions

$$\frac{\zeta_j - z}{\varrho} \qquad\qquad (j = 1, \ldots, p)$$

are of bound one in G. Hence so is the function

$$\varphi_\varepsilon(z) = \prod_{j=1}^{p} \left(\frac{\zeta_j - z}{\varrho} \right)^\varepsilon, \tag{281.1}$$

where $\varepsilon > 0$ is arbitrary. Now let $f(z)$ be any analytic function that is bounded in G and whose boundary values at all of the frontier points of G, with the possible exception of the ζ_j, are $\leqq 1$ in modulus. If we set

$$f_\varepsilon(z) = f(z)\, \varphi_\varepsilon(z), \tag{281.2}$$

then all of the boundary values of the function $f_\varepsilon(z)$, including those at the points ζ_j, are $\leqq 1$ in modulus, so that the function $f_\varepsilon(z)$ is of bound one in G for every (positive) value of ε. But at every interior point z of G, we have

$$f(z) = \lim_{\varepsilon = 0} f_\varepsilon(z),$$

which proves that $|f(z)| \leqq 1$ throughout G.

Unit Functions (§§ 282-285)

282. We shall now consider, in particular, functions that are analytic and of bound one in the circular disc $|z| < 1$. Among these functions, those that are continuous and have modulus unity at every point of the boundary $|z| = 1$ of the disc play a special role. We shall call functions of this kind *unit functions*.

If $E(z)$ and $E^*(z)$ are any two unit functions, then it is clear that the functions $E(z)E^*(z)$ and $E(E^*(z))$ are likewise unit functions.

We are now in a position to generalize the argument that was used in § 140, Vol. I, p. 135, to prove Schwarz's Lemma. We note first that if $f(z)$ is a function of bound one in $|z| < 1$ that can be written in the form $f(z) = E(z) \cdot g(z)$, where $E(z)$ is a unit function and $g(z)$ is analytic in the disc $|z| < 1$, then all of the boundary values of $g(z)$ at the points of the circle $|z| = 1$ are ≤ 1 in modulus, so that $g(z)$ must itself be of bound one.

This fact is fundamental for the theory of bounded functions. In particular, if $f(z)$ itself is a unit function, then $g(z)$ must likewise be a unit function.

283. Next we shall see how all unit functions can be calculated explicitly. A non-constant unit function $E(z)$ must have at least one zero in $|z| < 1$, according to the criterion at the end of § 138, Vol. I, p. 135. On the other hand, since no point of the boundary $|z| = 1$ can be a point of accumulation of zeros, $E(z)$ has only a finite number of zeros $z_1, \ldots, z_n$, where the z_ν are n not necessarily distinct numbers. Now the expression

$$\prod_{\nu=1}^{n} \frac{z_\nu - z}{1 - \bar{z}_\nu z} \tag{283.1}$$

represents a unit function the zeros of which coincide with the zeros of $E(z)$; hence we may write

$$E(z) = g(z) \prod_{\nu=1}^{n} \frac{z_\nu - z}{1 - \bar{z}_\nu z}, \tag{283.2}$$

where $g(z)$, according to the preceding section, is a unit function without zeros and hence is a constant of modulus unity. It follows that every unit function is of the form

$$E_n(z) = e^{i\vartheta} \prod_{\nu=1}^{n} \frac{z_\nu - z}{1 - \bar{z}_\nu z} \tag{283.3}$$

and is therefore a rational function whose numerator and denominator are polynomials of degree n. We shall call a function $E_n(z)$ of this kind a *unit function of degree n*.

If a is any point of the interior of the unit circle and if $E_n(z)$ is a unit function of degree n, then the function

$$E_n^*(z) = \frac{a - E_n(z)}{1 - \bar{a}\, E_n(z)}$$

is likewise a unit function of degree n, since its numerator and denominator clearly do not have any zeros in common. Hence $E_n^*(z)$ has n zeros, provided that each zero is counted with its proper multiplicity. But these zeros are simply those points of the disc at which $E_n(z) = a$ holds true; thus every value a ($|a| < 1$) is assumed the same number of times by $E_n(z)$, namely n times.

284. The totality of unit functions is part of a normal family the limit functions of which are not necessarily unit functions, though they must be functions of bound one. Thus, for example, the sequence of unit functions $f_\nu(z) = z^\nu$, $\nu = 1, 2, \ldots$ converges to the constant zero.

We shall now assign to every function $f(z)$ of bound one in the disc $|z| < 1$ a sequence of unit functions $E_1(z), E_2(z), \ldots$ that converges to $f(z)$, where $E_n(z)$ is a unit function of degree n.

To this end, let

$$f(z) = a_0 + a_1 z + \cdots + a_n z^n + \cdots \qquad (284.1)$$

be the Taylor expansion of $f(z)$. We define a function $g(z)$ as follows, and obtain its Taylor expansion:

$$g(z) = \frac{a_0 - f(z)}{z\,(1 - \bar{a}_0 f(z))} = b_0 + b_1 z + \cdots + b_{n-1} z^{n-1} + \cdots. \qquad (284.2)$$

By § 282, the function $g(z)$ is itself of bound one in $|z| < 1$. Now if $g^*(z)$ is any function of bound one having $b_0, b_1, \ldots, b_{n-1}$ as the first n coefficients of its Taylor series, then

$$f^*(z) = \frac{a_0 - z\,g^*(z)}{1 - \bar{a}_0 z\,g^*(z)} \qquad (284.3)$$

is a function of bound one that has $a_0, a_1, \ldots, a_n$ as the first $(n + 1)$ coefficients of its Taylor series. Moreover, if $g^*(z)$ is a unit function then so is $f^*(z)$.

Now if we assume we had an algorithm for assigning to every function $f(z)$ of bound one a unit function $E_n(z)$ of degree n having $a_0, \ldots, a_{n-1}$ as the first n coefficients of its Taylor series, then by means of this same algorithm we could assign to the function $g(z)$ of bound one a unit function $E_n^*(z)$

whose Taylor series starts off with $b_0 + b_1 z + \cdots + b_{n-1} z^{n-1}$. Then the unit function

$$E_{n+1}(z) = \frac{a_0 - z\,E_n^*(z)}{1 - \bar{a}_0\,z\,E_n^*(z)} \tag{284.4}$$

would be a unit function $E_{n+1}(z)$ of degree $(n+1)$ belonging to $f(z)$. But since

$$E_1(z) = \frac{a_0 - z}{1 - \bar{a}_0 z}$$

is known, we can actually determine successively, by the method just described, all the $E_n(z)$ belonging to $f(z)$. By the theorem of § 211 (*cf.* Vol. I, p. 209) it then follows that

$$f(z) = \lim_{n=\infty} E_n(z) \tag{284.5}$$

holds at every interior point of the disc $|z| < 1$. In this representation of the functions of bound one, the approximating functions $E_n(z)$ play a role similar to that of the polynomials that are the partial sums of a power series, and for some problems the former are actually preferable to the latter.

285. Let $w = E(z)$ be a unit function whose derivative $E'(z)$ vanishes nowhere in the disc $|z| < 1$. Then by the monodromy theorem (*cf.* § 232, Vol. I, p. 238), we can calculate the inverse function $z = \varphi(w)$ in the disc $|w| < 1$, and see immediately that $\varphi(w)$ is of bound one and that its boundary values are all of modulus unity. Hence the unit function $w = E(z)$ represents a one-to-one mapping of the two discs $|z| < 1$ and $|w| < 1$ onto each other, from which it follows that $E(z)$ is a unit function of degree one (*cf.* § 283). We therefore have the following theorem: *If $E(z)$ is a unit function of degree higher than the first, then its derivative $E'(z)$ must have at least one zero in the disc $|z| < 1$.*

G. Pick's Theorem (§§ 286-289)

286. The properties of unit functions that have been developed in the preceding sections will now enable us to derive a large number of results, of which *Schwarz's Lemma* is merely a first example. We proceed to establish an invariant formulation of Schwarz's Lemma, as follows.

Let $f(z)$ be a function of bound one in the unit circle that assumes at $z = z_0$ the value w_0. If $f(z) \not\equiv 1$, we have the relation

$$\frac{w_0 - f(z)}{1 - \bar{w}_0 f(z)} = \frac{z_0 - z}{1 - \bar{z}_0 z}\, g(z), \tag{286.1}$$

where $g(z)$, by § 282 above, is itself of bound one. From this it follows that

$$\left| \frac{w_0 - f(z)}{1 - \bar{w}_0 f(z)} \right| \le \left| \frac{z_0 - z}{1 - \bar{z}_0 z} \right|, \tag{286.2}$$

or, if we make use of the concept of pseudo-chordal distance introduced in § 87, Vol. I, p. 82, that

$$\psi(w_0, w) \le \psi(z_0, z). \tag{286.3}$$

If we consider the two discs $|z| < 1$ and $|w| < 1$ as representing non-Euclidean planes, then the non-Euclidean distances $E_n(z_0, z)$ and $E_n(w_0, w)$ are given by the equations

$$\left. \begin{aligned} \psi(z_0, z) &= \text{tgh}\, \frac{1}{2} E_n(z_0, z) \\[2mm] \psi(w_0, w) &= \text{tgh}\, \frac{1}{2} E_n(w_0, w) \end{aligned} \right\} \tag{286.4}$$

(cf. § 65, Vol. I, p. 55). Since tgh u is a monotonically increasing function (cf. equation (243.6), Vol. I, p. 252), we can replace relation (286.3) by the following:

$$E_n(w_0, w) \le E_n(z_0, z). \tag{286.5}$$

This interpretation of Schwarz's Lemma is due to G. Pick, and may be expressed as follows:

Any function $w = f(z)$ of bound one maps the non-Euclidean plane $|z| < 1$ onto itself, or onto part of itself, in such a way that the non-Euclidean distance of two image points under the mapping never exceeds the non-Euclidean distance between their pre-images. If these two distances are equal for even one pair of image points and the corresponding pair of original points, then the mapping must be a non-Euclidean motion that leaves all distances invariant.

The last part of the theorem follows immediately from equation (286.1) if we set $g(z) \equiv e^{i\vartheta}$.

287. Pick's theorem enables us to find an upper bound for $|f(z)|$ at any point z of the disc $|z| < 1$. We note that

$$\psi(0, w) = |w|, \quad \psi(0, w_0) = |w_0|, \quad \psi(w_0, w) \le \psi(z_0, z). \tag{287.1}$$

Hence if we set

$$|w| = \text{tgh}\, \frac{\omega}{2}, \quad |w_0| = \text{tgh}\, \frac{\omega_0}{2}, \quad \psi(z_0, z) = \text{tgh}\, \frac{\zeta}{2},$$

then we have—observing that the triangle inequality holds in non-Euclidean geometry, by (73.10), Vol. I, p. 64—

$$\omega \leq \omega_0 + E_n(w_0, w) \leq \omega_0 + \zeta \tag{287.2}$$

and hence

$$|w| \leq \operatorname{tgh} \frac{\omega_0 + \zeta}{2} = \frac{\operatorname{tgh} \omega_0/2 + \operatorname{tgh} \zeta/2}{1 + \operatorname{tgh} \omega_0/2 \operatorname{tgh} \zeta/2}.$$

This implies that

$$|f(z)| \leq \frac{|f(z_0)| + \psi(z_0, z)}{1 + |f(z_0)| \psi(z_0, z)} < 1. \tag{287.3}$$

This inequality can not be sharpened, since $f(z)$ can be chosen in such a way that, z_0 and z being given, the equality sign will hold in (287.3).

288. Let us consider the disc $|z| \leq r < 1$ interior to the unit circle, and any three points z_0, z_1, z_2 inside this disc. For any two of these points, say z_i and z_j, we have

$$E_n(z_i, z_j) \leq E_n(0, z_j) + E_n(0, z_i) < 2 E_n(0, r). \tag{288.1}$$

This implies (by § 87, Vol. I, p. 82) that

$$\psi(z_i, z_j) < \frac{2r}{1 + r^2} = h. \tag{288.2}$$

Now if $w = f(z)$ is any function of bound one, we may write

$$\psi(w_i, w) = \psi(z_i, z) |g_i(z)| \qquad (i = 1, 2, 3), \tag{288.3}$$

where the functions $g_i(z)$ are of bound one. We observe that by equations (288.3),

$$|g_0(z_1)| = |g_1(z_0)|$$

holds true and that therefore, by the result of the preceding section,

$$|g_1(z_2)| < \frac{|g_0(z_1)| + h}{1 + |g_0(z_1)| h} \tag{288.4}$$

holds. On the other hand,

$$|g_0(z_1)| < \frac{|g_0(z_0)| + h}{1 + |g_0(z_0)| h}. \tag{288.5}$$

Hence if $|g_0(z_0)| = \alpha < 1$ and if we set $2h/(1 + h^2) = k$, it follows that

$$|g_1(z_2)| < \frac{\alpha + k}{1 + \alpha k} = \lambda(r) < 1. \tag{288.6}$$

We have thus proved the following theorem: *If $f(z)$ is a function of bound one other than a unit function of the first degree, then we can assign to every positive number $r < 1$ a positive number $\lambda(r) < 1$ which is such that for any two points z_1, z_2 of the disc $|z| < r$, the following relation holds:*

$$\psi(w_1, w_2) < \lambda(r)\, \psi(z_1, z_2). \tag{288.7}$$

289. Let $w = f(z)$ be a function of bound one in the disc $|z| < 1$ and assume also that $f(z)$ is neither a constant nor represents a non-Euclidean motion (cf. § 82, Vol. I, p. 76). Let γ_z be a (closed) arc of a rectifiable curve without double points in $|z| < 1$, and let us assume first that $w = f(z)$ maps this arc one-to-one onto a Jordan arc γ_w in the disc $|w| < 1$. By § 88, Vol. I, p. 83, the non-Euclidean length of a curve equals twice the least upper bound of the pseudo-chordal lengths of all the inscribed polygonal trains. Since γ_z is a closed point set, it lies in some disc $|z| \leqq r < 1$. Therefore the non-Euclidean length L_z of γ_z is finite, so that γ_z is rectifiable in the non-Euclidean metric as well. If π_w is a polygonal train inscribed in γ_w and if Π_w denotes the pseudo-chordal length of π_w, then the vertices of π_w are the images of the vertices of a corresponding train π_z inscribed in γ_z; the pseudo-chordal length of π_z we denote by Π_z. By the preceding section, we have

$$2\,\Pi_w < 2\,\lambda(r)\,\Pi_z \leqq \lambda(r)\,L_z. \tag{289.1}$$

Since this relation holds for all polygonal trains inscribed in γ_w, it follows that

$$L_w \leqq \lambda(r)\,L_z. \tag{289.2}$$

The assumption that γ_z and γ_w are one-to-one images of each other can be dispensed with, since any rectifiable curve γ_z contained in $|z| \leqq r$ can be decomposed into at most denumerably many arcs each of which can be mapped one-to-one onto an arc of γ_w. Thus we have the following theorem: *If $f(z)$ is a function of bound one in $|z| < 1$, then it maps every closed[1] rectifiable arc γ_z onto a similar arc γ_w in the disc $|w| < 1$, and the respective non-Euclidean lengths L_z and L_w of these arcs satisfy the relation*

$$L_w \leqq L_z. \tag{289.3}$$

The equality sign holds in (289.3) only if the mapping $w = f(z)$ represents a non-Euclidean motion.

---

[1] Closed as a *point set*.

The Derivative of a Bounded Function ($\S\S$ 290-291)

290. Equation (286.1) can be written in the form

$$\frac{w_0 - f(z)}{z_0 - z} = \frac{1 - \bar{w}_0 f(z)}{1 - \bar{z}_0 z} g(z). \qquad (290.1)$$

If we let z tend to z_0 in (290.1), we obtain

$$f'(z_0) = \frac{1 - |f(z_0)|^2}{1 - |z_0|^2} g(z_0). \qquad (290.2)$$

Hence unless $f(z)$ represents a non-Euclidean motion, we have at every point $|z|$ of the interior of the unit circle that

$$|f'(z)| < \frac{1 - |f(z)|^2}{1 - |z|^2} \leqq \frac{1}{1 - |z|^2}. \qquad (290.3)$$

We have thus obtained the following theorem: *The modulus of the derivative of a function of bound one in $|z| < 1$ always satisfies*

$$|f'(z)| \leqq \frac{1 - |f(z)|^2}{1 - |z|^2}, \qquad (290.4)$$

and the equality sign holds only in the case of a non-Euclidean motion. In particular, in the disc $|z| \leqq r < 1$ we have in any case that

$$|f'(z)| \leqq \frac{1}{1 - r^2}. \qquad (290.5)$$

These bounds are the best bounds possible.

The result of the preceding section can be derived, in the case of a continuously differentiable arc γ_z, directly from relation (290.4), since (290.4) then implies that

$$\int_{\gamma_w} \frac{|dw|}{1 - |w|^2} \leqq \int_{\gamma_z} \frac{|dz|}{1 - |z|^2}, \qquad (290.6)$$

where the integrands represent the differentials of the respective non-Euclidean arc lengths.

Remark. From what has just been said, it follows that relation (290.6) can be used to derive once more Pick's theorem of $\S$ 286 above.

291. We shall next obtain a bound for $|f'(z)|$ under the additional assumption that $f(z)$ vanishes at $z = 0$. From this we obtain first, setting $z = 0$ in (290.1), that

$$w_0 = z_0\, g(0). \tag{291.1}$$

Furthermore, setting $|g(0)| = a$ we obtain from formula (287.3) the relation

$$|g(z_0)| \leqq \frac{a + |z_0|}{1 + a\,|z_0|}. \tag{291.2}$$

If we substitute these two results into (290.2), we find that

$$|f'(z_0)| \leqq \frac{(1 - a^2\,|z_0|^2)\,(a + |z_0|)}{(1 - |z_0|^2)\,(1 + a\,|z_0|)} = \frac{(1 - a\,|z_0|)\,(a + |z_0|)}{1 - |z_0|^2}. \tag{291.3}$$

The numerator of the right-hand side of this inequality increases monotonically in a up to the point

$$a_0 = \frac{1 - |z_0|^2}{2\,|z_0|}. \tag{291.4}$$

For sufficiently small values of $|z_0|$, more precisely for $|z_0| \leqq \sqrt{2} - 1$, we have $a_0 \geqq 1$, and the maximum of the right-hand side of (291.3) is obtained by setting $a = 1$. In this case,

$$|f'(z_0)| \leqq 1$$

holds. But if $|z_0| > \sqrt{2} - 1$, then we must set

$$a = a_0 = \frac{1 - |z_0|^2}{2\,|z_0|}$$

in order to obtain an upper bound for $|f'(z_0)|$. We have thus obtained the following theorem, which is due to Dieudonné:

If $f(z)$ is a function of bound one in $|z| < 1$ that vanishes at $z = 0$, then

$$|f'(z)| \leqq 1 \quad or \quad |f'(z)| \leqq \frac{(1 + |z|^2)^2}{4\,|z|\,(1 - |z|^2)}, \tag{291.5}$$

according to whether $|z| \leqq \sqrt{2} - 1 = 0.4142$ or $|z| > \sqrt{2} - 1$. These bounds are the best bounds possible.

The equality sign holds in the first case only if $g(z) \equiv 1$. In the second case it holds, as is easy to see, only if $g(z)$ is a unit function of degree one and $f(z)$ a unit function of degree two of the form

$$f(z) = e^{i\vartheta}\, z\, \frac{h + z}{1 + h\,z}. \tag{291.6}$$

The determination of h can easily be reduced to the case of real w_0 and z_0. In this case,

$$\frac{1 - z_0^2}{2\,z_0} = a = \frac{f(z_0)}{z_0} = \frac{h + z_0}{.1 + h\,z_0},$$

whence

$$h = \frac{1 - 3\,z_0^2}{z_0(1 + z_0^2)}.\tag{291.7}$$

It is remarkable that the upper bound for $|f'(z)|$ in the disc $|z| < 1$ is continuous, to be sure, but not analytic.

A Distortion Theorem (§ 292)

292. Let $f(z)$ be a function of bound one in $|z| < 1$ for which

$$f'(0) = b = 1 - \varepsilon^2$$

holds, where $\varepsilon \geq 0$. If $\varepsilon = 0$, then the results of § 290 above show that $f(z) = z$. We shall prove that in every disc $|z| < r < 1$, the functions of the set just described converge uniformly to z as ε tends to zero.

To this end, we set $f(0) = a$ and

$$\frac{a - f(z)}{1 - \bar{a}\,f(z)} = -z\,g(z),\tag{292.1}$$

where $g(z)$ is of bound one. Then

$$f(z) = \frac{a + z\,g(z)}{1 + \bar{a}\,z\,g(z)}\tag{292.2}$$

and

$$f(z) - a = \frac{z\,g(z)\,(1 - a\,\bar{a})}{1 + \bar{a}\,z\,g(z)}.\tag{292.3}$$

From this we calculate

$$f'(0) = g(0)\,(1 - a\,\bar{a}) = 1 - \varepsilon^2.\tag{292.4}$$

Hence $1 - \varepsilon^2 \leq 1 - a\,\bar{a}$ and $a = \varepsilon c$, where $|c| \leq 1$. It follows that

$$g(0) = \frac{1 - \varepsilon^2}{1 - \varepsilon^2\,c\,\bar{c}}\tag{292.5}$$

and

$$g(0) - b = \frac{\varepsilon^2\,(1 - \varepsilon^2)\,c\,\bar{c}}{1 - \varepsilon^2\,c\,\bar{c}} \leq \varepsilon^2.\tag{292.6}$$

Also,

$$1 - g(0)\, b = 1 - \frac{(1 - \varepsilon^2)^2}{1 - \varepsilon^2\, c\, \bar{c}} = \frac{(2 - c\, \bar{c})\, \varepsilon^2 - \varepsilon^4}{1 - \varepsilon^2\, c\, \bar{c}} < \frac{2\, \varepsilon^2}{1 - \varepsilon^2}. \qquad (292.7)$$

Now we set

$$g(z) = \frac{g(0) - z\, h(z)}{1 - g(0)\, z\, h(z)} \qquad (292.8)$$

and obtain

$$g(z) - b = \frac{g(0) - b - (1 - g(0)\, b)\, z\, h(z)}{1 - g(0)\, z\, h(z)}. \qquad (292.9)$$

These formulas show that for $|z| < r$,

$$|g(z) - b| \leqq \frac{\varepsilon^2\, (1 - \varepsilon^2) + 2\, \varepsilon^2\, r}{(1 - \varepsilon^2)\, (1 - r)}. \qquad (292.10)$$

Here we made use of the fact that $h(z)$ is of bound one. Now we have

$$f(z) - b\, z = \frac{a + z\, g(z) - b\, z - \bar{a}\, b\, z^2\, g(z)}{1 + \bar{a}\, z\, g(z)}. \qquad (292.11)$$

For $|z| < r$, finally,

$$\left.
\begin{aligned}
|f(z) - b\, z| &\leqq \frac{\varepsilon\, [1 + (1 - \varepsilon^2)\, r^2]\, (1 - \varepsilon^2)\, (1 - r) + r\, \varepsilon^2\, (1 - \varepsilon^2 + 2\, r)}{(1 - \varepsilon^2)\, (1 - r)\, (1 - \varepsilon\, r)} \\
&\leqq \varepsilon\, \frac{1 + r^2 - r - r^3 + r\, \varepsilon\, (1 + 2\, r)}{(1 - \varepsilon^2)\, (1 - r)\, (1 - \varepsilon\, r)} < \varepsilon\, \frac{1 + r\, \varepsilon\, (1 + 2\, r)}{(1 - \varepsilon^2)\, (1 - r)\, (1 - \varepsilon\, r)}.
\end{aligned}
\right\} \quad (292.12)$$

This shows that in the disc $|z| < r$, the expressions $f(z) - b\, z$ (where $b = 1 - \varepsilon^2$) converge to zero uniformly as ε goes to zero.[1]

---

[1] A slightly more general theorem can be established by means of a much shorter (though not quite as elementary) proof for which I am indebted to Mr. Erhard Schmidt. Let the function $f(z)$ of bound one be given by $f(z) = \sum\limits_{\nu=0}^{\infty} a_\nu\, z^\nu$. Then for $0 < r < 1$, $z = r\, e^{i\varphi}$

$$\sum_{\nu=0}^{\infty} |a_\nu|^2\, r^{2\nu} = \frac{1}{2\, \pi} \int_0^{2\pi} f(z)\, \bar{f}(z)\, d\varphi \leqq 1,$$

whence for $r = 1$,

$$\sum_{\nu=0}^{\infty} |a_\nu|^2 \leqq 1$$

follows. Hence if for any k,

$$|a_k^2| = 1 - \varepsilon^2,$$

then

$$\sum_{\nu \neq k} |a_\nu|^2 \leqq \varepsilon^2$$

and therefore, by Schwarz's Inequality,

$$|f(z) - a_k\, z^k|^2 \leqq \varepsilon^2 \sum_{\nu \neq k} r^{2\nu} < \frac{\varepsilon^2}{1 - r^2}.$$

By Rouché's theorem (*cf.* § 226, Vol. I, p. 229), it follows further that for ε sufficiently small (independently of the choice of a), the function $w = f(z)$ has at least one zero in $|z| < r$, and that this function is simple (schlicht) in some disc $|z| < \varrho$. To obtain the best possible bounds in this connection, one proceeds best by reversing the problem and going after the maximum of $|f'(0)|$ for all functions $f(z)$ of bound one that represent a simple mapping of a given disc $|z| \leqq r < 1$. This problem leads to extensive calculations but can be handled by methods similar to those used above.

Remark. The same method can be used to estimate the remainder of the Taylor series of $f(z) - a - bz$ in terms of ε and r.

Jensen's Theorem (§ 293)

293. Let $f(z)$ be a function of bound one that is known to have zeros at $z_1, \ldots, z_n$, all of these numbers being assumed to be distinct from $z = 0$. Then we deduce just as in § 283 above that $f(z)$ can be written in the form

$$f(z) = g(z) \prod_{\nu=1}^{n} \frac{z_\nu - z}{1 - \bar{z}_\nu z},$$

where $g(z)$ is also a function of bound one. From this it follows that

$$|f(0)| = |g(0)| \, |z_1 z_2 \ldots z_n| \leqq |z_1 z_2 \ldots z_n|. \tag{293.1}$$

This result, after re-norming the functions involved, is equivalent to the following theorem of J. L. Jensen (1859-1925): *Let $F(z)$ be regular in the disc $|z| < R$, let $F(0) = 1$, and let $z_1, \ldots, z_n$ be among the non-zero zeros of $F(z)$ in this disc. Then the least upper bound M of $|F(z)|$ in $|z| < R$ satisfies the inequality*

$$M \geqq \frac{R^n}{|z_1 z_2 \ldots z_n|}. \tag{293.2}$$

From (293.1) we can also derive an upper bound for the number of zeros in a disc $|z| < r < 1$ of any function $f(z)$ of bound one in $|z| < 1$ for which $F(0) = a_0$. For if n is the number of these zeros, we have

$$|a_0| < r^n, \tag{293.3}$$

whence

$$n < \frac{l \, |a_0|}{l \, r}. \tag{293.4}$$

An Application of Pick's Theorem (§ 294)

294. Let $f(z)$ be of bound one in the disc $|z| < 1$. We consider an arbitrary set of circles $K(z)$ with non-Euclidean centers at z and non-Euclidean radii $\varrho(z)$, and in the w-plane we consider the circles $\Gamma(z)$ with non-Euclidean centers at $w = f(z)$ and non-Euclidean radii $\varrho(z)$. If A_z is any point set contained in the union of the discs $K(z)$ and if the point set A_w of the w-plane is the image of A_z under the mapping $w = f(z)$, then by Pick's theorem, A_w must be contained in the union of the discs $\Gamma(z)$. We shall make use of this fact in what follows.

Let us assume that $f(z)$ is a real function, so that it maps the points of the real diameter of $|z| < 1$ onto points of the real diameter of $|w| < 1$. Now if we consider the set of all non-Euclidean discs of (non-Euclidean) radius ϱ and centers on the segment AB (see Fig. 34 below), we see that these discs cover the lens-shaped region $ANBMA$ bounded on either side by a (non-Euclidean) line of constant (non-Euclidean) distance from the segment AB. Our observation above now implies that to every point of this lens there corresponds a point $w = f(z)$ that lies within the corresponding lens in the disc $|w| < 1$.

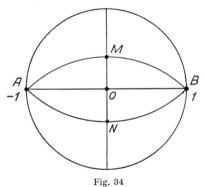

Fig. 34

Julia's Theorem (§§ 295-297)

295. Let us consider those non-Euclidean motions

$$w = e^{i\varphi} \frac{a - z}{1 - \bar{a} z} \qquad (|a| < 1), \qquad (295.1)$$

for which $z = 1$ is a fixed point; they are of the form

$$w = -\frac{1 - \bar{a}}{1 - a} \cdot \frac{a - z}{1 - \bar{a} z}. \qquad (295.2)$$

Writing

$$a = \frac{\lambda - 1}{\lambda + 1}, \quad 1 - a = \frac{2}{\lambda + 1}, \tag{295.3}$$

we obtain them in the form

$$w = -\frac{(\lambda - 1) - (\lambda + 1) z}{(\bar{\lambda} + 1) - (\bar{\lambda} - 1) z} = \frac{(1 + z) - \lambda (1 - z)}{(1 + z) + \bar{\lambda} (1 - z)}. \tag{295.4}$$

This yields

$$1 - w = \frac{(\lambda + \bar{\lambda}) (1 - z)}{(1 + z) + \bar{\lambda} (1 - z)}, \quad 1 + w = \frac{2 (1 + z) + (\bar{\lambda} - \lambda) (1 - z)}{(1 + z) + \bar{\lambda} (1 - z)}. \tag{295.5}$$

We now set $\lambda = \alpha + i\beta$ and note that by (295.3), the condition $|a| < 1$ can be replaced by $\alpha > 0$. We find that

$$\frac{1 - w}{1 + w} = \frac{\alpha (1 - z)}{(1 + z) - i \beta (1 - z)}. \tag{295.6}$$

This formula takes on a particularly simple form if we assume the point $z = -1$ to be a second fixed point of the transformation. For in this case $\beta = 0$, so that

$$\frac{1 - w}{1 + w} = \alpha \frac{1 - z}{1 + z}. \tag{295.7}$$

If we set

$$Z_n = \frac{u_n e^{i\vartheta_n} - z}{1 - u_n e^{-i\vartheta_n} z}, \quad W_n = \frac{v_n e^{i\psi_n} - w}{1 - v_n e^{-i\psi_n} w}, \tag{295.8}$$

where u_n and v_n are positive numbers < 1, then

$$W_n = e^{i\varphi_n} Z_n \qquad (n = 1, 2, \ldots) \tag{295.9}$$

represents a non-Euclidean motion. We shall show that under the assumptions

$$\lim_{n=\infty} u_n e^{i\vartheta_n} = \lim_{n=\infty} v_n e^{i\psi_n} = 1, \quad \lim_{n=\infty} \frac{1 - v_n}{1 - u_n} = \alpha, \tag{295.10}$$

it is possible to determine the numbers φ_n in (295.9) in such a way that (295.9) converges to (295.7). We first introduce the abbreviations

$$\zeta_n = e^{-i\vartheta_n} z, \quad \omega_n = e^{-i\psi_n} w. \tag{295.11}$$

Then we have

$$Z_n = e^{i\vartheta_n} \frac{u_n - \zeta_n}{1 - u_n \zeta_n}. \tag{295.12}$$

This implies that

$$1 + e^{-i\vartheta_n} Z_n = \frac{(1 + u_n)(1 - \zeta_n)}{1 - u_n \zeta_n},$$

$$1 - e^{-i\vartheta_n} Z_n = \frac{(1 - u_n)(1 + \zeta_n)}{1 - u_n \zeta_n}.$$

(295.13)

Similar formulas hold for W_n. Now the equation

$$\frac{1 + e^{-i\vartheta_n} Z_n}{1 - e^{-i\vartheta_n} Z_n} = \frac{1 + e^{-i\psi_n} W_n}{1 - e^{-i\psi_n} W_n}$$

(295.14)

holds identically if we set $W_n = e^{i\varphi_n} Z_n$ and take $\varphi_n = \psi_n - \vartheta_n$. It therefore represents a non-Euclidean motion. If we substitute the expressions (295.13) and the analogous expressions for the W_n into (295.14), we obtain these non-Euclidean motions in the form

$$\frac{1 - \omega_n}{1 + \omega_n} = \frac{1 - v_n}{1 - u_n} \cdot \frac{1 + u_n}{1 + v_n} \cdot \frac{1 - \zeta_n}{1 + \zeta_n},$$

(295.15)

and these motions map the point $u_n e^{i\vartheta_n}$ onto the point $v_n e^{i\psi_n}$ and, by (295.10), converge continuously to (295.7).

296. We now consider any function $f(z)$ of bound one in $|z| < 1$ that is not the constant unity, and we consider sequences of points z_n in the (interior of the) disc $|z| < 1$ that converge to $z = 1$. Let us assume also that $\lim f(z_n) = 1$. For all such sequences we either have

$$\lim_{n = \infty} \frac{1 - |f(z_n)|}{1 - |z_n|} = \infty,$$

(296.1)

or else there is a sequence of the kind specified for which the limit in (296.1) is a finite non-negative number α. We must then even have $\alpha > 0$, since by § 287,

$$|f(z)| \leq \frac{|f(0)| + |z|}{1 + |f(0)||z|},$$

(296.2)

whence

$$\frac{1 - |f(z)|}{1 - |z|} \geq \frac{1 - |f(0)|}{1 + |f(0)||z|} \geq \frac{1 - |f(0)|}{1 + |f(0)|},$$

(296.3)

from which

$$\alpha \geq \frac{1 - |f(0)|}{1 + |f(0)|} > 0$$

(296.4)

follows. If for a sequence $\{z_n\}$ the number α is finite, then with the notation

$$z_n = u_n e^{i\vartheta_n}, \quad f(z_n) = v_n e^{i\psi_n}$$

(296.5)

it follows that

$$\lim_{n=\infty} u_n = \lim_{n=\infty} v_n = 1, \quad \lim_{n=\infty} \frac{1-v_n}{1-u_n} = \alpha. \tag{296.6}$$

Let x be a fixed point on the real diameter of the disc $|z| < 1$ and let K_n be the circle that has $u_n\, e^{i\vartheta_n}$ as its non-Euclidean center and passes through the point x. The Moebius transformation (295.15) maps this circle onto a circle Γ_n of the w-plane having $w_n = f(z_n)$ as its non-Euclidean center and having the same non-Euclidean radius as K_n. The circles K_n converge to a circle K that is an oricycle (*cf.* § 83, Vol. I, p. 79) of the non-Euclidean

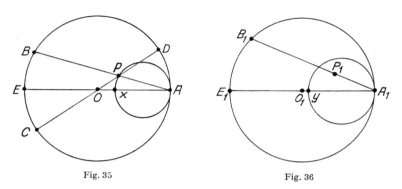

Fig. 35   Fig. 36

plane $|z| < 1$ and passes through the point $z = 1$ and $z = x$. Since the Moebius transformations (295.15) converge to (295.7), the images Γ_n of the circles K_n must converge to an oricycle Γ of the non-Euclidean plane $|w| < 1$ that passes through the points $w = 1$ and $w = y$, where y and x are related by

$$\frac{1-y}{1+y} = \alpha \frac{1-x}{1+x}. \tag{296.7}$$

Now if z is a point in the interior of the oricycle K, it must be contained in the interior of infinitely many of the circles K_n; by Pick's theorem, the point $w = f(z)$ must then be contained in the interior of infinitely many of the circles Γ_n and therefore cannot be outside the oricycle Γ. Since the mapping is neighborhood-preserving, the point $w = f(z)$ must even lie in the interior of Γ. Hence any boundary point of the disc K is mapped onto an interior point or a boundary point of Γ.

297. From a study of Figures 35 and 36 above it follows that

$$\frac{AP}{PB} = \frac{Ax}{xE} = \frac{1-x}{1+x}$$

and

$$\frac{A_1P_1}{P_1B_1} \leqq \frac{A_1y}{yE_1} = \frac{1-y}{1+y}.$$

Thus the result of the preceding section is expressed as follows in geometric terms:

$$\frac{A_1 P_1}{P_1 B_1} \leq \alpha \, \frac{AP}{PB}.$$

By § 158, Vol. I, p. 154, this can be written in the form

$$\frac{|1 - f(z)|^2}{1 - |f(z)|^2} \leq \alpha \, \frac{|1 - z|^2}{1 - |z|^2}. \tag{297.1}$$

Thus we have obtained the first part of the following theorem, which is due to G. Julia:

If $f(z)$ is a function of bound one in $|z| < 1$ that is not the constant unity and if $\{z_n\}$ is any sequence of points of the disc $|z| < 1$ that converges to $z = 1$ and for which $\lim f(z_n) = 1$, then either we have for all such sequences that

$$\lim_{n = \infty} \frac{1 - |f(z_n)|}{1 - |z_n|} = \infty, \tag{297.2}$$

or else there are finite positive real numbers a which are such that for all $|z| < 1$, the relation

$$\frac{|1 - f(z)|^2}{1 - |f(z)|^2} \leq \alpha \, \frac{|1 - z|^2}{1 - |z|^2} \tag{297.3}$$

holds. If, in particular, there is among these numbers a a value a_0 and in $|z| < 1$ a point z' for which the equality sign holds in (297.3), then the relation

$$\frac{|1 - f(z)|^2}{1 - |f(z)|^2} = \alpha_0 \, \frac{|1 - z|^2}{1 - |z|^2} \tag{297.4}$$

holds at all points inside the unit circle and $f(z)$ is a non-Euclidean motion of the form

$$f(z) = \frac{(1 + z) - (\alpha_0 + i\,\beta)\,(1 - z)}{(1 + z) + (\alpha_0 - i\,\beta)\,(1 - z)} \qquad (\alpha_0 > 0, \beta \text{ real}). \tag{297.5}$$

We shall now prove the second part of this theorem. If we denote by K' the oricycle through $z = 1$ and $z = z'$, then $w' = f(z')$ must lie on the image Γ' of K'. If z'' is any point of the non-Euclidean ray that joins $z = 1$ and $z = z'$, and if K'' is the oricycle through $z = 1$ and $z = z''$, then the image point $w'' = f(z'')$ lies inside or on the corresponding oricycle Γ'', and the pseudo-chordal distances $\psi(z', z'')$ and $\psi(w', w'')$ satisfy the relation

$$\psi(z', z'') \leq \psi(w', w''). \tag{297.6}$$

But by Pick's theorem,

$$\psi(z', z'') \geqq \psi(w', w''). \tag{297.7}$$

Therefore the two pseudo-chordal distances are equal, and the transformation $w = f(z)$ is a non-Euclidean motion. This last fact also follows from Pick's theorem. The non-Euclidean motion has $z = 1$ as a fixed point and is of the form (295.6), so that (297.5) is established.

The Angular Derivative (§§ 298-299)

298. Julia's theorem has a converse. If there exists a finite positive number α which is such that relation (297.3) holds at all points inside the unit circle, then we can show that there exist in the disc $|z| < 1$ sequences of points z_n for which

$$\lim_{n=\infty} z_n = \lim_{n=\infty} f(z_n) = 1 \tag{298.1}$$

and for which

$$\lim_{n=\infty} \frac{1 - |f(z_n)|}{1 - |z_n|} \tag{298.2}$$

exists and is $\leqq \alpha$. For by (296.7), the Euclidean radii

$$r = \frac{1-x}{2}, \quad \varrho = \frac{1-y}{2} \tag{298.3}$$

of the oricycles K and Γ satisfy the relation

$$\varrho = \frac{\alpha r}{1 - r(1 - \alpha)}. \tag{298.4}$$

But (297.3) implies that the real point $x = 1 - 2r$ of K is mapped onto a point $f(x)$ for which the relation

$$|1 - f(x)| \leqq 2\varrho \tag{298.5}$$

holds. Comparing the last relations, we find that

$$\frac{1 - |f(x)|}{1 - x} \leqq \frac{|1 - f(x)|}{1 - x} \leqq \frac{\varrho}{r} = \frac{\alpha}{1 - r(1 - \alpha)}. \tag{298.6}$$

Passage to the limit yields

$$\lim_{x=1} \frac{1 - |f(x)|}{1 - x} \leqq \lim_{x=1} \frac{|1 - f(x)|}{1 - x} \leqq \alpha, \tag{298.7}$$

from which our above statement follows immediately. We are now able to determine the smallest number α_0 for which the given function $f(z)$ satisfies relation (297.3) at every point of the disc $|z| < 1$. By (298.7), α_0 cannot be less than

$$\lim_{x=1} \frac{1 - |f(x)|}{1 - x}.$$

On the other hand, if α_0 stands for this expression, then there are sequences of real numbers x_n for which

$$\lim_{n=\infty} x_n = \lim_{n=\infty} f(x_n) = 1 \qquad (298.8)$$

and

$$\lim_{n=\infty} \frac{1 - |f(x_n)|}{1 - x_n} = \alpha_0 \qquad (298.9)$$

holds. Hence by the preceding two sections, we may also substitute the value α_0 for α in relations (298.6) and (298.7), and (298.6) then implies that

$$\overline{\lim_{x=1}} \frac{1 - |f(x)|}{1 - x} \leqq \overline{\lim_{x=1}} \frac{|1 - f(x)|}{1 - x} \leqq \alpha_0, \qquad (298.10)$$

while a comparison of (298.10) with (298.7) yields the fact that the two limits exist and are equal, so that

$$\lim_{x=1} \frac{1 - |f(x)|}{1 - x} = \lim_{x=1} \frac{|1 - f(x)|}{1 - x} = \alpha_0. \qquad (298.11)$$

The non-zero number α_0 which we have thus determined is positive, by (296.3); hence (298.11) shows that

$$\lim_{x=1} \frac{1 - |f(x)|}{|1 - f(x)|} = 1. \qquad (298.12)$$

If we set

$$1 - f(x) = \lambda e^{i\vartheta}, \qquad (298.13)$$

where λ is > 0 and ϑ is real, we obtain

$$\frac{1 - |f(x)|}{|1 - f(x)|} = \frac{2 \cos \vartheta - \lambda}{1 + \sqrt{1 - 2\lambda \cos \vartheta + \lambda^2}}. \qquad (298.14)$$

If x tends to unity, then (298.13) shows that λ must go to zero, whence $\cos \vartheta$ and therefore also $e^{i\vartheta}$ must, by (298.12) and (298.14), go to unity. Since

$$1 - f(x) = |1 - f(x)| e^{i\vartheta}$$

holds, we have thus obtained the following theorem:

For all functions $f(z)$ of the type considered in this section, and for real x, the limits

$$\lim_{x=1} \frac{1 - |f(x)|}{1 - x}, \quad \lim_{x=1} \frac{|1 - f(x)|}{1 - x}, \quad \lim_{x=1} \frac{1 - f(x)}{1 - x} \tag{298.15}$$

exist and are equal to each other.

299. The last result can be extended from real values x of z to sets of complex values of z that lie in a triangle having one of its vertices at $z = 1$

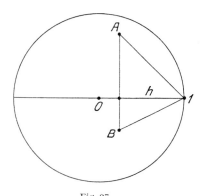

Fig. 37

and having the opposite side AB within $|z| < 1$ and perpendicular to the real axis (see Fig. 37).

By § 215, Vol. I, p. 215, all points z of the triangle $AB1$ satisfy the relation

$$\frac{|1 - z|}{1 - |z|} < M < \infty.$$

Hence if $\{z_n\}$ is any sequence from the triangular region that converges to $z = 1$, we have

$$\frac{1 - |f(z_n)|}{1 - |z_n|} \leqq \frac{|1 - f(z_n)|}{1 - |z_n|} \leqq M \left| \frac{1 - f(z_n)}{1 - z_n} \right|. \tag{299.1}$$

Unless for all such sequences we have

$$\lim_{n = \infty} \frac{1 - f(z_n)}{1 - z_n} = \infty, \tag{299.2}$$

it follows from Julia's theorem that (297.3) holds; there must then exist a number $a_0 < a$ that equals each of the three limits corresponding to those in (298.15).

In this latter case, we denote the altitude of triangle $AB1$ by h (cf. Fig. 37) and introduce the notations

$$r_n = \frac{\Re(1 - z_n)}{h}, \quad \varrho_n = \frac{\alpha_0 \, r_n}{1 - r_n \, (1 - \alpha_0)} \,. \tag{299.3}$$

We also set

$$1 - z = r_n \, (1 - t), \quad 1 - f(z) = \varrho_n \, (1 - \Phi_n(t)) \,. \tag{299.4}$$

From the geometric interpretation of Julia's theorem (cf. § 297 above), it follows that the functions $\Phi_n(t)$ are of bound one in the disc $|t| < 1$ and constitute a normal family. Relations (299.3) and (299.4) imply that

$$\Phi_n(t) - 1 = \frac{f(z) - 1}{\alpha_0 \, (z - 1)} \, (t - 1) \, [1 - r_n \, (1 - \alpha_0)], \tag{299.5}$$

where t and z are related by equation (299.4). In particular, if t is real then for every value of n, the corresponding z equals a real number x_n, and from $\lim r_n = 0$ we obtain

$$\lim_{n = \infty} \frac{f(x_n) - 1}{\alpha_0 \, (x_n - 1)} = 1, \quad \lim_{n = \infty} \Phi_n(t) = t. \tag{299.6}$$

Hence by Vitali's theorem (cf. § 191, Vol. I, p. 189), the $\Phi_n(t)$ converge uniformly to t on every closed point set contained in the disc $|t| < 1$.

We now return to the original sequence of z_n and we define the numbers t_n by the equations

$$1 - z_n = r_n \, (1 - t_n) \,.$$

Then by (299.3), all of the points t_n lie on the side AB of the triangle $AB1$ (if we consider the triangle as lying in the disc $|t| < 1$). Hence it follows from the last result above that if we set

$$\Phi_n(t_n) = t_n + \tau_n \tag{299.7}$$

then $\lim \tau_n = 0$. Equation (299.5) yields

$$\frac{1 - f(z_n)}{1 - z_n} = \frac{\alpha_0}{1 - r_n \, (1 - \alpha_0)} \left(1 - \frac{\tau_n}{1 - t_n}\right) \,.$$

Here,

$$\lim_{n = \infty} r_n = \lim_{n = \infty} \tau_n = 0, \quad \Re(1 - t_n) = h,$$

whence

$$\lim_{n=\infty} \frac{1-f(z_n)}{1-z_n} = \alpha_0. \tag{299.8}$$

By (299.6) and by § 188, Vol. I, p. 187, the derivatives $\Phi_n{}'(t)$ likewise form a sequence that converges uniformly to unity on the side AB of the triangle $AB1$. But by differentiating equations (299.4), we obtain

$$\Phi_n'(t) = f'(z) \frac{r_n}{\varrho_n}, \tag{299.9}$$

so that

$$\left.\begin{aligned} f'(z_n) &= \frac{\alpha_0}{1 - r_n(1-\alpha_0)} \Phi_n'(t_n), \\ \lim_{n=\infty} f'(z_n) &= \alpha_0. \end{aligned}\right\} \tag{299.10}$$

We have thus proved the following *theorem on the angular derivative*:

Let $f(z)$ be a function of bound one in the disc $|z| < 1$, and consider any triangle in this disc that has one of its vertices at $z = 1$. Then for any sequence $\{z_n\}$ of points from the interior of the triangle that converges to $z = 1$, the limit

$$\lim_{n=\infty} \frac{1-f(z_n)}{1-z_n} \tag{299.11}$$

exists and either always (that is, for every such sequence) equals infinity or always equals a positive number a_0. In the second case, we also have the relation

$$\lim_{n=\infty} f'(z_n) = \alpha_0, \tag{299.12}$$

and we refer to this number as the "angular derivative" of the function $f(z)$ at the point $z = 1$.

Further Properties of the Angular Derivative (§ 300)

300. The following remark gives a criterion for the existence of the angular derivative that is very convenient in many applications. From the results of the last sections it follows that a function $f(z)$ analytic in the disc $|z| < 1$ has an angular derivative at the point $z = 1$ if, first, $f(z)$ is of bound one in $|z| < 1$, second, the relation

$$\lim_{x=1} f(x) = 1$$

holds for real values x of z, and third, $|f'(x)| < M$ holds for $r_0 < x < 1$, where r_0 is a suitable number between 0 and 1. The third condition may also be replaced by $\overline{\lim_{x=1}} |f'(x)| < M$. These conditions are sufficient, since we may write

$$|1 - f(x)| = \left| \int_x^1 f'(x)\, dx \right| \leq M\, (1 - x), \quad r_0 < x < 1. \quad (300.1)$$

As a first application of this criterion, we can easily show that if $f_1(z)$ and $f_2(z)$ are two functions of bound one in $|z| < 1$ and if

$$f(z) = f_1(z)\, f_2(z), \quad\quad\quad (300.2)$$

then each one of these three functions has an angular derivative at $z = 1$ provided that the two others do. In fact, from, say,

$$\lim_{x=1} f(x) = \lim_{x=1} f_1(x) = 1$$

it follows that

$$\lim_{x=1} f_2(x) = 1.$$

Also,

$$f_2'(x) = \frac{f'(x) - f_2(x)\, f_1'(x)}{f_1(x)},$$

so that $f_2'(z)$ is bounded in some interval $r_0 < x < 1$. If we denote the angular derivatives of the above functions by α, α_1, and α_2, then

$$\alpha = \alpha_1 + \alpha_2, \quad\quad\quad (300.3)$$

which implies that $\alpha \geq \alpha_1$ and $\alpha \geq \alpha_2$.

Next we shall prove that if $\{f_n(z)\}$ is a sequence of functions each of whose terms $f_n(z)$ has an angular derivative α_n at the point $z = 1$, then any non-constant limit function $f(z)$ of the sequence also has an angular derivative α at $z = 1$ provided only that the sequence $\{\alpha_n\}$ has a finite upper bound; in this case,

$$\alpha \leq \lim_{n=\infty} \alpha_n$$

holds.

To prove this, we note that at every point z of the disc $|z| < 1$, the following relation holds:

$$\frac{|1 - f_n(z)|^2}{1 - |f_n(z)|^2} \leq \alpha_n \frac{|1 - z|^2}{1 - |z|^2}. \quad\quad\quad (300.4)$$

Also, in the sequence $\{\alpha_n\}$ there is a subsequence $\alpha_{n_1}, \alpha_{n_2}, \dots$ that converges to $\lim \alpha_n$; using this subsequence to pass to the limit in (300.4), we obtain

$$\frac{|1-f(z)|^2}{1-|f(z)|^2} \leqq \lim_{n=\infty} \alpha_n \cdot \frac{|1-z|^2}{1-|z|^2} \quad \text{for } |z| < 1, \quad (300.5)$$

and our statement now follows from §§ 296 ff.

The Angular Derivative and the Zeros of a Function (§§ 301-304)

301. We consider the unit function

$$E(z) = -\frac{1-\bar{z}_1}{1-z_1} \cdot \frac{z_1 - z}{1 - \bar{z}_1 z} \qquad (301.1)$$

and we note that

$$\left.\begin{aligned} E(1) &= 1, \\ E'(z) &= \frac{1-\bar{z}_1}{1-z_1} \cdot \frac{1-|z_1|^2}{(1-\bar{z}_1 z)^2} . \end{aligned}\right\} \qquad (301.2)$$

Therefore the function $E(z)$ has the angular derivative

$$\alpha' = E'(1) = \frac{1-|z_1|^2}{|1-z_1|^2} . \qquad (301.3)$$

We now consider an analytic function $f(z)$ that has a zero at $z = z_1$ and an angular derivative α at $z = 1$. If we set

$$f(z) = E(z)f_1(z),$$

then $f_1(z)$ must be of bound one and has, by the preceding section, an angular derivative α_1 for which $\alpha = \alpha' + \alpha_1$ holds. This together with (301.3) yields the inequality

$$\alpha \geqq \frac{1-|z_1|^2}{|1-z_1|^2} . \qquad (301.4)$$

Remark. If $z_1 = 0$, then $\alpha' = 1$ and $\alpha \geqq 1$, whence we immediately deduce the following *theorem of Löwner:*

Let $w = f(z)$ *be a function of bound one in* $|z| < 1$ *for which* $f(0) = 0$, *and assume that this function maps an arc of length s of the circle* $|z| = 1$ *onto an arc of length σ of the circle* $|w| = 1$. *Then we must have* $\sigma \geqq s$.

302. Let $f(z)$ have the angular derivative α and a finite or infinite number of zeros z_ν . Then by the preceding section,

$$\alpha \geq \sum \frac{1 - |z_\nu|^2}{|1 - z_\nu|^2} = \alpha'. \tag{302.1}$$

From § 158, Vol. I, p. 154 and from Fig. 38 below, we infer that

$$\frac{1 - |z_\nu|^2}{|1 - z_\nu|^2} = \frac{q_\nu \, p_\nu}{p_\nu^2} = \frac{q_\nu}{p_\nu} = \frac{1 + x_\nu}{1 - x_\nu}. \tag{302.2}$$

This observation enables us to determine the most general distribution of zeros z_ν for which

$$\sum \frac{1 - |z_\nu|^2}{|1 - z_\nu|^2} = \alpha' \tag{302.3}$$

holds. To this end, we choose any sequence of positive numbers ϱ_ν for which

$$\alpha' = \sum \varrho_\nu \tag{302.4}$$

holds; we then determine x_ν from the equation

$$\frac{1 + x_\nu}{1 - x_\nu} = \varrho_\nu, \tag{302.5}$$

and we finally construct the oricycles (cf. § 83, Vol. I, p. 79) through $z = 1$ and $z = x_\nu$. If we now choose an arbitrary point z_ν on each of these oricycles,

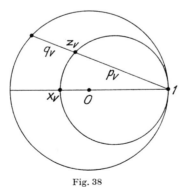

Fig. 38

relation (302.3) ensues. If there are infinitely many numbers ϱ_ν, the points z_ν can always be chosen in such a way as to make the set of their points of accumulation coincide with any pre-assigned closed subset of the circle $|z| = 1$. In particular, the point $z = 1$ may be the only point of accumulation. We now introduce the unit functions

$$f_k(z) = \prod_{\nu=1}^{k} E_\nu(z) \qquad (k = 1, 2, \ldots), \quad (302.6)$$

whose respective angular derivatives are given by

$$\alpha_k = \sum_{\nu=1}^{k} \varrho_\nu. \qquad (302.7)$$

Let $\{f_{n_j}(z)\}$ be a convergent subsequence of the sequence $\{f_k(z)\}$, and let

$$\varphi(z) = \lim_{j=\infty} f_{n_j}(z) \qquad (302.8)$$

be the limit of this subsequence. If G_1 is a subregion of the disc $|z| < 1$ that does not contain any of the points z_ν, then all of the $f_{n_j}(z)$ are $\neq 0$ in G_1. Hence by Hurwitz's theorem (cf. § 198, Vol. I, p. 194), $\varphi(z)$ is either the constant zero or a non-constant function of bound one having its (single or multiple) zeros at the points z_ν. In the latter case, $\varphi(z)$ must have by § 300 above, an angular derivative α^* for which

$$\alpha^* \leqq \lim_{j=\infty} \alpha_{n_j} = \alpha'$$

holds. But since we can write

$$\varphi(z) = f_{n_j}(z)\, g_{n_j}(z) \qquad (j = 1, 2, \ldots),$$

it follows that, on the other hand, $\alpha^* > \alpha_{n_j}$ $(j = 1, 2, \ldots)$, whence we see that the angular derivative of $\varphi(z)$ at $z = 1$ must equal α'.

If all $z_\nu \neq 0$, then (301.1), (302.6), and (302.8) yield

$$|\varphi(0)| = \prod_{\nu=1}^{\infty} |E_\nu(0)| = \prod_{\nu=1}^{\infty} |z_\nu|. \qquad (302.9)$$

Setting

$$|z_\nu| = 1 - \varepsilon_\nu,$$

we obtain by our construction above that

$$\varepsilon_\nu = 1 - |z_\nu| \leqq 1 + x_\nu \leqq 2\,\varrho_\nu,$$

which implies that the sum $\sum_{\nu=1}^{\infty} \varepsilon_\nu$ is finite. Hence the product on the right-hand side of (302.9) is likewise finite and different from zero. In this case, therefore, $\varphi(z)$ is not a constant, and this holds also in the case that a finite number of the z_ν are zero.

Now let

$$\psi(z) = \lim_{k=\infty} f_{m_k}(z)$$

be a second function that fits the specifications laid down for $\varphi(z)$. Then for every natural number j,

$$|\psi(z)| \leq |f_{n_j}(z)|$$

holds, so that $|\psi(z)| \leq |\varphi(z)|$. But in the same way it follows that $|\varphi(z)| \leq |\psi(z)|$, and we therefore conclude, by § 144, Vol. I, p. 139, that

$$\psi(z) = e^{i\vartheta}\,\varphi(z) \quad \text{for} \quad |z| < 1,$$

where ϑ is a real number. Since each of the functions $\varphi(z)$ and $\psi(z)$ has an angular derivative at $z = 1$, it follows that if we approach $z = 1$ along a straight line then

$$\lim_{z=1} \varphi(z) = \lim_{z=1} \psi(z) = 1,$$

whence $e^{i\vartheta} = 1$.

Using the same argument as in the proof of Vitali's theorem (*cf.* § 191, Vol. I, p. 189), we find that the sequence $\{f_k(z)\}$ itself converges in the disc $|z| < 1$ and that *the equation*

$$f(z) = \prod_{\nu=1}^{\infty} E_{\nu}(z) \tag{302.10}$$

defines a non-constant function of bound one having the angular derivative α' *and the zeros* z_ν.

303. Let λ be a point of the disc $|z| < 1$. If $f(z)$ has an angular derivative α at $z = 1$ and if we set

$$\left.\begin{aligned}
g(z) &= -\frac{1-\overline{\lambda}}{1-\lambda}\cdot\frac{\lambda-f(z)}{1-\overline{\lambda}f(z)}, \\[2mm]
g'(z) &= \frac{1-\overline{\lambda}}{1-\lambda}\cdot\frac{1-\lambda\overline{\lambda}}{(1-\overline{\lambda}f(z))^2}\,f'(z),
\end{aligned}\right\} \tag{303.1}$$

then $g(z)$ has an angular derivative

$$\beta = g'(1) = \frac{1-|\lambda|^2}{|1-\lambda|^2}\,\alpha. \tag{303.2}$$

If we denote the zeros of $g(z)$ by z_ν —they are the points where $f(z)$ assumes the value λ—we have by (302.1) that

$$\alpha \geqq \frac{|1-\lambda|^2}{1-|\lambda|^2} \sum \frac{1-|z_\nu{}^2|}{|1-z_\nu|^2} , \tag{303.3}$$

and this inequality cannot be sharpened.

304. Let α be assigned, and let x be a point of the negative real axis that lies inside the unit circle. For every point z_ν lying within the oricycle through $z = 1$ and $z = x$, we have

$$\frac{1-|z_\nu|^2}{|1-z_\nu|^2} > \frac{1+x}{1-x}. \tag{304.1}$$

If we denote by n the number of λ-places of $f(z)$ within the oricycle (*i.e.* points within the oricycle at which $f(z) = \lambda$), then by (303.3),

$$n < \alpha \frac{1-|\lambda|^2}{|1-\lambda|^2} \cdot \frac{1-x}{1+x}. \tag{304.2}$$

The disc $|z| < r < 1$, where $x = -r$, lies within the above oricycle. Hence if n_0 is the number of λ-places of $f(z)$ in the disc $|z| < r$, then

$$n_0 < \alpha \frac{1-|\lambda|^2}{|1-\lambda|^2} \cdot \frac{1+r}{1-r}. \tag{304.3}$$

If in particular we set $\lambda = f(0)$, we must have $n_0 \geqq 1$ for all $r > 0$, and we obtain

$$\alpha \geqq \frac{|1-f(0)|^2}{1-|f(0)|^2}. \tag{304.4}$$

This inequality cannot be sharpened, and it is clearly better than (296.4).

An Application of the Poisson Integral (§§ 305-306)

305. Consider a real function $\psi(\zeta)$ that is defined and sectionally continuous on the unit circle $|\zeta| = 1$ and whose values lie between two positive numbers α and β. We wish to construct a function that is analytic in the disc $|z| < 1$ and whose modulus on the boundary of this disc coincides with $\psi(\zeta)$ at all those points at which $\psi(\zeta)$ is continuous.

To this end, we substitute

$$\varphi(t) = l \, \psi(e^{it}) \tag{305.1}$$

in the integral on the right-hand side of (148.11), Vol. I, p. 145, and we obtain in this way a function $g(z)$ whose real part is represented by a Poisson integral (*cf.* § 151, Vol. I, p. 147) that is continuous and equal to $l\psi(\zeta)$ at all points of continuity of $\psi(\zeta)$. Then the function

$$f(z) = e^{g(z)} \qquad (305.2)$$

is regular and distinct from zero in the disc $|z| < 1$, and the modulus $|f(e^{it})|$ coincides with $\psi(e^{it})$ at all points of continuity of $\psi(\zeta)$. Thus we see that within certain limits, we can assign the values of $|f(z)|$ at will. Of course, the function $f(z)$ constructed above is not the only one that satisfies the requirements, since every function of the form

$$f^*(z) = f(z)E(z),$$

where $E(z)$ is any unit function, will do as well.

306. The construction given in the preceding section enables us, in particular, to obtain functions $f(z)$ of bound one devoid of zeros in $|z| < 1$ and equal in modulus to the constant $\mu < 1$ on a given arc α of the unit circle

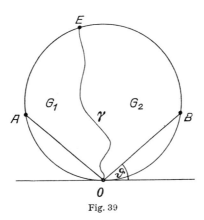

Fig. 39

and equal to unity on the complementary arc β. For such an $f(z)$, the real part of $lf(z)$ equals the product of $l\mu$ by the harmonic measure (*cf.* § 158, Vol. I) of the arc α. By § 158, Vol. I, p. 154, the level lines of $|f(z)|$ are in this case arcs of circles that connect the end points of α. If we denote once more by δ the angle between such a circular arc and the arc β (*cf.* Fig. 23, Vol. I, p. 156), then on the circular arc we have, by (158.5), the relation

$$|f(z)| = \mu^{\frac{\delta}{\pi}}. \qquad (306.1)$$

This particular function is used as a majorant in many proofs.

Continuity of Bounded Functions under Approach Within a Sector (§§ 307-308)

307. Let $f(z)$ be of bound one in the disc $|z - i| < 1$. We consider two chords AO and OB of equal length (see Fig. 39), and a Jordan arc γ

that joins the point O to a point E on the boundary of the disc and lies within the sector bounded by the rays OA and OB. Let us assume that on γ,

$$|f(z)| \leq \mu < 1 \tag{307.1}$$

holds. The arc γ divides the disc into two regions G_1 and G_2, each of which is bounded by a closed Jordan curve.

Now we construct, as shown in the two preceding sections, two auxiliary functions $\varphi_1(z)$ and $\varphi_2(z)$ regular and non-zero in the disc $|z - i| < 1$

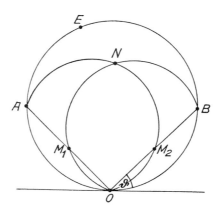

Fig. 40

which are such that $|\varphi_1(z)| = \mu$ on the arc OB and $|\varphi_1(z)| = 1$ on the arc $BEAO$, while $|\varphi_2(z)| = \mu$ on the arc AO and $|\varphi_2(z)| = 1$ on the arc $OBEA$.

Each of these functions exceeds μ, in absolute value, at every interior point of the arc γ. This implies that

$$|f(z)| < |\varphi_1(z)|$$

in the region G_1, and

$$|f(z)| < |\varphi_2(z)|$$

in the region G_2, and hence in any case

$$|f(z)| < \max \left(|\varphi_1(z)|, |\varphi_2(z)| \right) \tag{307.2}$$

for all points z of the disc $|z - i| < 1$.

Now let M_1 and M_2 be the midpoints of the chords AO and OB (see Fig. 40 above), and consider the circular arcs BNM_1O and OM_2NA. On the first of these arcs, $|\varphi_1(z)|$ is a constant and equals a number $\mu^{k(\vartheta)}$, where $k(\vartheta)$ is between 0 and 1 and can easily be calculated from formula (306.1). Similarly $|\varphi_2(z)|$ is constant on the arc OM_2NA and also equal to $\mu^{k(\vartheta)}$.

Hence in the lens-shaped region $O M_2 N M_1 O$ we have

$$\max \left(|\varphi_1(z)|, |\varphi_2(z)| \right) < \mu^{k(\vartheta)},$$

so that by (307.2),

$$|f(z)| < \mu^{k(\vartheta)}, \qquad\qquad (307.3)$$

and thus for all sequences $\{z_n\}$ of points inside the sector AOB that converge to the point O, we have that

$$\overline{\lim_{n=\infty}} |f(z_n)| \leq \mu^{k(\vartheta)}.$$

308. Let us now assume that $f(z)$ is of bound one in the disc $|z-i| < 1$ and that $f(z)$ converges to the number a as z approaches the point O along the curve γ. Given any positive ε, we choose μ_0 so small that

$$\mu_0^{k(\vartheta)} < \varepsilon$$

holds, and construct in the disc of Fig. 39 the circle $|z - i\varrho| = \varrho$, where we select ϱ sufficiently small to insure that on the intersection OE_1 of γ and $|z - i\varrho| < \varrho$, the inequality

$$\left| \frac{f(z) - a}{2} \right| < \mu_0$$

holds. Now we apply the results of the preceding section to the function

$$\frac{f(z) - a}{2},$$

and the disc $|z - i\varrho| < \varrho$, obtaining a lens-shaped region with an angle $> \pi - 2\vartheta$ which is such that in its interior,

$$|f(z) - a| < 2\varepsilon$$

holds. From this it follows that $f(z)$ converges to a for any approach of z to O within the angular sector AOB. We have thus proved the following theorem:

If the bounded function $f(z)$ converges to the number a as z approaches the boundary point O along a Jordan arc γ, then $f(z)$ converges to a also if z approaches O along any other Jordan arc γ' ending at O and lying entirely within the angular sector AOB.

Two Theorems of E. Lindelöf (§ 309)

309. A slight modification of the above construction yields the following theorem, which is due to E. Lindelöf:

Let $f(z)$ be regular and of bound one in the disc $|z - i| < 1$. Let $f(z)$ be continuous at every point ζ of an arc OCB of the boundary of the disc (see Fig. 41 below), and assume that $f(\zeta)$ converges to 0 as ζ approaches

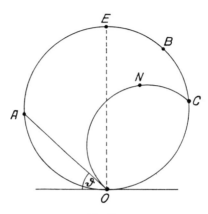

Fig. 41

O along this arc. Then the function $f(z)$ is continuous at O whenever z approaches O from within the circular segment $OCBAO$ (where AO is the chord, not the arc).

To prove this theorem, let us first consider a circular arc CNO that is tangent to the chord AO at O and whose radius is arbitrarily small. Let $\varphi(z)$ be the non-zero analytic function in the disc $|z - i| < 1$ whose modulus equals the constant μ on the arc OC and equals the constant unity on the complementary arc. Within the lens-shaped region $OCNO$, we then have

$$|\varphi(z)| < \mu^{\frac{\vartheta}{\pi}}.$$

If we choose $\mu = \max |f(\zeta)|$ on the arc OC, then the following relation holds everywhere in the disc $|z - i| < 1$:

$$|f(z)| \leq |\varphi(z)|.$$

As C tends to O, μ and $\mu^{\vartheta/\pi}$ converge to zero. This implies that $f(z)$ is continuous at O if z is allowed to approach O from within an arbitrary segment $OCBA'O$ of the circular disc, where A' may be arbitrarily close to A on the arc AB. But since the choice of A itself was arbitrary, we have thus proved the theorem stated at the beginning of this section.

It is noteworthy that the conclusion of the theorem does not depend on the behavior of the function $f(z)$ on the arc AO.

If $f(\zeta)$ is continuous on the arc AO as well and if the limits of $f(\zeta)$ for $\zeta \to 0$ exist and are equal to a and to b for ζ on AO and on OB respectively, then these two limits a and b must be equal provided only that $f(z)$ is bounded. For by our last result, the function $f(z)$ must converge along the diameter EO to both a and b. In this case, $f(z)$ is continuous at O, relative to the entire closed disc. Hence if $a \neq b$ for a function $f(z)$ that is regular in $|z - i| < 1$ and satisfies all of the above continuity conditions on the boundary, then $f(z)$ cannot be bounded. In fact, in this case *every* point ω of the complex plane must be a boundary value of $f(z)$ at O. This is clear for $\omega = a$ and $\omega = b$; but if ω is different from both a and b, then it follows from the result just obtained that the function

$$\frac{1}{f(z) - \omega}$$

cannot be bounded in any neighborhood of the point[1] O. Therefore ω must be a boundary value of $f(z)$. Note, however, that even if $a = b$ the function $f(z)$ may still have an essential singularity at O. In this case, $f(z)$ is of course not bounded. An example of this possibility is given by the function

$$f(z) = e^{-\frac{1}{z^2}}.$$

These results are also due to Lindelöf.

Fatou's Theorem (§§ 310-311)

310. In this and in the next few sections we shall derive several facts that require the use of the Lebesgue integral. The most important and remarkable theorem of this kind is due to P. Fatou (1878-1929), which we state as follows:

Every single-valued analytic function $f(z)$ bounded in the disc $|z| < 1$ is continuous, under approach within an angular sector (cf. § 307 above), at a set of boundary points on $|z| = 1$ whose linear measure always equals 2π.

---

[1] For, any neighborhood of O contains some lens-shaped region R that is the intersection of the disc $|z - i| < 1$ and a disc $|z| < \varepsilon$. As shown in § 314 below, we can map this region R onto the disc $|u - i| < 1$ by means of a function $z = \psi(u)$. By the result obtained in the present section, the function $g(u) = f(\psi(u))$ cannot be bounded in $|u - i| < 1$, so that the function $f(z)$ cannot be bounded in the region R.

In other words, the exceptional points, at which

$$\lim_{r=1} f(r\, e^{i\vartheta})\ \cdot$$

fails to exist, always constitute a set of linear measure zero. To be sure, for certain functions this set of measure zero may be very complicated; it may, for instance, be everywhere dense and non-denumerable on any arc of the boundary $|z| = 1$.

Because of the result obtained in § 308 above, we need prove the theorem only for radial approach to the boundary. Also, we may assume without loss of generality that $f(0) = 0$, since this can always be achieved by merely adding a constant.

Let $f(z)$, then, be regular in $|z| < 1$, and let $|f(z)| < M$ in this disc. We introduce the function

$$F(\varrho, \vartheta) = \int_0^\vartheta f(\varrho\, e^{i\vartheta})\, d\vartheta = \int_\varrho^{\varrho e^{i\vartheta}} \frac{f(z)}{i\,z}\, dz. \qquad (310.1)$$

The second integral in this relation can be taken along any path that joins the points $z = \varrho$ and $z = \varrho\, e^{i\vartheta}$ and lies entirely within $|z| < 1$, since $f(z)/iz$ is regular in the disc $|z| < 1$. Thus $F(\varrho, \vartheta)$ is a single-valued function in $|z| < 1$, whence in particular,

$$F(\varrho, -\pi) = F(\varrho, \pi) \qquad (310.2)$$

follows. Now by (310.1),

$$|F(\varrho + \varDelta\varrho, \vartheta) - F(\varrho, \vartheta)| \leqq \left| \int_\varrho^{\varrho + \varDelta\varrho} \frac{f(z)}{i\,z}\, dz \right| + \left| \int_{\varrho e^{i\vartheta}}^{(\varrho + \varDelta\varrho) e^{i\vartheta}} \frac{f(z)}{i\,z}\, dz \right| < 2\,M\,|\varDelta\varrho|. \qquad (310.3)$$

Here we have used the fact that

$$\left| \frac{f(z)}{z} \right| < M$$

holds, by Schwarz's Lemma. On the other hand, if we fix ϱ and let ϑ vary we obtain

$$|F(\varrho, \vartheta + \varDelta\vartheta) - F(\varrho, \vartheta)| < M\,|\varDelta\vartheta|. \qquad (310.4)$$

From (310.3) we infer that

$$F(\vartheta) = \lim_{\varrho=1} F(\varrho, \vartheta) \qquad (310.5)$$

exists for every ϑ, and that the convergence is uniform. By (310.4), the function $F(\vartheta)$ satisfies the relation

$$\left| \frac{F(\vartheta + \varDelta\vartheta) - F(\vartheta)}{\varDelta\vartheta} \right| \leq M,$$

from which we see that $F(\vartheta)$ is continuous and that its difference quotients are bounded.

We now set $z = r\,e^{i\vartheta}$ and apply the Poisson integral to the circle $|z| = \varrho < 1$, where $r < \varrho$, obtaining

$$f(z) = \frac{1}{2\pi} \int_{-\pi}^{\pi} f(\varrho\,e^{i\varphi}) \frac{\varrho^2 - r^2}{\varrho^2 - 2\,r\,\varrho \cos(\varphi - \vartheta) + r^2}\, d\varphi.$$

Upon integrating by parts, we see from (310.2) that the first resulting term (the one which is *not* an integral) vanishes, so that

$$f(z) = -\frac{1}{2\pi} \int_{-\pi}^{\pi} F(\varrho, \varphi) \frac{d}{d\varphi} \frac{\varrho^2 - r^2}{\varrho^2 - 2\,r\,\varrho \cos(\varphi - \vartheta) + r^2}\, d\varphi.$$

The left-hand side of this equation is independent of ϱ. Since the integrand converges to a continuous function of φ as ϱ tends to unity, we may set $\varrho = 1$ in the last formula, obtaining

$$f(z) = -\frac{1}{2\pi} \int_{-\pi}^{\pi} F(\varphi) \frac{d}{d\varphi} \frac{1 - r^2}{1 - 2\,r \cos(\varphi - \vartheta) + r^2}\, d\varphi. \tag{310.6}$$

An analogous formula holds in the case that $f(z)$ is a constant C; for in this case, we can write

$$C = \frac{1}{2\pi} \int_{-\pi}^{\pi} C \cdot \frac{1 - r^2}{1 - 2\,r \cos(\varphi - \vartheta) + r^2}\, d\varphi,$$

which after an integration by parts yields

$$C = \frac{C(1 - r^2)}{1 + 2\,r \cos\vartheta + r^2} - \frac{1}{2\pi} \int_{-\pi}^{\pi} C\,\varphi\, \frac{d}{d\varphi} \frac{1 - r^2}{1 - 2\,r \cos(\varphi - \vartheta) + r^2}\, d\varphi. \tag{310.7}$$

In particular, for $C = 1$ and $\vartheta = 0$,

$$-\frac{1}{2\pi} \int_{-\pi}^{\pi} \varphi\, \frac{d}{d\varphi} \frac{1 - r^2}{1 - 2\,r \cos\varphi + r^2}\, d\varphi = 1 - \frac{1 - r^2}{(1 + r)^2} = \frac{2}{1 + \dfrac{1}{r}}. \tag{310.8}$$

Let $e^{i\vartheta_0}$ be a point of the unit circle at which $F(\varphi)$ has a finite derivative $F'(\vartheta_0)$. We shall show that in this case,

$$\lim_{r=1} f(r\, e^{i\vartheta_0}) = F'(\vartheta_0) \tag{310.9}$$

holds. Here it suffices to take $\vartheta_0 = 0$, since we can reduce the general case to the special case $\vartheta_0 = 0$ by a rotation of the coordinate system. By (310.6) and (310.7),

$$f(r) - F'(0)$$
$$= -F'(0)\,\frac{1-r}{1+r} - \frac{1}{2\pi}\int_{-\pi}^{\pi}[F(\varphi) - \varphi\,F'(0)]\,\frac{d}{d\varphi}\,\frac{1-r^2}{1-2\,r\cos\varphi + r^2}\,d\varphi.$$

Now we select a positive number $\lambda < \pi$ and set

$$H(r, \lambda) = -\frac{1}{2\pi}\int_{-\lambda}^{\lambda}[F(\varphi) - \varphi\,F'(0)]\,\frac{d}{d\varphi}\,\frac{1-r^2}{1-2\,r\cos\varphi + r^2}\,d\varphi \tag{310.10}$$

and

$$J(r, \lambda) = -\frac{1}{2\pi}\left\{\int_{-\pi}^{-\lambda} + \int_{\lambda}^{\pi}\right\} \tag{310.11}$$

(with the same integrand), so that

$$f(r) - F'(0) = -F'(0)\,\frac{1-r}{1+r} + H(r, \lambda) + J(r, \lambda) \tag{310.12}$$

holds. If we note that (310.1) and (310.5) imply that $F(0) = 0$, and if we set

$$F(\varphi) = \varphi\,F'(0) + \varphi\,\eta(\varphi), \tag{310.13}$$

and denote the l. u. b. of $|\eta(\varphi)|$ in the interval from $-\lambda$ to λ by $h(\lambda)$, we find that

$$\lim_{\lambda=0} h(\lambda) = 0. \tag{310.14}$$

From (310.10) and (310.13) it follows that

$$H(r, \lambda) = -\frac{1}{2\pi}\int_{-\lambda}^{\lambda}\varphi\,\eta(\varphi)\,\frac{d}{d\varphi}\,\frac{1-r^2}{1-2\,r\cos\varphi + r^2}\,d\varphi,$$

and if we note that

$$-\varphi\,\frac{d}{d\varphi}\,\frac{1-r^2}{1-2\,r\cos\varphi + r^2} = \frac{2\,r\,(1-r^2)\,\varphi\sin\varphi}{(1-2\,r\cos\varphi + r^2)^2} \geqq 0 \tag{310.15}$$

holds, we obtain

$$|H(r, \lambda)| \leqq - \frac{h(\lambda)}{2\pi} \int_{-\lambda}^{\lambda} \varphi \frac{d}{d\varphi} \frac{1-r^2}{1-2r\cos\varphi+r^2} \, d\varphi$$

$$< - \frac{h(\lambda)}{2\pi} \int_{-\pi}^{\pi} \varphi \frac{d}{d\varphi} \frac{1-r^2}{1-2r\cos\varphi+r^2} \, d\varphi,$$

and hence finally, by (310.8),

$$|H(r, \lambda)| < \frac{2\,h(\lambda)}{1+\dfrac{1}{r}} < h(\lambda). \tag{310.16}$$

In order to obtain a bound for $J(r, \lambda)$, we first observe that by (310.4) and (310.5),

$$|F(\varphi)| < \pi M$$

holds in the interval of integration, and that in the same interval, we have (cf. § 152, Vol. I, p. 148)

$$\left| \frac{d}{d\varphi} \frac{1-r^2}{1-2r\cos\varphi+r^2} \right| < \frac{2r(1-r^2)}{(1-2r\cos\lambda+r^2)^2} < \frac{2(1-r^2)}{(1-\cos^2\lambda)^2}.$$

Hence (310.11) yields

$$|J(r, \lambda)| < \frac{2\pi(M+|F'(0)|)}{\sin^4\lambda}(1-r^2). \tag{310.17}$$

Finally, we obtain from (310.12), (310.16) and (310.17) that

$$|f(r) - F'(0)| < h(\lambda) + \left\{ \frac{2\pi(M+|F'(0)|)}{\sin^4\lambda} + \frac{|F'(0)|}{(1+r)^2} \right\}(1-r^2). \tag{310.18}$$

Given any positive number ε, then by (310.14) we can choose λ so small that $h(\lambda) < \varepsilon/2$. It then follows from (310.17) that for sufficiently small values of $1-r^2$,

$$|f(r) - F'(0)| < \varepsilon. \tag{310.19}$$

We have thus derived as a first result the fact that for every ϑ_0 where $F(\vartheta)$ is differentiable, the given function $f(z)$ converges to the value $F'(\vartheta_0)$ as z approaches $e^{i\vartheta_0}$ radially.

To complete the proof of Fatou's theorem, we shall now make use of the following basic theorem of Lebesgue: *If a real function is defined on an interval I and if its difference quotients are bounded on I, then the function is differentiable everywhere on I except possibly on a set of linear measure zero.*[1]

According to this theorem, both the real and the imaginary part of $F(\varphi)$ are differentiable except at most on a set of measure zero, and this, together with the preliminary result stated above, proves Fatou's theorem.

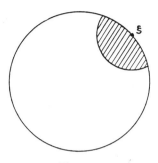

Fig. 42

311. We shall prove next an important generalization of Fatou's theorem. We consider a function $f(z)$ that is regular or merely meromorphic in the disc $|z| < 1$ and the boundary values of which at a certain point ζ of the boundary $|z| = 1$ fail to cover the Riemann sphere completely. Then there exists at least one number ω, finite or infinite, that is distinct from every boundary value at ζ.

If $\omega = \infty$ then the function $g(z) = f(z)$ is bounded in a certain neighborhood of ζ within the disc. If ω is finite, the same statement holds true for the function

$$g(z) = \frac{1}{f(z) - \omega}.$$

In either case, $g(z)$ is bounded in a certain lens (see Fig. 42 above). This lens can be mapped onto the disc $|u| < 1$ by means of a function $z = \psi(u)$ composed of elementary transformations (*cf.* § 314 below). The function $g(\psi(u))$ is also bounded in $|u| < 1$, so that Fatou's theorem applies to it. Interpreted in terms of the original function $f(z)$, this means that the conclusions of Fatou's theorem apply to $f(z)$ in a certain neighborhood of the point ζ.

This means that *if the boundary points for which*

$$\lim_{r=1} f(r\,e^{i\vartheta})$$

---

[1] *Cf.* C. Carathéodory, *Vorlesungen über reelle Funktionen*, 2nd edition (Chelsea Publishing Co., New York 1948). p. 589.

*fails to exist constitute a set of positive Lebesgue measure on every boundary
arc that contains the point ζ, then the set of boundary values of f(z) at ζ must
cover the entire Riemann sphere.*

Generalization of Poisson's Integral (§ 312)

312. The method by which we proved Fatou's theorem will also enable us
to greatly generalize the theory of the Poisson integral.

Let $f(z)$ be a real function that is bounded and Lebesgue-measurable[1] in
the interval $-\pi < \varphi < \pi$. If we set $z = r\,e^{i\vartheta}$, the formula

$$U(r, \vartheta) = \frac{1}{2\pi} \int_{-\pi}^{\pi} f(\varphi)\,\frac{1 - r^2}{1 - 2r\cos(\varphi - \vartheta) + r^2}\,d\varphi \qquad (312.1)$$

defines a function that is harmonic in the disc $|z| < 1$. The function

$$F(\varphi) = \int_{0}^{\varphi} f(\vartheta)\,d\vartheta$$

is continuous and has bounded difference quotients that are subject to all of
the pertinent inequalities of § 310 above. It follows that for all φ for which
$F(\varphi)$ has a finite derivative $F'(\varphi)$, the equation

$$\lim_{r=1} U(r, \varphi) = F'(\varphi) \qquad (312.2)$$

holds. But by a theorem of Lebesgue theory,[2] we have

$$F'(\varphi) = f(\varphi)$$

except possibly on a set of measure zero, whence we deduce that everywhere,
except possibly on a set of measure zero,

$$\lim_{r=1} U(r, \varphi) = f(\varphi). \qquad (312.3)$$

This result should be compared with Schwarz's theorem of § 150 ff., Vol. I,
p. 146 ff.

---

[1] Carathéodory, *loc. cit.* p. 374 ff.
[2] *Loc. cit.*, p. 589.

The Theorem of F. and M. Riesz (§ 313)

313. We shall now prove the following theorem: *Let the function $f(z)$ be analytic and bounded in the disc $|z| < 1$, say $|f(z)| < M$, and let e be a Lebesgue-measurable point set on the circle $|z| = 1$ which is such that*

$$\lim_{r=1} f(r \, e^{i\vartheta})$$

exists and equals zero at every point of e. Then if the Lebesgue measure $m(e)$ of e is positive, the function $f(z)$ must vanish identically.

To prove this, let e' be the set that is the complement of e on $|z| = 1$, and let us assume first that the Lebesgue measure of e' is positive. Let $u(r \, e^{i\vartheta})$ be a harmonic function that assumes the constant value $A/m(e)$ almost everywhere on e (that is, everywhere on e except possibly on a subset of measure zero), and the value $A/[m(e) - 2\pi]$ almost everywhere on e'. Here, A stands for an arbitrary positive number. Then it follows from the preceding section that

$$u(0) = m(e) \cdot \frac{A}{m(e)} + [2\pi - m(e)] \, \frac{A}{m(e) - 2\pi} = 0.$$

Let $v(r \, e^{i\vartheta})$ be the harmonic function conjugate to $u \, (r \, e^{i\vartheta})$, which we can and do choose in such a way that $v(0) = 0$ (*cf.* § 150, Vol. I, p. 146 ff.). Then the function $g(z) = e^{u + iv}$ is regular inside the unit circle and satisfies $g(0) = 1$ and $|g(z)| = e^{u}$. Therefore $|g(z)|$ is bounded in the disc $|z| < 1$, just as is $u(z)$. Also, according to the result of the preceding section, the following relation holds almost everywhere on e' for the radial limit of $g(z)$:

$$\lim_{r=1} \left| g(r \, e^{i\varphi}) \right| = e^{\frac{A}{m(e) - 2\pi}}.$$

The function $f(z) g(z)$ is likewise analytic and bounded inside the unit circle. Hence by Fatou's theorem, we can apply the Cauchy Integral Formula to this function not only for the circles $|z| = r < 1$ but even for the unit circle $|z| = 1$ itself, since by a well-known theorem of Lebesgue we can in the case of bounded sequences interchange the two operations of taking the limit and of integrating. In particular, by formula (135.5), Vol. I, p. 132, we have

$$f(0) = f(0) \, g(0) = \frac{1}{2\pi} \int_{-\pi}^{\pi} f(e^{i\varphi}) \, g(e^{i\varphi}) \, d\varphi = \frac{1}{2\pi} \int_{e'} f(e^{i\varphi}) \, g(e^{i\varphi}) \, d\varphi,$$

since the integrand is zero on the set e. From this it follows that

$$|f(0)| = \frac{1}{2\pi} \left| \int_{e'} f(e^{i\varphi}) \, g(e^{i\varphi}) \, d\varphi \right| \leq \frac{1}{2\pi} \, e^{\frac{A}{m(e) - 2\pi}} \int_{e'} |f(e^{i\varphi})| \, d\varphi < M \, e^{\frac{A}{m(e) - 2\pi}}.$$

Here, A may be any positive number, as large as we please; hence $f(0) = 0$.

Now if we set $f_1(z) = f(z)/z$, then $f_1(z)$ is also bounded, and its boundary values agree with those of $f(z)$ in modulus. Therefore we may apply the above discussion to $f_1(z)$ in place of $f(z)$ and conclude that $f_1(0) = 0$. Similarly, the functions $f_n(z) = f_{n-1}(z)/z$, $(n = 2, 3, \ldots)$ must vanish at $z = 0$, so that by § 143, Vol. I, p. 138, we must have $f(z) \equiv 0$.

If $m(e') = 0$, then it follows from well-known properties of the Lebesgue integral that $f(z)$ must vanish identically, and we have thus completed the proof of the theorem of F. and M. Riesz.

At the same time, we have obtained the following result:

If $f(z)$ is a non-constant bounded function in $|z| < 1$ and a any complex number, then the set of points on the boundary $|z| = 1$ at which $f(z)$ assumes the value a is of linear measure zero.

Hence for any given arc on $|z| = 1$, the values assumed by the radial limits—the existence of which is insured by Fatou's theorem—form a non-denumerable set of numbers. For, the union of denumerably many sets of measure zero would itself amount to a set of measure zero, so that its measure could not equal that of the given arc.

CHAPTER TWO

CONFORMAL MAPPING

Elementary Mappings (§ 314)

314. We can map certain simple regions onto the interior $|z| < 1$ of the unit circle by combining Moebius transformations with the elementary conformal mappings that we studied in §§ 246 ff. and 254 ff. (Vol. I, p. 256 ff. and

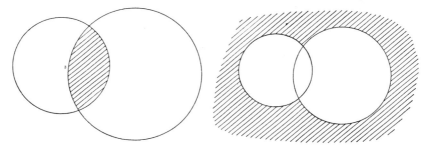

Fig. 43

p. 263 ff.). The two most important cases that we shall need in the sequel are that of the general lens and that of the crescent of angle zero.[1]

Consider the region bounded by two circular arcs (see Fig. 43) that intersect in the two points w_0 and w_1 at the angle $\pi\lambda$, where $0 < \lambda < 2$. In order to map this region (the "general lens," or "general crescent") onto the disc $|z| < 1$, we first set

$$u = e^{i\vartheta} \frac{w - w_0}{w - w_1}.$$ (314.1)

This transformation maps the lens onto an (infinite) sector bounded by two rays emanating from $u = 0$. Let us choose ϑ in (314.1) in such a way that one of these rays coincides with the positive real axis. Then if we set

$$v = u^{\frac{1}{\lambda}} = e^{\frac{1}{\lambda} l u},$$ (314.2)

---

[1] The terms *lens* and *crescent* are applied to any region bounded by two intersecting circular arcs. (The German term is *Kreisbogenzweieck*.)

the above sector is mapped onto the half-plane $\Im v > 0$ (*cf.* § 255, Vol. I, p. 264), and this half-plane can be mapped onto the disc $|z| < 1$ by means of another Moebius transformation, for instance by

$$z = \frac{v - i}{v + i} \, . \qquad\qquad (314.3)$$

The desired mapping function is the product of the transformations (314.1), (314.2), and (314.3). We note that the two boundary arcs of the lens are mapped analytically onto two complementary arcs of the circle $|z| = 1$, except that the analyticity of the mapping breaks down at the two "vertices"

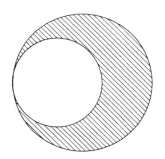 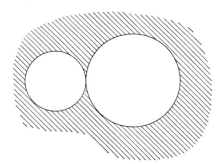

Fig. 44

of the lens; but even at those, the mapping is still continuous.

The limiting case $\lambda = 2$ can readily be given a meaning, as follows: It represents the mapping of the complex plane with a cut along a circular arc, onto the interior of a circle.

Returning to the general case, it is easy to verify that any given arc of a circle in $|z| < 1$ that connects the images on $|z| = 1$ of w_0 and w_1 has as its pre-image, in the above mapping, an arc of a circle through the interior of the lens; and the latter arc forms with any one of the boundary arcs of the lens an angle that is proportional to λ; this follows easily from § 254, Vol. I, p. 263. At the vertices of the lens, the mapping is not conformal; it is referred to, at these points, as a *quasi-conformal mapping*.

If $\lambda = 0$ (see Fig. 44), the two points w_0 and w_1 coincide, and with a proper choice of α and β, the Moebius transformation

$$u = \frac{\alpha w + \beta}{w - w_0} \qquad\qquad (314.4)$$

maps the given region onto an infinite strip of width π, bounded by two parallel lines one of which coincides with the real u-axis. This strip is mapped by

$$v = e^u$$

onto the half-plane $\Im v > 0$, and this in turn is mapped onto $|z| < 1$ by (314.3). In this case too, there are two complementary arcs on $|z| = 1$ that are the analytic images of the two boundary arcs of the given crescent.

The Riemann Mapping Theorem for Bounded Regions (§§ 315-323)

315. Let a be a real number for which $0 < a < 1$. The Riemann surface of two sheets that is cut along $|w| = 1$ and has a branch point at $w = a^2$ is mapped by

$$\frac{a^2 - w}{1 - a^2 w} = \left(\frac{a - z}{1 - a z} \right)^2 \tag{315.1}$$

conformally onto the disc $|z| < 1$. From (315.1) it follows that

$$w = z \frac{h - z}{1 - h z}, \qquad h = \frac{2a}{1 + a^2} < 1, \qquad \frac{dw}{dz} = 2 \frac{(a - z)(1 - a z)}{(1 + a^2)(1 - h z)^2}. \tag{315.2}$$

Hence in the disc $|z| \leqq 1$ we have $dw/dz \neq 0$ everywhere except at $z = a$, $w = a^2$. We also know from (14.11), Vol. I, p. 13, that at every point of this disc,

$$\frac{h - z}{1 - h z} \leqq \frac{h + |z|}{1 + h |z|},$$

where the function

$$\frac{h + |z|}{1 + h |z|} = 1 - \frac{(1 - h)(1 - |z|)}{1 + h |z|}$$

increases monotonically with $|z|$. Then for every ζ satisfying $|z| < \zeta < 1$

$$|w(z)| = \left| z \frac{h - z}{1 - h z} \right| \leqq |z| \frac{h + |z|}{1 + h |z|} < \zeta \frac{h + \zeta}{1 + h \zeta}. \tag{315.3}$$

In particular,

$$|w(z)| < a^2 \tag{315.4}$$

if we choose for ζ the positive root of the equation

$$\zeta \frac{h + \zeta}{1 + h \zeta} = a^2, \qquad h = \frac{2a}{1 + a^2}, \tag{315.5}$$

i.e. if we set

$$\zeta = a \, \frac{-(1-a^2) + \sqrt{2(1+a^4)}}{1+a^2} \, . \tag{315.6}$$

From this we obtain

$$\zeta - a^2 = \frac{a}{1+a^2} \left\{ -1 - a + a^2 - a^3 + \sqrt{2(1+a^4)} \right\}$$

$$= \frac{a(1-a)^3(1+a)}{(1+a) - a^2(1-a) + \sqrt{2(1+a^4)}} = \frac{a(1-a)^3}{\left(1 - a^2 \dfrac{1-a}{1+a}\right) + \sqrt{2 \dfrac{1+a^4}{(1+a)^2}}} \, .$$

Since

$$1 - a^2 \frac{1-a}{1+a} < 1, \qquad \frac{1+a^4}{1+2a+a^2} < 1,$$

we finally have

$$\zeta - a^2 > \frac{a(1-a)^3}{1+\sqrt{2}} > \frac{2a(1-a)^3}{5} \, . \tag{315.7}$$

We have thus obtained the following result.

The function $w = f(z)$ *defined by* (315.1) *maps the closed disc*

$$|z| \leqq a^2 + \frac{2a(1-a)^3}{5} \tag{315.8}$$

conformally onto a point set lying in the interior of the circle $|w| = a^2$.

This result remains valid if the branch point $w = a^2$ is moved to the point $w = a^2 e^{i\vartheta}$ by means of simultaneous rotations of the w-plane and the z-plane, through the same angle. Instead of (315.2), we must set, in this case,

$$w = z \, \frac{h \, e^{i\vartheta} - z}{e^{i\vartheta} - h \, z} = \varphi(a, \vartheta, z), \tag{315.9}$$

and we then have

$$\frac{dw}{dz}\bigg|_{z=0} = h = \frac{2a}{1+a^2} > 0.$$

316. Let G be a region in the disc $|w| < 1$ of any connectivity—finite or even infinite—and let A be the closed complement of G in $|w| \leqq 1$. We assume that the center of the disc is an interior point of G and that the distance a^2 between $w = 0$ and the set A is less than unity. Then A contains at least one point of the form

$$w^* = a^2 \, e^{i\vartheta}. \tag{316.1}$$

We now introduce the unit function

$$w = w_1 \, \frac{h \, e^{i\vartheta} - w_1}{e^{i\vartheta} - h \, w_1} = \varphi(a, \vartheta, w_1), \qquad h = \frac{2a}{1+a^2} \, , \tag{316.2}$$

where a and ϑ are as in (316.1), and we denote by A_1 the set of points of the disc $|w_1| \leq 1$ that are mapped onto points of A by (316.2). Let a_1^2 be the distance from $w_1 = 0$ to the set A_1. Then the set A_1 contains at least one point of the form

$$w_1^* = a_1^2 e^{i\vartheta_1}. \tag{316.3}$$

As above, we set

$$w_1 = w_2 \frac{h_1 e^{i\vartheta_1} - w_2}{e^{i\vartheta_1} - h_1 w_2} = \varphi(a_1, \vartheta_1, w_2), \qquad h_1 = \frac{2 a_1}{1 + a_1^2}. \tag{316.4}$$

Now we denote by A_2 the set of points of the disc $|w_2| \leq 1$ that are mapped by (316.4) onto points of A_1, and we denote by a_2^2 the distance from $w_2 = 0$ to A_2.

Continuing in this way, we obtain an infinite sequence of closed point sets $A_1, A_2, \ldots$ and two infinite sequences of numbers $a_1, a_2, \ldots$ and $\vartheta_1, \vartheta_2, \ldots$. We note that all of the positive numbers $a_k \, (k = 1, 2, \ldots)$ are < 1.

Now if ζ_k is the positive root of the equation

$$\zeta \frac{h_k + \zeta}{1 + h_k \zeta} = a_k^2 \qquad \left(h_k = \frac{2 a_k}{1 + a_k^2} \right),$$

then the transformation $w_k = \varphi(a_k, \vartheta_k, w_{k+1})$ maps the disc $|w_{k+1}| < \zeta_k$ onto a point set of the w_k-plane that contains no points of A_k. Hence we always have $a_{k+1}^2 \geq \zeta_k$. This together with (315.7) yields

$$a_{k+1}^2 - a_k^2 \geq \zeta_k - a_k^2 > \frac{2 a_k (1 - a_k)^3}{5}$$

and further, since $a_{k+1} + a_k < 2$,

$$a_{k+1} > a_k + \frac{a_k (1 - a_k)^3}{5}. \tag{316.5}$$

Therefore

$$a_1 < a_2 < \ldots$$

and

$$\lim_{k = \infty} a_k = 1. \tag{316.6}$$

317. Let us consider a sequence of unit functions

$$f_1(z), f_2(z), \ldots, \tag{317.1}$$

defined successively by the equations

$$f_1(z) = \varphi(a, \vartheta, z), \quad f_{n+1}(z) = f_n(\varphi(a_n, \vartheta_n, z)) \quad (n = 1, 2, \ldots). \tag{317.2}$$

Then $f_n(z)$ is a unit function of degree 2^n and satisfies $f_n(0) = 0$, $f_n'(0) > 0$.

We also note that

$$w = f_n(z) \tag{317.3}$$

maps every point of the disc $|z| < 1$ that is not in A_n—hence in particular, every point of the disc $|z| < a_n^2$—onto a point of G. At all of these points, we have

$$f_n'(z) \neq 0. \tag{317.4}$$

318. We shall study some further properties of the functions $f_n(z)$. Let $0 < r < 1$, and denote by $B_n(r)$ the point set in the w-plane that is the image of the closed disc $|z| \leqq r$ under the mapping (317.3). A point of $B_n(r)$ may of course have more than one pre-image in $|z| \leqq r$. Since $|\varphi(a_n, \vartheta_n, z)| < |z|$, it follows from (317.2) that

$$B_{n+1}(r) \leq B_n(r). \tag{318.1}$$

Hence if $\varDelta_n(r)$ stands for the distance (which may be zero) between the two closed sets $B_n(r)$ and A, we must have

$$\varDelta_1(r) \leqq \varDelta_2(r) \leqq \cdots. \tag{318.2}$$

For all n for which $r < a_n^2$, the closed point set $B_n(r)$ lies in the region G, and we therefore have

$$\lim_{n = \infty} \varDelta_n(r) > 0. \tag{318.3}$$

A second property of the function $f_n(z)$ may be regarded in a certain sense as the converse of the first. Let w_0 be any point of G, and let it be connected to $w = 0$ by a path γ_w lying in (the interior of) G. Then by (317.4), we can find for every n a path $\gamma_z(n)$ that lies in $|z| < 1$, emanates from $z = 0$, and is mapped by (317.3) onto γ_w. Now we can prove the following theorem:
All of these paths $\gamma_z(n)$ lie in a fixed disc

$$|z| \leqq r_\gamma, \tag{318.4}$$

the radius r_γ of which is < 1.

To prove this, we first note that for every point z of $\gamma_z(n)$ we can solve the equation $w = f_n(z)$ for z, obtaining the inverse function $z = g_n(w)$. If we denote the minimum of the distance between γ_w and A by δ, then the function

$$\psi(u) = g_n(w + \delta u) \tag{318.5}$$

is regular and of bound one in the disc $|u| < 1$. Hence by (290.4), we have

$$|\psi'(0)| \leqq 1 - |\psi(0)|^2, \tag{318.6}$$

where by (318.5), we must set

$$\psi(0) = g_n(w) = z, \quad \psi'(0) = \delta\, g'_n(w) = \delta\, \frac{dz}{dw}.$$

But this implies that

$$\delta \left| \frac{dz}{dw} \right| \leqq 1 - |z|^2,$$

whence, by integrating, we obtain

$$\int\limits_{\gamma_z(n)} \frac{|dz|}{1 - |z|^2} \leqq \frac{1}{\delta} \int\limits_{\gamma_w} |dw|. \tag{318.7}$$

The first of these integrals is equal to the non-Euclidean length Λ_n of $\gamma_z(n)$, while the right-hand side represents the Euclidean length L of γ_w divided by δ. Therefore,

$$\Lambda_n \leqq \frac{L}{\delta},$$

and we need only set

$$r_\gamma = \operatorname{tgh} \frac{L}{2\,\delta} < 1$$

to complete the proof of the above statement.

319. We are now able to prove that the sequence $\{f_n(z)\}$ converges. Since this sequence is normal in the disc $|z| < 1$, it contains subsequences $\{f_{n_j}(z)\}$ for which

$$\lim_{j=\infty} f_{n_j}(z) = f(z), \tag{319.1}$$

the convergence in (319.1) being continuous.

Now let z be any (interior) point of the disc $|z| < 1$, and select a number r for which $|z| < r < 1$. We also introduce the notation

$$w_n = f_n(z). \tag{319.2}$$

Then if δ_n stands for the distance from w_n to A, we have by the preceding section that

$$\delta_n \geqq \Lambda_n(r). \tag{319.3}$$

Also, from (319.1),

$$w = f(z) = \lim_{j=\infty} w_{n_j},$$

and by (318.3) and (319.3) we have

$$\lim_{j=\infty} \delta_{n_j} \geqq \lim_{j=\infty} \Lambda_{n_j}(r) > 0. \tag{319.4}$$

From this we conclude that every point $w = f(z)$ is an interior point of G.

Let us now consider once more the paths $\dot{\gamma}_w$ and $\gamma_z(n)$ introduced in the preceding section, and let $z^{(n)}$ be the point of $\gamma_z(n)$ that is mapped onto the point w_0 by (317.3). If z^* is a point of accumulation of the set $\{z^{(n_j)}\}$, then the sequence $n_1, n_2, \ldots$ contains a subsequence $n_1', n_2', \ldots$ for which

$$z^* = \lim_{j = \infty} z^{(n'_j)} \tag{319.5}$$

holds. All of the points $z^{(n)}$ lie in the disc $|z| \leq r_\gamma$. Hence

$$f(z^*) = \lim_{j = \infty} f_{n'_j}(z^{(n'_j)}) = w_0 . \tag{319.6}$$

Now let $\gamma_w^*(n)$ be the image under $w = f_n(z)$ of the line-segment joining $z = 0$ and $z = z^{(n)}$, and let γ_w^* be the image under $w = f(z)$ of the segment joining $z = 0$ and $z = z^*$. We note that for all values of n for which $a_n^2 > r_\gamma$, the curve $\gamma_w^*(n)$ is *topologically equivalent*, or *homotopic*,[1] to the given curve γ_w and has the same end point w_0. But since the curves $\gamma_w^*(n_j)$ converge uniformly to $\gamma_w^{*\prime}$, the curve γ_w^* must also be homotopic in G to the curve γ_w. We have thus obtained the following result:

Every point z of the disc $|z| < 1$ is mapped by $w = f(z)$ onto an interior point of the region G. For every path γ_w that lies in G and joins $w = 0$ to a point w_0, there is at least one point z^* such that

$$w_0 = f(z^*) \tag{319.7}$$

and such that the image γ_w^* of the line-segment joining $z = 0$ and $z = z^*$ is homotopic in G to the given path γ_w. Finally, at every point z of the disc $|z| < 1$ we have

$$f'(z) \neq 0 .$$

The last statement is an immediate consequence of Hurwitz's theorem (§ 198, Vol. I, p. 194) if we only note that in every disc $|z| < r < 1$, the derivative $f_n'(z)$ is $\neq 0$ for all sufficiently large n. Therefore the function

$$z = g(w) = \lim_{n = \infty} g_n(w)$$

---

[1] Two curves γ_w and γ_w^* lying in the interior of G and having the same end points w_0 and w_1 are said to be *homotopic in G* if they can be approximated to any desired degree of closeness by polygonal paths whose union is a sum of closed polygons lying, along with their interiors, entirely in G. In this case, the closed curve that is obtained by taking γ_w from w_0 to w_1, and γ_w^* back from w_1 to w_0, can be shrunk to any one of its points by means of a continuous deformation that takes place entirely within G.

not only exists in a neighborhood of the point $w = 0$ but can also be continued along any path γ_w within G (*cf.* § 232, Vol. I, p. 236 ff.).

320. We shall now prove, on the basis of the properties established in the preceding section, that the mapping function $w = f(z)$ is uniquely determined.

To this end, let $\varphi(t)$ be regular in $|t| < 1$ and let every point t of this disc be mapped by $w = \varphi(t)$ onto a point of the region G. Assume also that to every curve γ_w in G that joins $w = 0$ to a second point $w = w_0$, there corresponds at least one curve γ_t in $|t| < 1$ that joins $t = 0$ to $t = t_0$. Finally, let $\varphi'(t) \neq 0$ in $|t| < 1$, let $\varphi(0) = 0$, and $\varphi'(0) > 0$.

Now if t is any point of $|t| < 1$ and if γ_w is the image under $w = \varphi(t)$ of the line-segment joining the center $t = 0$ of the disc to the point t, then by the theorem of § 319, the pre-image under $w = f(z)$ of the curve γ_w is a curve γ_z that joins $z = 0$ to a second point z of the disc $|z| < 1$. Thus we are led to a function $z = \psi(t)$ regular in a certain neighborhood of t. By the monodromy theorem, $\psi(t)$ must be a single-valued regular function everywhere in $|t| < 1$, and it satisfies $\psi(0) = 0$ and $\psi'(0) > 0$. By interchanging the roles of t and z in the above, we similarly obtain a function $t = \chi(z)$ of bound one in $|z| < 1$, which is the inverse of $z = \psi(t)$ and for which $\chi(0) = 0$ and $\chi'(0) > 0$. But by Schwarz's Lemma we have $\psi'(0) \leq 1$ and $\chi'(0) \leq 1$, which together with $\chi'(0)\psi'(0) = 1$ yield $\psi(t) \equiv t$. Therefore $t = z$ and $\varphi(z) \equiv f(z)$.

By the same method as was used in the proof of Vitali's theorem (§ 191, Vol. I, p. 189), we now find that the original sequence $\{f_n(z)\}$ itself converges to $f(z)$, introduced in § 319 above merely as the limit of the subsequence $\{f_{n_j}(z)\}$.

321. The function $z = g(w)$ introduced at the end of § 319 need not be single-valued. In other words, the mapping $w = f(z)$ may assign to two different points z' and z'' the same image point w_0, so that

$$f(z') = f(z'') = w_0$$

holds. But in this case, the images in G of the two line-segments joining $z = 0$ to $z = z'$ and to $z = z''$ cannot be homotopic in G. For if they were, then we should be able to transform the path $z'Oz''$ formed by the two segments by means of a continuous deformation into a curve $\bar{\gamma}_z$ that joins z' to z'' and whose image in G is a closed curve $\bar{\gamma}_w$ passing through w_0 and having a diameter (as a point-set) that is as small as we please. But since $f'(z') \neq 0$, there is a neighborhood $U_{z'}$ of the point z' that does not contain the point z'' and is mapped one-to-one onto a neighborhood U_{w_0} of w_0. This leads to a contradiction if the diameter of set $\bar{\gamma}_w$ is so small that this curve γ_w lies wholly within U_{w_0}; for then $\bar{\gamma}_z$ would lie wholly in $U_{z'}$ and thus could not join z' to z''.

322. If, in particular, the region G is simply-connected, then any two paths γ_w and γ_w' that join $w = 0$ to $w = w_0$ are homotopic in G. In this case, there is therefore one and only one point z_0 in $|z| < 1$ that is mapped by $w = f(z)$ onto a given point w_0. Hence by the monodromy theorem, the function $z = g(w)$ is single-valued in G and the mapping $w = f(z)$ is simple (schlicht). *Cf.* § 200, Vol. I, p. 196.

323. Let G be a simply-connected region of the w-plane that may or may not contain the point at infinity in its interior and whose frontier contains at least two distinct points A_1 and B_1 (see Fig. 45 below).

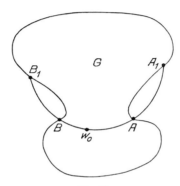

Fig. 45

Let w_0 be an interior point of G that is not at infinity. We construct the arc $A_1 w_0 B_1$ of the circle determined by these three points (this arc may degenerate into a line-segment or into a ray). Let A be the first frontier point of G that is encountered on the (directed) sub-arc $w_0 A_1$, and let B be the corresponding point on the complementary sub-arc $w_0 B_1$. Then all of the interior points of the arc $A w_0 B$ are interior points of G, and its end-points A and B are frontier points of G.

We now map the w-plane onto a u-plane, by means of a Moebius transformation, in such a way that the points A, w_0, and B of the w-plane are mapped onto the points 0, 1, and ∞ respectively of the u-plane. The image of the region G is then a simply-connected region G_1 of the u-plane that has the points $u = 0$ and $u = \infty$ as frontier points and contains all of the points of the positive real axis in its interior. We now set $u = v^4$; then among the regions of the v-plane that correspond to G_1, there is one that contains the point $v = 1$ in its interior. This region, which like G_1 itself is simply-connected, we denote by G_2. It lies entirely in the half-plane $\Re v > 0$; for if G_2 contained a point v^* for which $\Re v^* \leqq 0$, then G_2 would contain a Jordan arc joining $v = 1$ to v^*. Then let P be the first point of the imaginary axis that is encountered as the Jordan arc is traversed from $v = 1$ to $v = v^*$, and let Q

be the last point of the real axis encountered on the sub-arc $1P$. The sub-arc PQ, which we denote by γ_0, would then lie either in the first or in the fourth quadrant of the v-plane. Under $u = v^4$, the arc γ_0 would be mapped onto a curve γ_u lying in G_1 and having its end-points on the positive real axis of the u-plane. By adding a piece of the real axis, if necessary, to γ_u, we would thus have obtained a closed Jordan curve containing the point $u = 0$ in its interior. But such a curve cannot exist, because G_1 is a simply-connected region that contains neither $u = 0$ nor $u = \infty$ as interior points.

Now if we set

$$t = \frac{v-1}{v+1},$$

then the half-plane $\Re v > 0$ is mapped onto the interior $|t| < 1$ of the unit circle $|t| = 1$. We have thus obtained the following result:

Every simply-connected region whose frontier contains at least two distinct points can be mapped onto a bounded region by means of elementary transformations.

Combining this result with that of the preceding section, we obtain the *Riemann Mapping Theorem*:

Every simply-connected region having at least two distinct frontier points can be mapped one-to-one and conformally onto the interior of the unit circle. The mapping function $w = f(z)$ is determined uniquely if we assign to a given line element[1] in the region G a definite line element in the disc $|z| < 1$.

The Koebe-Faber Distortion Theorem (§§ 324-329)

324. Let G be a simply-connected region of the w-plane that does not contain the point at infinity in its interior. Assume that the disc $|w| < 1$ lies in G and that the point $w = 1$ is a frontier point of G.

Let us consider the two-sheeted Riemann surface having its branch points at $w = 1$ and $w = \infty$. The transformation

$$1 - w = u^2 \qquad (324.1)$$

maps this surface onto the simple u-plane; the two points $u = \pm 1$ correspond to the two points of the Riemann surface that lie "over" $w = 0$.

The transformation (324.1) maps every curve in G that emanates from $w = 0$ onto two curves of the u-plane. The set of all curves of the u-plane

---

[1] A *line element* consists of a point z_0 along with a direction through z_0. Thus the last condition is met if we assign, say, the conditions $w_0 = f(z_0)$, $f'(z_0) > 0$.

that can be obtained in this way and that, in particular, emanate from $u = +1$, covers a simply-connected region that we shall denote by G_u.

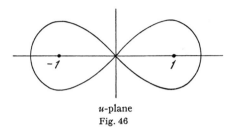

u-plane
Fig. 46

If u_0 is any complex number, then the region G_u cannot contain both of the points $\pm u_0$. For if it did, then we could join these two points by a path γ_u entirely within G_u; to γ_u there would correspond in G a closed curve γ_w, a single point w_0 of which would correspond to the two end-points $\pm u_0$ of γ_u. Since G is simply-connected, we could transform γ_w by means of a continuous deformation into a curve passing through w_0 and having an arbitrarily small diameter. But since the end-points of the image curve γ_u remain fixed throughout this deformation, we would thus be led to a contradiction.

Equation (324.1) transforms the circle $|w| = 1$ into a lemniscate of the u-plane whose equation in polar coordinates is

$$\varrho^2 = 2 \cos 2 \vartheta \qquad (324.2)$$

This lemniscate (see Fig. 46 above) is symmetric with respect to the point $u = 0$, and of the two finite regions bounded by its loops, one must lie entirely within G_u while the other, by what we have just proved, cannot contain any point of G_u. The transformation

$$t = \frac{1 - u}{1 + u}, \qquad u = \frac{1 - t}{1 + t} \qquad (324.3)$$

maps the lemniscate (324.2) onto the closed curve C of Fig. 47 below, which has a double point at $t = 1$ and also consists of two loops.

The transformation (324.3) maps G_u onto a simply-connected region G_t that lies wholly within one of these two loops and contains the other loop in its interior. Also, by elimination of u from (324.1) and (324.3), we obtain the equations

$$t = \frac{1 - \sqrt{1 - w}}{1 + \sqrt{1 - w}} = \frac{(1 - \sqrt{1 - w})^2}{w}, \qquad w = \frac{4 t}{(1 + t)^2}. \qquad (324.4)$$

From this it follows that for $|w| = 1$,

$$|t| < (1 + \sqrt{2})^2 \tag{324.5}$$

holds. Since the two loops of the curve C are mapped onto each other by

$$t' = \frac{1}{t}$$

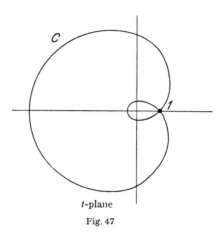

t-plane

Fig. 47

we also have that for $|w| = 1$,

$$|t| > (1 + \sqrt{2})^{-2}. \tag{324.6}$$

From this we see that G_t lies in the disc (324.5) and contains the disc complementary to (324.6) in its interior. Finally, if we set

$$t = (1 + \sqrt{2})^2 z,$$

then G_t is mapped onto a simply-connected region G_z of the z-plane that lies in the interior $|z| < 1$ of the unit circle and contains the disc $|z| < (1 + \sqrt{2})^{-4}$ in its interior. Neither G nor G_u contains the point at infinity in its interior; therefore the point $t = -1$ is not in the interior of G_t, and the point $z = -(1 + \sqrt{2})^{-2}$ is not in the interior of G_z.

325. Let G^* be a simply-connected subregion of G that is bounded by an analytic curve γ_w and contains the point $w = 0$ in its interior. The transformation (324.1) maps G^* onto two separate regions of the u-plane, one of which contains the point $u = 1$ while the other contains $u = -1$. The boundaries of these regions are likewise analytic curves, which we denote by γ_u' and γ_u''. If u' is any point of γ_u', then $u'' = -u'$ is a point of γ_u''. The two regions are in turn mapped by (324.3) onto two separate simply-connected regions of the t-plane. One of these contains the point $t = 0$ and will be denoted by G_t^*; this region is the interior of a closed analytic curve γ_t'. The other region is the exterior of a closed analytic curve γ_t''. Since these two regions of the t-plane have no points in common, γ_t' must lie inside γ_t''. Finally, the transformation $\tau = 1/t$ maps the two curves γ_t' and γ_t'' onto each other.

326. Before proceeding along the above lines, we shall derive in this section some properties of the function lz that will be needed in the sequel. We begin by noting that relation (159.5) of Vol. I, p. 157, *viz.*

$$\int_\gamma u \, dv = \int\int_G |f'(z)|^2 \, dx \, dy > 0,$$

remains valid also in the case that G is a doubly-connected region bounded by two curves γ' and γ'', the function $f(z)$ being single-valued in G. Then

$$\int_{\gamma''} u \, dv \geqq \int_{\gamma'} u \, dv, \tag{326.1}$$

provided that the curve γ' is inside the curve γ''. Also, if the point $z = 0$ lies in the interior of the region bounded by γ', then

$$lz = l\varrho \, e^{i\psi} = l\varrho + i\,\psi$$

is regular but not single-valued in the annular region G. However, we still have

$$\int_{\gamma''} l\varrho \, d\psi > \int_{\gamma'} l\varrho \, d\psi, \tag{326.2}$$

because the differential $d\psi$ is single-valued in the region G. Assume now that the two curves γ' and γ'', like those at the end of the preceding section, are the images of each other under $z'' = 1/z'$; then

$$\int_{\gamma''} l\varrho \, d\psi = -\int_{\gamma'} l\varrho \, d\psi,$$

so that (326.2) implies that

$$\int_{\gamma'} l\varrho \, d\psi \leqq 0. \tag{326.3}$$

Now let $\varphi(z)$ be a function that is regular and non-zero in the closed disc $|z| \leqq 1$. We set

$$F(z) = z\,\varphi(z),$$
$$F(e^{i\vartheta}) = \varrho(\vartheta)\,e^{i\psi(\vartheta)}.$$

$$(326.4)$$

By our assumptions concerning $\varphi(z)$, the function $l\varphi(z)$ is regular in $|z| \leq 1$, and on the circle $|z| = 1$ we have

$$l\,\varphi(e^{i\vartheta}) = l\,[F(e^{i\vartheta})\,e^{-i\vartheta}] = l\,\varrho + i\,(\psi - \vartheta). \qquad (326.5)$$

If we denote the circle $|z| = 1$ by $\varkappa$ it follows from (159.5), Vol. I, p. 157 that

$$\int_{\varkappa} l\,\varrho\,d(\psi - \vartheta) \geq 0. \qquad (326.6)$$

On the other hand, a use of the Mean Value Theorem yields

$$l\,|F'(0)| = l\,|\varphi(0)| = \Re\,l\,\varphi(0) = \frac{1}{2\pi}\int_0^{2\pi} l\,\varrho\,d\vartheta. \qquad (326.7)$$

Hence by (326.6),

$$l\,|F'(0)| \leq \frac{1}{2\pi}\int_{\varkappa} l\,\varrho\,d\psi. \qquad (326.8)$$

327. We again consider the region G introduced in § 324 above and the mapping

$$w = f(z) \qquad (f(0) = 0,\ f'(0) > 0), \quad (327.1)$$

which maps the disc $|z| < 1$ onto this region G. If r is a positive number < 1, we set

$$g(z) = f(r\,z), \qquad (327.2)$$

and by (324.4) obtain

$$F(z) = \frac{1 - \sqrt{1 - g(z)}}{1 + \sqrt{1 - g(z)}} = \frac{g(z)}{\left(1 + \sqrt{1 - g(z)}\right)^2}. \qquad (327.3)$$

By § 324 above, $t = F(z)$ maps the closed disc $|z| \leq 1$ onto the region G_t^* whose properties we indicated in § 325 and whose boundary we shall now denote by γ' (instead of by γ_t' as in § 325). Since the function $F(z)$ is simple, $\varphi(z) = F(z)/z$ is regular and nowhere equal to zero, and with the notation (326.4), relation (326.8) holds true. But by (327.3) and (327.2),

$$F'(0) = \frac{g'(0)}{4} = \frac{r}{4}\,f'(0). \qquad (327.4)$$

Hence by (326.8),

$$l\left|\frac{r}{4}f'(0)\right| \leq \frac{1}{2\pi}\int_0^{2\pi}\psi'(\vartheta)\,l\,\varrho\,d\vartheta = \frac{1}{2\pi}\int_\gamma l\,\varrho\,d\psi. \qquad (327.5)$$

By § 325, γ' lies inside an analytic curve γ'' that is the image of γ' under $\tau = 1/t$. Hence by the preceding section, the right-hand side of (327.5) satisfies the inequality (326.3), so that

$$|f'(0)| \leq \frac{4}{r},$$

and since this holds for all $r < 1$, we finally obtain

$$|f'(0)| \leq 4. \qquad (327.6)$$

If we study the elementary mappings (324.1) and (324.3), which upon elimination of u yield the second equation of (324.4), we see that the equation

$$w = \frac{4z}{(1+z)^2}. \qquad (327.7)$$

represents a mapping of the disc $|z| < 1$ onto the simple w-plane cut along the positive real axis from $w = 1$ to $w = \infty$. This region satisfies the conditions imposed on the region G in § 324. Also, we note that $w'(0) = 4$. This shows that (327.6) gives the best possible bound.

We note furthermore that in relation (326.3), the left-hand side cannot vanish unless γ' and γ'' coincide, i.e. unless γ' coincides with the unit circle $|z| = 1$, since the double integral in (159.5) vanishes only in this case. From this it follows that the equality sign can hold in (327.6) only if the region is the w-plane with the cut as described above.

328. Let G be an arbitrary simply-connected region of the w-plane that contains the point $w = 0$ but does not contain $w = \infty$, and whose frontier has at least two distinct points. Let $w = f(z)$ be a function that maps the disc $|z| < 1$ onto the region G and for which $f(0) = 0$. Let z_0 be any point inside the unit circle, let $w_0 = f(z_0)$ be its image in G, and denote the distance of w_0 from the frontier of G by $a(w_0)$. We set

$$v = \frac{z_0 - z}{1 - z_0 z}, \qquad z = \frac{z_0 - v}{1 - z_0 v}. \qquad (328.1)$$

We also put

$$g(v) = \frac{1}{a}\left\{f\left(\frac{z_0 - v}{1 - z_0 v}\right) - w_0\right\}. \qquad (328.2)$$

Then the function $\omega = g(v)$ maps the disc $|v| < 1$ onto a simply-connected region of the ω-plane that does not contain the point $\omega = \infty$ and whose frontier is at unit distance from the point $\omega = 0$. Then according to the preceding section,

$$|g'(0)| \leq 4,$$

whence by (328.2),

$$|f'(z_0)| \leq \frac{4\,a(w_0)}{1-|z_0|^2}. \tag{328.3}$$

We summarize the results of the last two sections in the following *distortion theorem of Koebe and Faber*:

Let G be a simply-connected region of the w-plane that does not contain the point $w = \infty$ in its interior. Let $w = f(z)$ be a function that maps the disc

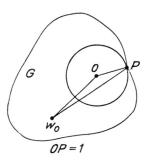

$$OP = 1$$

Fig. 48

$|z| < 1$ *onto G. Then if $a(w)$ stands for the distance of the point w from the frontier of G, we must have*

$$|f'(z)| \leq \frac{4\,a(w)}{1-|z|^2}, \quad (|z| < 1,\ w = f(z)). \tag{328.4}$$

The equality sign holds if and only if the region G is a simple plane with a cut along a ray and the point w lies on the extension of this ray.

329. We now again make the assumption that the distance from the point $w = 0$ to the frontier of G is equal to unity. Then for every point w_0 of G,

$$a(w_0) \leq 1 + |w_0|, \tag{329.1}$$

and relation (328.3) implies that

$$\frac{|dw|}{1+|w|} \leq \frac{4\,|dz|}{1-|z|^2}, \tag{329.2}$$

whence by integration we obtain

$$l\,(1 + |w|) \leqq 2\,l\,\frac{1 + |z|}{1 - |z|}.$$

Therefore,

$$|w| \leqq \left(\frac{1 + |z|}{1 - |z|}\right)^2 - 1 = \frac{4\,|z|}{(1 - |z|)^2}. \tag{329.3}$$

If the distance from $w = 0$ to the frontier of G equals a and if r is a positive number < 1, then it follows from (329.3) that the following relation holds for $|z| < r$:

$$|f(z)| < \frac{4\,r\,a}{(1 - r)^2}.$$

From this we deduce the following fact: Let $\mathfrak{G}$ be a set of simply-connected regions G each of which contains the point $w = 0$ but does not contain the point $w = \infty$, and assume that for none of the regions G the distance a of its frontier from $w = 0$ exceeds a fixed number M; then the functions $w = f(z)$ with $f(0) = 0$ that map $|z| < 1$ onto the regions G constitute a family of functions that is bounded in the small (cf. § 185, Vol. I, p. 184) in $|z| < 1$ and is therefore normal in $|z| < 1$.

If we note that by the above definition of the numbers a and regions G, the disc $|w| < a$ always lies in the corresponding region G, and that the inverse function $z = \varphi(w)$ of $w = f(z)$ is of bound one in the disc $|w| < a$, it follows by Schwarz's Lemma that

$$|\varphi'(0)| \leqq \frac{1}{a},$$

and hence that

$$|f'(0)| \geqq a. \tag{329.4}$$

Therefore the above condition involving M may be replaced by the condition that

$$|f'(0)| < M \tag{329.5}$$

hold for the functions $f(z)$ of the family; the new condition likewise insures that the family is normal in the disc $|z| < 1$, since it follows from (329.5) and (329.4) that the set of numbers a is bounded.

The Mapping of Doubly-Connected Regions (§§ 330-331)

330. If G is a doubly-connected region of the w-plane, then the frontier of G consists of two disjoint continua, C_1 and C_2. Let us assume that at least one of these, say C_1, contains more than one point. Then the (simply-connected) region G_1 bounded by C_1 and containing C_2 in its interior can be mapped, according to the Riemann Mapping Theorem, onto the disc $|t| < 1$ by a mapping function whose inverse we denote by

$$w = \varphi(t). \tag{330.1}$$

We must now make a distinction between the case in which C_2 consists of one point and that in which it consists of more than one point. In the first of these cases we can clearly arrange, by a proper norming of the mapping (330.1), that the image of G will be the punctured disc

$$0 < |t| < 1. \tag{330.2}$$

We now consider the part lying inside the circle $|t| = 1$ of the Riemann surface having a logarithmic branch point at $t = 0$ (cf. § 249, Vol. I, p. 258), and we map this region by means of the transformation

$$\omega = l\,t \tag{330.3}$$

onto the half-plane $\Re \omega < 0$. We map into the z-plane by means of

$$\omega = \frac{z + 1}{z - 1}, \tag{330.4}$$

and finally, using the function in (330.1) above, into the w-plane by means of

$$w = \varphi(e^{\omega}) = f(z). \tag{330.5}$$

We could also have obtained the function $f(z)$ by the method of §§ 315-320, paying due attention to normalizing it properly.

Now if

$$z_0 = \frac{\omega_0 + 1}{\omega_0 - 1} \tag{330.6}$$

is a point of the disc $|z| < 1$ that corresponds to a point w_0 of the given region G, then the points z_ν $(\nu = \pm 1, \pm 2, \ldots)$ that are obtained from (330.6) by the substitution of $\omega_0 + 2\nu\pi i$ for ω_0 will also correspond to w_0. The transition from z_0 to one of the points z_ν can always be represented by a limiting rotation (cf. § 82, Vol. I, p. 78) of the non-Euclidean plane $|z| < 1$. Hence the function $w = f(z)$ maps the disc $|z| < 1$ conformally onto a Riemann surface that has a logarithmic branch point at C_2 and whose frontier consists of the continua C_1 and C_2. This Riemann surface, being mapped continuously onto $|z| < 1$, is simply-connected; we call it the *universal covering surface*[1] of G. Using the notation of § 318 above, we see that every closed path γ_w corresponds under $w = f(z)$ either to a closed path γ_z or to an open path whose end-points are the images of each other under a limiting rotation of the non-Euclidean plane $|z| < 1$.

331. Next we consider the case in which each of the two continua C_1 and C_2 that constitute the frontier of G contains more than one point. We again start by mapping the simply-connected region G_1 bounded by C_1, and containing C_2 in its interior, onto the inside of a circle C_1'; then C_2 is mapped onto a continuum C_2'. We then map the simply-connected region bounded by C_2' and containing C_1' onto the inside of a circle C_2'' and note that the image C_1'' of the circle C_1' under this last mapping must be a closed analytic curve. Therefore we can assume from the very beginning, without loss of generality, that C_1 is the unit circle $|w| = 1$ and that C_2 is a closed analytic curve that lies in $|w| < 1$ and loops around $w = 0$.

In the present case, the transformation

$$\omega = l\,w \tag{331. 1}$$

maps the covering surface of G—that is, the Riemann surface of infinitely many sheets all lying between C_1 and C_2—onto a kind of strip of the ω-plane, bounded by the imaginary axis C_1^* and an analytic curve C_2^* that lies in the half-plane $\Re\,\omega < 0$. Since the curve C_2^* is periodic, the strip is mapped onto itself by the transformations

$$\omega_\nu = \omega + 2\,\nu\,\pi\,i \quad (\nu = 0, \pm 1, \pm 2, \ldots). \tag{331. 2}$$

Now we map the interior of this (simply-connected) strip onto the disc $|z| < 1$ by means of a function

$$\omega = \psi(z) \tag{331. 3}$$

and we then have in the product $w = f(z)$ of the transformations (331.1) and (331.3) a mapping function that has the same properties as the function $f(z)$ described in the result of § 319 above. To each of the congruence transformations (331.2) of the strip there corresponds a non-Euclidean motion S_ν of the non-Euclidean plane $|z| < 1$. We set $S_1 = S$ and note that S_ν is obtained by iteration of S, so that we can write

$$S_\nu = S\,S\,\ldots\,\nu\text{- times} = S^\nu.$$

We shall see shortly that S cannot be a rotation of the non-Euclidean plane;

---

[1] The concept of universal covering surface is discussed more fully in §§ 336 ff. below.

meanwhile, the following reasoning shows that it cannot be a limiting rotation either:

Let G be a doubly-connected region all of whose congruence transformations S_v are limiting rotations. Then there exists a Moebius transformation

$$z = \frac{\alpha u + \beta}{\gamma u + \delta}$$

that maps the disc $|z| < 1$ onto the half-plane $\Re u < 0$, and under which the limiting rotation $S_1 = S$ of the z-plane corresponds to the Euclidean translation $u' = u + 2\pi i$ of the u-plane. Setting $t = e^u$ and $w = \varphi(t)$, we thus arrive at a one-to-one mapping of the region G onto the punctured disc $0 < |t| < 1$. The function $\varphi(t)$ is bounded and simple. By Riemann's theorem of § 133, Vol I, p. 131, we can extend $\varphi(t)$ to a function regular in the whole disc $|t| < 1$ by setting $\varphi(0) = w_0$. The extended function must likewise be simple; for if there were a non-zero $t = t'$ for which $\varphi(t') = w_0$, then since $\varphi(t)$ is neighborhood-preserving there would be a point t_1 near $t = 0$ and a point t_2 near t' for which $t_1 \neq t_2$ and $\varphi(t_1) = \varphi(t_2)$, and φ could not be simple in the punctured disc. But now it follows that the continuum C_2 would have to consist of the single point w_0.

Thus S must be a non-Euclidean translation, and as such it is a Moebius transformation with two distinct fixed points F_1 and F_2 that lie on the unit circle $|z| = 1$. We now consider in the v-plane a strip

$$|\Re v| < h. \tag{331. 4}$$

We can map this strip one-to-one onto the disc $|z| < 1$ by means of a transformation $z = \psi(v)$, and we can norm this transformation in such a way that the two ends (the portions near $v = \infty$) of the strip are mapped onto neighborhoods of the two fixed points F_1 and F_2. If we do this, then the non-Euclidean translation S corresponds to a Euclidean translation of the strip onto itself. The magnitude of this translation depends on h; we can make it equal to $2\pi i$ by choosing h suitably.

We now set

$$v = l\,\omega.$$

Then the function

$$w = e^{f(\psi(l\,\omega))} = F(\omega)$$

represents a one-to-one mapping of a circular annulus onto the doubly-connected region G. We have thus obtained the following result:

Let G be any doubly-connected region whose frontier consists of two disjoint continua, each of them containing more than one point; then G can be mapped *one-to-one and conformally onto a concentric circular annulus.*

If R_1 and R_2 are the radii of the two concentric circles of the annulus, then

$$\frac{R_2}{R_1} = e^{2h},$$

and this ratio is therefore a number that is uniquely determined by the region G; it is called the *modulus* of the region G. From this we derive the following corollary:

Two doubly-connected regions can be mapped conformally onto each other if and only if their moduli are the same.

The Group of Congruence Transformations (§§ 332-335)

332. We return to a problem that came up briefly in § 321. We saw in that section that the function $w = f(z)$ of § 319 (the function that maps the disc $|z| < 1$ onto the given region G) need not be simple in $|z| < 1$, i.e. that $f(z)$ may assume the same value at different points of the disc $|z| < 1$. We shall call any two such points *equivalent*.

If z_1 and z_2 are equivalent points, let us write

$$z = \frac{z_1 - u}{1 - \bar{z}_1 u}, \qquad z' = \frac{z_2 - u'}{1 - \bar{z}_2 u'}. \tag{332.1}$$

If we substitute the first of these expressions into $w = f(z)$ and recall that $f'(z)$ does not vanish in $|z| < 1$, we see that a certain neighborhood of $u = 0$ is mapped onto a simple neighborhood of $w_0 = f(z_1)$. The latter neighborhood may in turn be considered as the image under $w = f(z)$ of a certain neighborhood of z_2 (since the points z_1 and z_2 are equivalent), and it may also be considered as the image of a certain neighborhood of $u' = 0$, in virtue of the second relation in (332.1). Hence we have established the existence of a one-to-one relation

$$u' = \varphi(u) \qquad\qquad (\varphi(0) = 0) \quad (332.2)$$

in a certain neighborhood of $u = 0$, and with the aid of the theorem in § 319, we see that $\varphi(u)$ can be continued analytically along every path in $|u| < 1$ and is therefore, by the monodromy theorem, regular and single-valued in the whole disc $|u| < 1$. In this argument, the roles of u and u' are clearly interchangeable, so that we can produce similarly a single-valued regular function

$$u = \psi(u'), \tag{332.3}$$

and this must of course be the inverse of (332.2). Both $\varphi(u)$ and $\psi(u')$ are of bound one and vanish at the origin, so that by Schwarz's Lemma,

$$u' = e^{i\vartheta} u;$$

hence by (332.1), the relation connecting z and z' must represent a non-Euclidean motion S which is such that $f(z) = f(z')$; thus the motion S carries

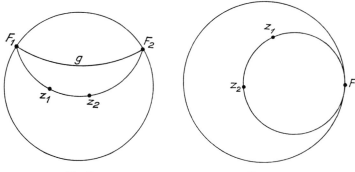

Fig. 49   Fig. 50

every point into an equivalent point (under $w = f(z)$), and in particular it carries z_1 into z_2.

If S' is another non-Euclidean motion of this kind, carrying every point z of the non-Euclidean plane $|z| < 1$ into an equivalent point, then the product

$$S'' = S'S$$

of the two motions S and S' has the same property. The same holds for the motion S^{-1} inverse to S. Therefore the non-Euclidean motions of the kind described constitute a group $\mathfrak{S}$.

Any function $f(z)$ for which the relation

$$f(z) = f(Sz)$$

holds for every element S of the group $\mathfrak{S}$ is called an *automorphic function* of the group $\mathfrak{S}$.

None of the above motions S can be a non-Euclidean rotation. For if z_0 is the fixed point of such a rotation, then every neighborhood of z_0 would have to contain two equivalent points z_1 and z_2; but this is impossible, since there are neighborhoods of z_0 that are mapped one-to-one onto a part of the region G. Hence each of the motions S must be either a *limiting rotation* or a *translation* along a non-Euclidean line (*cf.* § 82, Vol. I, p. 78).

If z_1 is any point of the disc $|z| < 1$ and $z_2 = Sz_1$ a point equivalent to z_1 under $w = f(z)$, we consider (resuming once more the notation of § 319) a curve γ_2 that joints z_1 and z_2. The curve γ_z is mapped by $w = f(z)$ onto a closed curve γ_w lying in the region G. Now if S is, first, a non-Euclidean translation of the non-Euclidean plane $|z| < 1$ with fixed points F_1 and F_2, then the two points z_1 and z_2 must lie on a line of constant (non-Euclidean) distance from the non-Euclidean line g whose end-points are F_1 and F_2. Hence this line of constant distance from g is mapped onto itself by the translation S (see Fig. 49).

Second, if S is a limiting rotation, then z_1 and z_2 both lie on the oricycle that passes through z_1 and through the only fixed point F that S has in this case (see Fig. 50). This oricycle is mapped onto itself by S. Here as in the first case, any path γ_z that joints the two equivalent points z_1 and z_2 is mapped by $w = f(z)$ onto a closed curve γ_w of the region G.

333. Any given curve γ_w of the region G is the image of an infinite number of curves $\gamma_z^{(\nu)}$ of the disc $|z| < 1$, and these pre-images are permuted among themselves by every motion of the group $\mathfrak{S}$. Since all of these curves $\gamma_z^{(\nu)}$ have the same non-Euclidean length, we can introduce a metric in G by assigning this common length to the image curve γ_w as its length.[1] We shall denote this length by $L_G(\gamma_w)$.

We recall (cf. § 316 above) that the region G lies in the disc $|w| < 1$. Considering this disc as a non-Euclidean plane and denoting the non-Euclidean length of γ_w by $\Lambda(\gamma_w)$, we have by Pick's theorem of § 289 that

$$\Lambda(\gamma_w) < L_G(\gamma_w). \tag{333. 1}$$

Now let G' be any region that lies in $|w| < 1$ and contains G. In accordance with §§ 315-321, let

$$w = \varphi(u) \qquad (\varphi(0) = 0,\ \varphi'(0) > 0) \tag{333. 2}$$

be a function that maps the disc $|u| < 1$ onto the region G'. The points of $|u| < 1$ that are mapped onto (interior) points of G form an open subset of $|u| < 1$ that can always be represented as a union of at most denumerably many regions, and these regions are permuted among themselves by the transformations T of a group $\mathfrak{T}$ of motions of the non-Euclidean plane $|u| < 1$. We denote by G^* that one among these regions which contains the point $u = 0$ in its interior. Let

$$u = \psi(z) \qquad (\psi(0) = 0,\ \psi'(0) > 0) \tag{333. 3}$$

be a function that maps the disc $|z| < 1$ onto the region G^*.

---

[1] If the region G is multiply-connected, the concept of distance between two of its points can be established only under certain restrictive conditions, but we shall not have to deal with this case.

Let γ_w be a path in G that joins the point $w = 0$ to any other point $w = w_0$ of G. Since this path also lies in G', there is, among the (possibly infinitely many) paths in $|u| < 1$ that correspond to γ_w by (333.2), a definite path γ_u emanating from $u = 0$. This path γ_u must necessarily lie in G^*. Similarly, there is in the disc $|z| < 1$ a path γ_z emanating from $z = 0$ that is mapped onto γ_u by (333.3). Then the function

$$w = f(z) = \varphi(\psi(z)) \tag{333.4}$$

maps the path γ_z onto the path γ_w. This function $w = f(z)$ has all of the properties required of $f(z)$ in § 319, and it must therefore coincide with the mapping function $w = f(z)$ of § 319.

We shall denote the non-Euclidean lengths of the curves γ_z, γ_u and γ_w in the non-Euclidean planes $|z| < 1$, $|u| < 1$ and $|w| < 1$ by $\Lambda(\gamma_z)$, $\Lambda(\gamma_u)$ and $\Lambda(\gamma_w)$ respectively, as before. Then with the notation introduced earlier in this section, we have

$$L_G(\gamma_w) = L_{G^*}(\gamma_u) = \Lambda(\gamma_z).$$

Moreover,

$$L_{G'}(\gamma_w) = \Lambda(\gamma_u),$$

and by Pick's theorem,

$$\Lambda(\gamma_u) < L_{G^*}(\gamma_u),$$

and similarly

$$\Lambda(\gamma_w) < L_{G'}(\gamma_w).$$

A comparison of these relations yields the following theorem:

If G and G' are two regions lying in the disc $|w| < 1$ which are such that G contains the point $w = 0$ and is itself a subregion of G', then with the above notation we have the following inequalities:

$$\Lambda(\gamma_w) < L_{G'}(\gamma_w) < L_G(\gamma_w). \tag{333.5}$$

Here, G' is assumed to coincide neither with $|w| < 1$ nor with G.

334. The results of the preceding section enable us to establish a criterion for deciding whether a substitution S of the group $\mathfrak{S}$ is a limiting rotation or a translation of the non-Euclidean plane $|z| < 1$.

Assume first that we are dealing with a translation S along a non-Euclidean line e. Without loss of generality, we may assume e to be the real axis (see Fig. 51 below). If z_1 is any point and z_2 its image under the translation S, let z_1' and z_2' be the points at which the non-Euclidean perpendiculars to e, through z_1 and z_2 respectively, intersect e. Then S maps z_1' onto z_2', and the distance $s = E_n(z_1', z_2')$ is an invariant that indicates the magnitude of the translation. On the other hand, s may be regarded as the non-Euclidean distance between the above two perpendiculars, so that we certainly have $E_n(z_1, z_2) \geqq s$. Every path γ_z that joins z_1 and z_2 is likewise of a non-Euclidean length $\geqq s$. Now if γ_w is the image under $w = f(z)$ of such a path γ_z, then γ_w is a closed

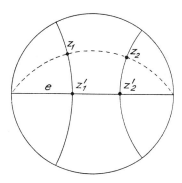

Fig. 51

curve in G whose length $L_G(\gamma_w)$, in the metric of § 333, is $\geqq s$. The same holds for all curves γ_w^* that are homotopic to γ_w in G, since any such γ_w^* may be regarded as the image of a path γ_z^* whose one end-point is mapped onto the other by S. Therefore in the metric just mentioned, the lengths of the curves homotopic to γ_w have a non-zero lower bound.

Next, assume that S is a limiting rotation and that it maps a point z_1 onto a point z_2. These two points then lie on an oricycle ω that is tangent to the circle $|z| = 1$ at the fixed point F of the limiting rotation. The two non-Euclidean lines through F that pass through z_1 and z_2 respectively are parallel. Let z_1^* and z_2^* be their respective intersections with a second oricycle ω^* emanating from F. Now as the diameter of ω^* is allowed to go to zero, the non-Euclidean distance $E_n(z_1^*, z_2^*)$ must likewise converge to zero. The easiest way to see this is to map $|z| < 1$ onto a Poincaré half-plane (*cf.* § 84, Vol I, p. 79) in such a way that F is mapped onto the point at infinity; then z_1 and z_2 lie on a parallel to the real axis, and so do z_1^* and z_2^*; finally, if h and h^* are the respective distances of these parallels from the real axis, then $E_n(z_1^*, z_2^*)$ goes to zero as $1/h^*$ does.

We have thus derived the criterion announced at the beginning of this section, which can be stated as follows:

Let γ_w be a closed curve in G that is not homotopic to zero, i.e. that cannot be shrunk to an interior point of G without having to pass over frontier points of G. To γ_w there corresponds a transformation S of the group $\mathfrak{S}$.

Then S is either a translation or a limiting rotation of the non-Euclidean plane $|z| < 1$, according to whether the lengths of the curves homotopic to γ_w, in the L-metric of § 333, have a non-zero or zero greatest lower bound.

335. Now let γ_w be a closed curve in the region G that is the image of a path γ_z having two distinct end-points z_1 and z_2. Then there is in the group $\mathfrak{S}$ a transformation S that maps z_1 onto z_2. We can then find in G a closed Jordan curve γ_w^* that contains all of the points of γ_w in its interior and stays within a distance ε of γ_w; moreover, γ_w^* can be selected in such a way that

$$L_G(\gamma_w^*) < L_G(\gamma_w) + \varepsilon \qquad (335.\,1)$$

holds. We can obtain such a Jordan curve γ_w^*, for instance, by constructing small circles about certain of the double points (if any) of γ_w and by replacing certain portions of γ_w by suitable arcs of these circles (see Fig. 52).

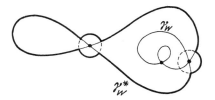

γ_w has three double points

γ_w^* is the heavier line

Fig. 52

Inside γ_w^* there must be at least one point that does not belong to G; for otherwise, γ_w and γ_w^* could be shrunk by means of a continuous deformation to curves that lie within an arbitrarily small disc in G, so that z_1 and z_2 could not be distinct points, as they in fact are.

Let us then consider first the case that every curve γ_w^* of the kind specified above contains at least two distinct points P_1 and P_2 that do not belong to G. We pass through P_1 and P_2 a non-Euclidean line e of the non-Euclidean plane $|w| < 1$; let the end-points of e be Q_1 and Q_2 (see Fig. 53). Let R_1 be the first and R_2 the last point of intersection of e and γ_w^* as e is traversed from Q_1 to Q_2. The points R_1 and R_2 subdivide γ_w^* into two Jordan arcs, and each of these has an L-length (cf. § 333 above) that exceeds the non-Euclidean length of the segment $R_1 R_2$ of e, and therefore also exceeds $E_n(P_1, P_2)$. But by (335.1), this implies that

$$L_G(\gamma_w) + \varepsilon > L_G(\gamma_w^*) > 2\,E_n(P_1,\,P_2),$$

and hence also that

$$L_G(\gamma_w) \geqq 2\, E_n(P_1,\, P_2). \tag{335.2}$$

Relation (335.2) holds also for every closed curve $\gamma_w{'}$ that is homotopic in G to γ_w. Therefore by the criterion of § 334, the non-Euclidean motion S must in this case be a translation.

Next we consider the case that there exists at least one Jordan curve γ_w^* of the kind specified in whose interior there lies one and only one point P that does not belong to G. Then P is an isolated point of the frontier of G, and

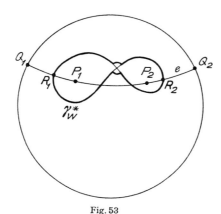

Fig. 53

there exists at least one punctured disc $\varkappa$ that has its center at P and otherwise belongs to G. By a continuous deformation within G, we can then transform γ_w^* and γ_w (which has no points exterior to γ_w^*) into a pair of curves that share all of the specified properties of γ_w^* and γ_w and lie within $\varkappa$. If k is an arbitrarily small disc concentric with $\varkappa$, then the homotopic image of γ_w just obtained must in turn be homotopic to the boundary of k traversed n times, where n is some non-zero integer (*cf.* § 330 above).

Let the radii of $\varkappa$ and of k be ϱ and r, respectively. By means of the function $w = lt$, we map the punctured disc $\varkappa$ onto the Poincaré half-plane and we find that

$$L_\varkappa(k) = \frac{2\,\pi}{l\dfrac{\varrho}{r}}. \tag{335.3}$$

The L-length of the boundary of $\varkappa$ traversed n times is n times the quantity in (335.3). Since this quantity goes to zero if r does, and since by § 333,

$$L_G(k) < L_\varkappa(k)$$

holds (the punctured disc $\varkappa$ being a subset of G), it follows that there are curves homotopic to γ_w in G whose L-lengths are as small as we please. Therefore by the criterion of § 334 above, S must be a limiting rotation.

We have thus shown that the group $\mathfrak{S}$ cannot contain any limiting rotations among its elements S unless the closed set A consisting of the points of $|\,w\,| \leqq 1$ that do not belong to G (cf. § 316 above) contains isolated points.

The Universal Covering Surface (§§ 336-338)

336. Once more, let

$$w = f(z) \tag{336. 1}$$

be the mapping function whose existence was demonstrated in §§ 315-320. If the region G_w is multiply-connected, then for any given point a_0 of the disc $|\,z\,| < 1$ there are infinitely many equivalent points

$$\{a_j\} = a_0, a_1, a_2, \ldots . \tag{336. 2}$$

In what follows, we shall stick to a fixed point a_0, and therefore to a fixed set (336.2). If z is any point of $|\,z\,| < 1$ that is distinct from all of the a_j, then there are at most a finite number of points of (336.2) within or on the non-Euclidean circle with center at z that passes through a_0. Among these there is at least one point, say a_{n_1}, which has the smallest (non-Euclidean) distance from the center z, i.e. for which $E_n(a_{n_1}, z)$ is a minimum. For certain positions of z, there may be several points of (336.2) that qualify.

Now let S_{n_1} be that non-Euclidean motion of the group $\mathfrak{S}$ (cf. § 332 above) which maps the point a_{n_1} onto a_0, and let the image of z under this motion be denoted by z_0. Then

$$E_n(a_0, z_0) \leqq E_n(a_j, z_0) \tag{336. 3}$$

holds for $j = 1, 2, \cdots$. We wish to determine the set of all those points z_0 for which (336.3) holds true, and to this end we construct the non-Euclidean perpendicular bisector μ_j of the (non-Euclidean) line-segment $a_0 a_j$. Then μ_j divides $|\,z\,| < 1$ into two non-Euclidean half-planes. One of these contains a_0, and we denote it by U_j. Each of the open point sets U_j is convex in the non-Euclidean sense, that is to say that if z' and z'' are any two of its points, the set U_j contains the non-Euclidean line-segment joining z' and z''.

Any disc $|z| < r < 1$ intersects only a finite number of the lines[1] μ_j. Hence we can find an $N = N(r)$ such that $|z| < r$ lies in the interior of U_j for all $j > N$. The intersection of the half-planes $U_1, U_2, \cdots, U_N$ and the disc $|z| < r$ is a convex non-Euclidean polygon with a finite number of sides and vertices and a finite number of boundary arcs that belong to $|z| = r$. The interior region of this polygon consists of all those points of $|z| < r$ that are closer to a_0 than to any other point of the set (336.2). If we let r tend to unity,

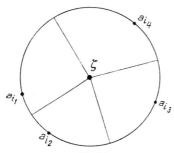

Fig. 54

we obtain in the limit a convex polygon with at most denumerably many vertices and a finite or infinite number of sub-arcs of $|z| = 1$. We shall denote the interior of this limiting polygon by F_0; it consists of all those points of $|z| < 1$ that are closer to a_0 than to any other point of (336.2).

Let S_n be that element of the group $\mathfrak{S}$ which carries a_n into a_0, and let us denote the image of F_0 under S_n^{-1} by F_n. Then F_n consists of all those points that are closer to a_n than to any other point of (336.2). Thus for any point z_n of F_n, we have

$$E_n(a_n, z_n) < E_n(a_0, z_n);$$

therefore z_n cannot belong to F_0, and it follows that the regions $F_0, F_1, \cdots$ are mutually disjoint. Since the motions of $\mathfrak{S}$ distribute the points $z_1', z_2', \cdots$ equivalent to a given point z_0' of F_0 into the various regions F_ν, we conclude further that no two points z' and z'' of F_0 can be equivalent.

Now let ζ be any point of $|z| < 1$ that is not contained in the open point-set $F_0 + F_1 + \ldots$; then the set of points a_i that have the smallest possible distance from ζ contains at least *two* distinct points, since ζ would otherwise have to belong to one of the sets F_j. Hence there exists a circle with ζ as its non-Euclidean center that passes through the points $a_{i_1}, \ldots, a_{i_p}$ $(p \geqq 2)$ but does not have any of the points a_j in its interior. Fig. 54 illustrates this circle, under the assumption that ζ is at $z = 0$.

---

[1] This is seen easily if we note that for a given r, the non-Euclidean circle with center at a_0 and non-Euclidean radius, ϱ contains the disc $|z| < r$ in its interior if ϱ is sufficiently large. For every point a_j that lies outside the non-Euclidean circle with center at a_0 and non-Euclidean radius 2ϱ, the corresponding μ_j lies entirely outside the disc $|z| < r$.

We are led in this way to a well-defined convex polygon whose vertices, in order, are $a_{i_1}, \ldots, a_{i_p}$. The perpendiculars from ζ onto the sides of this polygon subdivide a sufficiently small neighborhood of ζ into p parts that are easily seen to lie in the regions $F_{i_1}, F_{i_2}, \ldots, F_{i_p}$, respectively. Therefore the point ζ belongs to the frontier of each of these p regions. Hence every point of $|z| < 1$ is either an interior point or a frontier point of one of the various regions F_j, and the totality of regions F_j plus their frontiers may be regarded as a kind of mosaic that covers $|z| < 1$ completely. Every point ζ that is not contained in any of the F_j is equivalent to at least one point ζ_0 of the frontier of F_0. For our above ζ, we obtain such an equivalent ζ_0 by mapping any one of the regions $F_{i_1}, \ldots, F_{i_p}$ onto F_0 by means of a non-Euclidean motion belonging to the group $\mathfrak{S}$. This yields in fact p *distinct* points $\zeta_{i_1}, \ldots, \zeta_{i_p}$ of the frontier of F_0 that are equivalent to ζ and therefore also to each other. For if any two of these points, say ζ_{i_1} and ζ_{i_2}, coincided, then the transformation $S_{i_1} S_{i_2}^{-1}$ would have ζ as a fixed point and would therefore have to be elliptic, and we know this to be impossible by § 332 above. In our "tiling" of the unit disc $|z| < 1$, each of the $\zeta_{i_1}, \ldots, \zeta_{i_p}$ is a point at which p of the regions F_j meet. The points of the frontier of F_0 for which $p \geqq 3$ coincide with the vertices of the polygon that bounds F_0; at every interior point of any of the sides of this polygon, we must have $p = 2$. From this we infer that the sides of the polygon must be equivalent in pairs.

337. Let us now consider the region G_w which is the image under (336.1) of the disc $|z| < 1$. By the results obtained above, we know that any two distinct (interior) points of F_0 are mapped onto two distinct (interior) points of G_w, in other words that the mapping of F_0 into G_w given by $w = f(z)$ is simple. Furthermore, every point of G_w is the image of at least one interior or frontier point of F_0. The sides of the bounding polygon of F_0 are mapped onto certain curves in G_w, two distinct sides being mapped, in general, onto two curves that have no interior points in common; but whenever the two sides of the polygon are equivalent, their image curves coincide. Every vertex ζ_0 of the frontier of F_0 is mapped onto a point $\omega_0 = f(\zeta_0)$ at which p ($p \geqq 3$) of the image curves meet, since $w = f(z)$ maps Fig. 54 one-to-one and conformally onto a neighborhood of ω_0.

Let us now cut G_w along all of the curves that correspond to the frontier of F_0. Then the residual subset G^* of G_w (i.e. G_w minus the above curves) is the image under $w = f(z)$ of the simply-connected region F_0; hence G^* is itself a simply-connected region. We note that each of the regions F_j is mapped by $w = f(z)$ onto this same region G^*. Now we consider an infinite number of specimens of G^* that we denote by $G_0^*, G_1^*, \ldots$, and we assign to G_j^* the convex region F_j. We note that because of their convexity, no two distinct regions F_i and F_j can meet along more than one of their sides; also, that any two of the finite number of regions that meet at a point ζ_0 must have a side of their frontiers in common; and finally, that any given disc $|z| < r < 1$ is covered by a finite number of the regions F_j.

Now consider two regions F_i and F_j whose frontiers have a side s_{ij} in common, and let G_i^* and G_j^* be the corresponding specimens of the image region G^*. To s_{ij} there corresponds in the w-plane a certain curve σ_{ij}, and every sufficiently small neighborhood of any given point of s_{ij} is mapped one-to-one onto a neighborhood of the corresponding point of σ_{ij}. We now join one of the "banks" or "sides" of σ_{ij} in the region G_i^* with the opposite bank of σ_{ij} in G_j^*; by what has been said above, the choice of the banks to be joined here is quite unambiguous. We first apply this process of joining to finitely many specimens and finitely many curves, the specimens being chosen in such a way that their pre-images in the z-plane cover a given disc $|z| < r < 1$, and we then imagine the process continued indefinitely as r is allowed to tend to 1. In the limit, we obtain a simply-connected Riemann surface which is the one-to-one image of $|z| < 1$. Our entire construction of this surface seems to have depended on our initial choice of the point a_0 in $|z| < 1$; but the resulting surface is actually independent of this choice, as can easily be seen by an argument like the one in § 320 above.

The Riemann surface "over" G_w that we have thus obtained is called the *canonical universal covering surface of G_w*. In its place we can use, whenever it is more convenient, the subdivision or "tiling" of the disc $|z| < 1$ by means of the regions F_i. The region F_0 can be extended, by adding a portion of its frontier to the region itself, to a so-called *fundamental region F_0^**, i.e. to a point set that is disjoint from every one of its equivalent sets F_j^* and that together with these equivalent sets covers the *entire* (interior of the) disc $|z| < 1$ exactly once. The simplest way of obtaining such a fundamental region is to add to F_0 only one of every two equivalent sides of the frontier polygon, and to retain only one vertex from every system of p equivalent vertices of this polygon as described in § 336. This particular construction always yields a *connected* point set as a fundamental region (*cf.* § 100, Vol. I, p. 96).

338. In conclusion, we wish to show that each of the regions F_j has frontier points that lie *on* the circle $|z| = 1$. To this end, we select a sequence of distinct points

$$w_1, w_2, w_3, \ldots$$

in G_w in such a way that the sequence converges to a point of the frontier of G_w, or more generally, in such a way that the points of the sequence have no point of accumulation in (the interior of) G_w. In $|z| < 1$, we consider any sequence of points

$$z_1', z_2', z_3', \ldots \tag{338.1}$$

for which $f(z_\nu') = w_\nu$ $(\nu = 1, 2, \ldots)$ holds. Then the sequence (338.1) cannot have a point of accumulation in (the interior of) $|z| < 1$; for if it did have one, say z_0', then $w_0 = f(z_0')$ would be an interior point of G_w that would also be a point of accumulation of the sequence $w_1, w_2, \cdots$. Now if F_j^* is any fundamental region, then for every point z_ν' of (338.1) there is an equivalent point z_ν in F_j^*. Since all of the points of accumulation of the sequence $\{z_\nu\}$ lie on $|z| = 1$, it follows that the frontier of F_j^*, and hence also the frontier of the open set F_j, must have points in common with $|z| = 1$.

Simultaneous Conformal Mapping of Nested Annular Regions (§§ 339-340)

339. The following problem is of importance in the theory of uniformization. Consider an infinite sequence of complex planes, which we shall call the z_1-plane, z_2-plane, etc., and consider in each z_n-plane two simply-connected regions $G_n^{(n)}$ and $G_n^{(n-1)}$ which are such that $G_n^{(n)}$ contains $G_n^{(n-1)}$ and both contain the origin $z_n = 0$. The problem we set ourselves is to find a sequence of

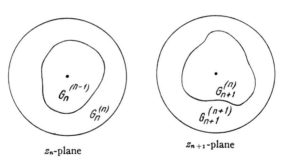

z_n-plane z_{n+1}-plane

Fig. 55

regions $G^{(1)}, G^{(2)}, \ldots$ in a w-plane, and a sequence of mapping functions $w = \varphi^{(n)}(z_n)$, having the following properties:

1. Each region $G^{(n)}$ contains the origin $w = 0$ in its interior, and is itself contained in the next region $G^{(n+1)}$;

2. For $n = 2, 3, \ldots$, the function

$$w = \varphi^{(n)}(z_n) \qquad (\varphi^{(n)}(0) = 0, \ \varphi^{(n)\prime}(0) > 0)$$

maps the region $G^{(n)}$ conformally onto the region $G_n^{(n)}$, and at the same time maps $G^{(n-1)}$ conformally onto $G_n^{(n-1)}$.

Without loss of generality, we may assume that the desired regions $G_n^{(n)}$ are circular discs of radii r_n, since we could map any other $G_n^{(n)}$ onto such a disc which must then contain the image of the region $G_n^{(n-1)}$. Assume then that the region $G_n^{(n)}$ coincides with the disc $|z| < r_n$, and let

$$z_{n+1} = f_{n+1}^{(n)}(z_n) \quad (f_{n+1}^{(n)}(0) = 0,\ f_{n+1}^{(n)\prime}(0) > 0) \quad (339.1)$$

be the function that maps this disc onto the region $G_{n+1}^{(n)}$. The radius r_n being given, $f_{n+1}^{(n)\prime}(0)$ is proportional to r_{n+1} and we can always determine r_{n+1} in such a way that

$$f_{n+1}^{(n)\prime}(0) = 1 \quad (339.2)$$

holds.

Now we set $r_1 = 1$, and we stipulate that (339.2) hold for $n = 1, 2, \cdots$. Then the radii r_n and the functions (339.1) are uniquely determined. We define additional functions by setting

$$f_{n+2}^{(n)}(z_n) = f_{n+2}^{(n+1)}(f_{n+1}^{(n)}(z_n)), \quad (339.3)$$

$$f_{n+k}^{(n)}(z_n) = f_{n+k}^{(n+1)}(f_{n+1}^{(n)}(z_n)). \quad (339.4)$$

The functions (339.3) can all be determined provided that we know all of the functions in (339.1). Similarly, the functions $f_{n+3}^{(n)}(z_n)$ can all be determined once we have all of the functions (339.1) and (339.3). Continuing in this way, we obtain all of the functions $f_{n+k}^{(n)}(z_n)$. We note that all of the functions (339.4) satisfy

$$f_{n+k}^{(n)}(0) = 0, \quad f_{n+k}^{(n)\prime}(0) = 1. \quad (339.5)$$

340. Now we observe that for fixed n, the functions (339.4) represent conformal mappings of the disc $|z_n| < r_n$ onto simple, simply-connected regions. Hence it follows from the last result of § 329 and from (339.5) that the sequence $\{f_{n+k}^{(n)}(z_n)\}$, $(k = 1, 2, \ldots)$, constitutes a normal family of functions. Therefore there exists a sequence of numbers $k_1^{(n)}, k_2^{(n)}, \ldots$ which are such that the sequence $\{f_{n+k_p^{(n)}}^{(n)}(z_n)\}$, $(p = 1, 2, \ldots)$, converges continuously in the disc $|z_n| < r_n$. We have a convergent subsequence of this kind for every n, and by Cantor's Diagonal Process (*cf.* § 92, Vol. I, p. 90) we can therefore select independently of n a sequence of numbers $k_1, k_2, \ldots$ which are such that for every n, we have

$$\lim_{p=\infty} f_{n+k_p}^{(n)}(z_n) = \varphi^{(n)}(z_n) \quad (n = 1, 2, \ldots). \quad (340.1)$$

By (339.5), the limit function $\varphi^{(n)}(z_n)$ cannot be a constant. Being the limit of functions $f_{n+k_p}(z_n)$ simple in the disc $|z_n| < r_n$, the function $\varphi^{(n)}(z_n)$ is itself simple in this disc (cf. § 200, Vol. I, p. 197) and it therefore maps $|z_n| < r_n$ onto a simple, simply-connected region $G^{(n)}$. The functions $\varphi^{(n)}(z_n)$ and the regions $G^{(n)}$, however, furnish a solution of our problem, as we shall see presently. For upon replacing the subscript k by k_p in (339.4) and then passing to the limit, we obtain the equation

$$\varphi^{(n)}(z_n) = \varphi^{(n+1)}\left(f^{(n)}_{n+1}(z_n)\right),\tag{340.2}$$

which implies that the second of the two specified conditions is met.

Also, the numbers r_n are monotonically increasing with n; for if we had $r_{n+1} < r_n$, it would follow from Schwarz's Lemma that $|f^{(n)'}_{n+1}(0)| < 1$, since the function $z_{n+1} = f^{(n)}_{n+1}(z_n)$ maps the disc $|z_n| < r_n$ onto a subregion of the disc $|z_{n+1}| < r_{n+1}$. Hence $r_n \leqq r_{n+1}$ and we must have either

$$\lim_{n=\infty} r_n = \infty \tag{340.3}$$

or

$$\lim_{n=\infty} r_n = R. \tag{340.4}$$

These two cases have to be discussed separately.

Assume first that (340.3) holds, and denote the distance of the point $w = 0$ from the frontier of the region $G^{(n)}$ by a_n. Since $\varphi^{(n)'}(0) = 1$, the Koebe-Faber distortion theorem (cf. § 328) implies that $a_n \geqq r_n/4$ and therefore that

$$\lim_{n=\infty} a_n = \infty,$$

which means that the nested regions $G^{(n)}$ will cover any pre-assigned disc $|w| < r$ if n is chosen sufficiently large.

In the second case, i.e. if (340.4) holds, we note that our construction implies that

$$|f^{(n)}_{n+k_p}(z_n)| < r_{n+k_p} < R,$$

so that in the limit,

$$|\varphi^{(n)}(z_n)| < R \qquad (|z_n| < r_n)$$

holds. Here, all of the nested regions $G^{(n)}$ lie within the disc $|w| < R$, and their union is a simply-connected region H that is likewise contained in $|w| < R$. Let the conformal mapping of H onto the disc $|t| < R$ be given by the function $t = \psi(w)$, with $\psi(0) = 0$, $\psi'(0) > 0$. Then by Schwarz's Lemma,

$$\psi'(0) \geqq 1 \tag{340.5}$$

must hold. On the other hand, the functions

$$t = \Psi^{(n)}(z_n) = \psi(\varphi^{(n)}(z_n))$$

give the mapping of $|z_n| < r_n$ onto a subregion of $|t| < R$. It then follows from $\varphi^{(n)'}(0) = 1$ that $\Psi^{(n)'}(0) = \psi'(0)$. But by Schwarz's Lemma

$$\Psi^{(n)'}(0) \leq \frac{R}{r_n}.$$

Therefore

$$\psi'(0) \leq \frac{R}{r_n},$$

and by (340.4) we thus obtain $\psi'(0) \leq 1$. This together with (340.5) yields $\psi'(0) = 1$, which is possible only if $\psi(w) \equiv w$, in which case H must coincide with the disc $|w| < R$. It follows from this that any given smaller disc that is concentric with $|w| < R$ will be covered by the regions $G^{(n)}$ if n is large enough.

CHAPTER THREE

THE MAPPING OF THE BOUNDARY
The Schwarz Reflection Principle (§§ 341-342)

341. Let G_w be a simply-connected region of the w-plane that is its own mirror image under a reflection in the real axis, i.e. that is symmetric with respect to the real axis, and assume that the real point w_0 is an interior point

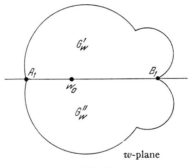

Fig. 56

of G_w. Then there is a segment $A_1 B_1$ of the real axis that contains the point w_0 in its interior and whose end points A_1 and B_1 are points of the frontier of G_w (see Fig. 56).

Let the function

$$w = \psi(t) \tag{341.1}$$

represent a conformal mapping of the open disc $|t| < 1$ onto the region G_w under which the point $t = 0$ is mapped onto $w = w_0$ while $\psi'(0) > 0$. We denote the points of intersection of the circle $|t| = 1$ and the real axis of the t-plane by A_2 and B_2 (see Fig. 57 below), and we denote the disc $|t| < 1$ by G_t. Both G_w and G_t are transformed onto themselves by the reflections in the segments $A_1 B_1$ and $A_2 B_2$ respectively. It follows from this that the equation $\bar{w} = \psi(\bar{t})$ also represents a conformal mapping of G_t onto G_w, for which

$\overline{\psi}(0) = w_0$ and $\overline{\psi}'(0) > 0$. Since there can be only one mapping of this kind, it follows that

$$\overline{\psi}(\overline{t}) = \psi(t). \tag{341.2}$$

Hence if $\psi(t)$ is developed in a Taylor series, the coefficients of the series must all be real. This implies that under the mapping (341.1), the segments $A_1 B_1$ and $A_2 B_2$ correspond to each other, and from this it follows further that the regions G_w' and G_t' (see Figs. 56 and 57) correspond to each other.

Now we map the disc $|z| < 1$ onto the half-disc G_t' by means of a function $t = \chi(z)$; then the function $w = f(z) = \psi(\chi(z))$ maps the disc $|z| < 1$ onto the region G_w'. But the function $t = \chi(z)$ can be constructed in terms of elementary transformations (cf. § 314 above), and if we follow

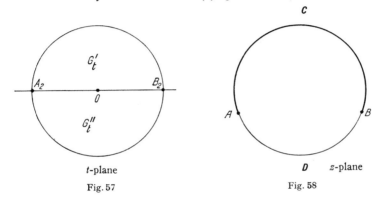

t-plane

Fig. 57

z-plane

Fig. 58

this through we find that the segment $A_2 B_2$ corresponds to an arc of the circle $|z| = 1$ with two (distinct) end-points A and B (see Fig. 58). Moreover, the inverse function $z = \omega(t)$ is regular in the whole disc $|t| < 1$ and represents a conformal mapping of this disc onto the z-plane cut along the arc BCA. Under this mapping, two complex conjugates t and $\overline{t}$ correspond to two points z and $z^* = 1/\overline{z}$ that are images of each other under inversion (reflection) in the circle $|z| = 1$. Similarly, the function $w = f(z)$ is regular on the arc ADB and maps the two points z and z^* that are inverses of each other with respect to the circle, onto two points w and $\overline{w}$ that are symmetric images of each other in the real axis of the w-plane.

The results just obtained are known as the *Schwarz Reflection Principle*.

342. The Schwarz Reflection Principle can be generalized considerably. Let $f(z)$ be a function meromorphic in the disc $|z| < 1$ and assume that on an arc AB of the boundary $|z| = 1$, all of the boundary values of $f(z)$ (cf. § 99, Vol. I, p. 95) are either real or infinite (see Fig. 59). Then the function

$$g(z) = \frac{f(z) - i}{f(z) + i} \tag{342.1}$$

is meromorphic at every point of the disc $|z| < 1$. At every point ζ of the arc AB, all of the boundary values of $|g(z)|$ are equal to 1, since the mapping

$$\omega = \frac{w-i}{w+i}$$

transforms the real axis of the w-plane onto the circle $|\omega| = 1$. If ζ is an interior point of the arc AB, we can choose a natural number n so large that the two following requirements are met: First, if the boundaries of the two discs

$$|z| < 1, \qquad |z - \zeta| < \frac{1}{n} \tag{342.2}$$

intersect at the points C and D, then the arc CD of $|z| = 1$ is a subarc of AB; and second, the relation

$$\frac{1}{2} < |g(z)| < 2 \tag{342.3}$$

holds at every point z that lies in the intersection of the two discs (342.2).

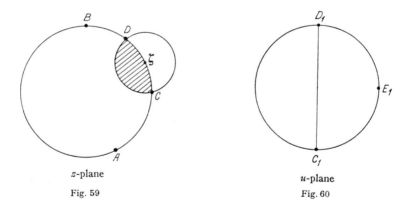

z-plane

Fig. 59

u-plane

Fig. 60

For otherwise, we should be able to assign to every natural number n a point z_n inside the unit circle for which

$$|z_n - \zeta| < \frac{1}{n}$$

holds and which satisfies one of the two relations $|g(z_n)| \geqq 2$ and $|g(z_n)| \leqq 1/2$. But then $|g(z)|$ would have at ζ a boundary value different from unity, contrary to what we noted earlier.

Let us now map the shaded lens of Fig. 59 onto the disc $|u| < 1$ (see Fig. 60) by means of a function

$$z = \psi(u) \tag{342.4}$$

in such a way that the arc $C\zeta D$ is mapped onto the semicircle $C_1 E_1 D_1$ that lies in the half-plane $\Re u > 0$, and let us set

$$h(u) = g(\psi(u)). \tag{342.5}$$

Then by the above,

$$\frac{1}{2} < |h(u)| < 2;$$

therefore one of the branches of the logarithm of $h(u)$ is regular in $|u| < 1$ and has a bounded real part in this disc. We introduce the notation

$$\lambda(r, \vartheta) = \Re l\, h(r\, e^{i\vartheta}) \qquad (0 < r < 1). \tag{342.6}$$

Then if u is any point of the disc $|u| < 1$ and if $|u| < r < 1$, we have by Poisson's Integral Formula (cf. §§ 150-152, Vol. I, p. 146 ff. and formula (148.11), Vol. I, p. 145) that

$$l\, h(u) = \frac{l\, h(0) - \overline{l\, h(0)}}{2} + \frac{1}{2\pi} \int_0^{2\pi} \lambda(r, \vartheta)\, \frac{r\, e^{i\vartheta} + u}{r\, e^{i\vartheta} - u}\, d\vartheta. \tag{342.7}$$

Since for $0 \le \vartheta < \pi/2$ and for $3\pi/2 < \vartheta < 2\pi$ all of the boundary values of $|h(u)|$ are $= 1$, so that

$$\lim_{r=1} \lambda(r, \vartheta) = 0$$

holds true, it follows from letting r tend to unity in (342.7) and setting

$$\lambda(\vartheta) = \lim_{r=1} \lambda(r, \vartheta)$$

that

$$l\, h(u) = \frac{l\, h(0) - \overline{l\, h(0)}}{2\cdot} + \frac{1}{2\pi} \int_{\pi/2}^{3\pi/2} \lambda(\vartheta)\, \frac{e^{i\vartheta} + u}{e^{i\vartheta} - u}\, d\vartheta. \tag{342.8}$$

But this representation of $l h(u)$ shows that $l h(u)$ is regular on the semicircle $C_1 E_1 D_1$; the same holds true for $h(u)$, and therefore $g(z)$ must be regular at every point of the arc $C\zeta D$; the same then applies to $f(z)$. We have thus proved the following theorem:

Let $f(z)$ be meromorphic in the disc $|u| < 1$, and let all of the boundary values of $f(z)$ on an arc AB of $|u| = 1$ be real or infinite. Then if ζ is any point of the arc AB, the function $f(z)$ either is regular and real at ζ or else has a pole at ζ.

This theorem is remarkable in that it shows the regularity of the function $f(z)$ on the arc AB to depend only on the distribution of the boundary values; it does not require the assumption of continuity of the function on the arc.

We note that in the above proof, we needed the given meromorphic function $f(z)$ only in a certain neighborhood of the arc AB, so that the theorem goes through whenever we can find for every interior point ζ of the arc AB a lens CDC (see Fig. 59 above) in which $f(z)$ is meromorphic.

Conformal Mapping of the Region Inside a Jordan Curve (§§ 343-346)

343. Let γ_w be a Jordan curve (simple closed curve, *cf.* § 106, Vol. I, p. 100) and let G_w be the finite region bounded by γ_w (the "inside" of γ_w). Since γ_w is a one-to-one continuous image of the circle $e^{i\varphi}$, there exist two continuous periodic functions $x(\varphi)$ and $y(\varphi)$ for which the points of γ_w are given by

$$w(\varphi) = x(\varphi) + i\, y(\varphi). \tag{343.1}$$

For any two values φ_1 and φ_2 of φ that are not congruent modulo 2π, we have

$$z(\varphi_1) \neq z(\varphi_2).$$

Let the function

$$w = f(z) \tag{343.2}$$

represent a one-to-one conformal mapping of the disc $|z| < 1$ onto the region G_w. Let A be any point of the curve γ_w, and consider a sequence $\{w_\nu\}$ of points of G_w converging to A. By (343.2), the points w_ν are the images of (uniquely determined) points z_ν of the disc $|z| < 1$ that have no point of accumulation in the interior of this disc. We shall prove that the sequence $\{z_\nu\}$ has one and only one point of accumulation A'.

To this end, assume that the sequence $\{z_\nu\}$ had, besides A', an additional point of accumulation B'. By Fatou's theorem (*cf.* § 310), there are two radii $O'P_1'$ and $O'P_2'$ of the circle $|z| = 1$ whose end-points P_1' and P_2' are separated by the points A' and B' and along which the function (343.2) converges to certain boundary values ω_1 and ω_2, respectively. We also assume

P_1' and P_2' to be chosen in such a way that no two of the ω_1, ω_2, and A coincide (see Figs. 61 and 62).

The mapping (343.2) transforms the broken line $P_1'O'P_2'$ into a Jordan arc $\omega_1 O \omega_2$ that is a cross cut of the region G_w (cf. § 113, Vol. I, p. 105). This cross cut divides G_w into two subregions G_w' and G_w'' whose pre-images under $w = f(z)$ are the sectors $O'P_1'A'P_2'$ and $O'P_2'B'P_1'$ of the disc $|z| < 1$. Now if the point A lies, say, on the frontier of G_w', then the distance

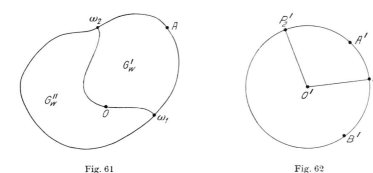

Fig. 61   Fig. 62

between A and the subregion G_w'' is not zero, so that the sequence $\{w_\nu\}$, which converges to A, cannot have more than finitely many of its points lying in G_w'' or on the frontier of G_w''. The pre-images of these points therefore also constitute a finite set, consisting of all those members of the sequence $\{z_\nu\}$ that lie in the sector $O'P_2'B'P_1'$; thus B' cannot possibly be a point of accumulation of the sequence $\{z_\nu\}$. The result we have obtained may be stated as follows:

The mapping (343.2) makes it possible to associate with every point A of the Jordan curve γ_w a point A' of the circle $z = e^{i\vartheta}$ with the following property: For every sequence of points $\{w_\nu\}$ that converges to A, the sequence of pre-images $\{z_\nu\}$, (under the mapping (343.2)) converges to A'.

This correspondence between the points of γ_w and the points of $|z| = 1$ can therefore be expressed by means of a single-valued function

$$\vartheta = \lambda(\varphi) \tag{343.3}$$

that is periodic and has period 2π.

We can easily show that the function (343.3) is continuous. To this end, consider a convergent sequence of numbers $\varphi_1, \varphi_2, \ldots$ whose limit is φ_0, and let $A_1, A_2, \ldots$ be the points of γ_w that correspond to the φ_i by virtue of (343.1); the A_i converge to a point A_0 of γ_w. We must prove that if

$A_1', A_2', \dots$ are the points of the circle $|z| = 1$ that correspond to $A_1, A_2, \dots$ under the relation (343.3) and if A_0' similarly corresponds to A_0, then the sequence $A_1', A_2', \dots$ converges to A_0'. But this is almost self-evident, because we can determine a sequence of interior points $w_1, w_2, \dots$ of G_w in such a way that the distance between w_ν and A_ν, and the distance between the corresponding points z_ν and A_ν', are both less than $1/\nu$. Then $\lim w_\nu = A_0$, so that by our last theorem $\lim z_\nu = A_0'$.

344. Next we wish to prove that every subarc γ_w^* of the Jordan curve γ_w contains pairs of points whose pre-images on $|z| = 1$ under the mapping (343.3) induced by (342.2) are two distinct points.

Let M be an interior point of the arc γ_w^* (see Fig. 63 below). Then M has a non-zero distance δ from the complementary arc of the Jordan curve γ_w.

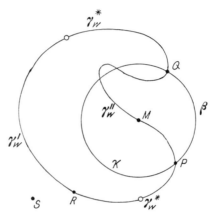

Fig. 63

Let $\varkappa$ be a circle whose center is at M and whose radius is less than δ. If we denote the outside of γ_w (the region exterior to γ_w) by H_w, then H_w must contain points that lie inside $\varkappa$, since M is on the frontier of H_w. Now any two points of H_w can be joined within H_w by continuous curves; therefore H_w must contain points of the circle $\varkappa$ itself. Hence there is at least one arc β of $\varkappa$ that lies in H_w and whose end-points P and Q lie on γ_w. Also, P and Q must be distinct, since a similar reasoning shows that at least one (non-zero) arc of $\varkappa$ must lie in G_w.

By our construction, the two points P and Q lie on γ_w^*. We wish to show that the points P_1 and Q_1 of $|z| = 1$ that correspond to P and Q under $w = f(z)$ are distinct.

P and Q divide γ_w into two Jordan arcs γ_w' and γ_w''. We consider the (closed) Jordan curves $\beta + \gamma_w'$ and $\beta + \gamma_w''$, which bound two finite regions that we denote by G_w' and G_w''. If G_w'' contains a point of G_w, then it must contain all of G_w. Let us assume that G_w'' is a subregion of H_w. Then every point R of γ_w' lies outside G_w'', and in any neighborhood of R there are points S that belong neither to G_w nor to G_w''. We can easily show that S must also lie outside G_w'; for there are points T that belong neither to G_w nor to G_w' nor to G_w'', and if we join such a point T to S by a continuous curve that avoids G_w, this curve can meet the frontier of G_w' only in points of β (if at all); we can then arrange by means of a continuous deformation of the curve that it meets neither γ_w nor β. Hence S lies outside G_w'.

Since S is outside G_w' and R is on the frontier of G_w', all the points of G_w that lie in a sufficiently small neighborhood of R must be (interior) points of G_w', whence it follows that the whole region G_w must be inside the Jordan curve $\beta + \gamma_w'$, i.e. that G_w is a subregion of G_w'. Thus we always have, if necessary after interchanging the symbols for the above curves γ_w' and γ_w'' (and likewise those for G_w' and G_w''), that G_w' contains G_w.

Let us now map the circular arc β onto a segment of the real axis of a t-plane by means of a Moebius transformation, and let the image of G_w' under this transformation be the region G_t'. We then map G_t' by means of $t^4 = u$, similarly as in § 323, onto the interior region G_u' of a Jordan curve of the u-plane, in such a way that G_u' lies in the upper half-plane while the image of β is a segment of the real axis of the u-plane. By the Schwarz Reflection Principle it is now evident that when G_u' is mapped in turn onto $|v| < 1$, the images of P and Q are two distinct points P_2 and Q_2 on $|v| = 1$. At the same time, the v-image of γ_w'' is a cross cut γ_v of $|v| < 1$, and that of G_w is a region G_v bounded by an arc of the circle $|v| = 1$ and by the cross cut γ_v''. Finally, when G_v is mapped onto $|z| < 1$, the points P_2 and Q_2 are mapped onto two distinct points P_1 and Q_1 on $|z| = 1$, and we have proved the result stated at the beginning of this section.

345. It is now easy to prove that under our original mapping (343.2), two distinct points A and B of γ_w always are the images (actually not under $w = f(z)$ but under the induced mapping (343.3)) of two distinct points A_1 and B_1. To this end, we shall borrow a fact that will be proved in the next section, namely that A and B can always be joined by a cross cut q of G_w. Assuming the truth of this statement, we infer from it that under the conformal mapping of $|z| < 1$ onto G_w, the cross cut q is the image of a curve q_1 that has at most two points A_1 and B_1 in common with the circle $|z| = 1$ and must therefore be a cross cut of the disc $|z| < 1$. But the points A and B divide the Jordan curve γ_w into two arcs on each of which, by the preceding section, there are pairs of points whose pre-images are likewise pairs of distinct points; also, the two subregions into which q divides G_w are the images of two non-empty subregions into which q_1 divides $|z| < 1$; hence A_1 and B_1 cannot coincide.

Now if $z_1, z_2, \ldots$ is a sequence of points of the disc $|z| < 1$ that converges to a point of $|z| = 1$, then the images $w_1, w_2, \ldots$ of these points cannot have more than one point of accumulation A on the curve γ_w. Hence the relation between the quantities ϑ and φ of § 343 can be expressed not only by (343.3), but also in the inverse form

$$\varphi = \mu(\vartheta). \tag{345.1}$$

Just as we have shown $\lambda(\varphi)$ to be continuous (§ 343), we can prove the same for $\mu(\vartheta)$; it follows further that both $\lambda(\varphi)$ and $\mu(\vartheta)$ are monotonically increasing and cannot be constant on any interval of their domain of definition. This implies that the *order* of any three points A_1, B_1, C_1 of the circle $|z| = 1$ is preserved by the mapping (343.3)—or (345.1)—for their images A, B, C on the curve γ_w; in other words, the mapping leaves the cyclic order of any three points intact. We have at last arrived at the following theorem:

If there exists a one-to-one and bi-continuous mapping of the frontier of a simply-connected region onto a circle (in other words, if the frontier is the topological image of a circle), then any conformal mapping of the region onto an open circular disc induces a corresponding mapping, of the kind mentioned, of the frontier of the region onto the frontier of the disc.

It clearly follows that a similar correspondence of their frontiers is induced by any conformal mapping of one Jordan region G_u (i.e., simply-connected region whose frontier is a Jordan curve) onto another Jordan region G_v. This follows from the fact that the mapping of G_u onto G_v can always be accomplished by first mapping G_u onto the disc $|t| < 1$, and then mapping this disc onto G_v; the theorem applies at each of the two steps.

On the basis of the above theorem, we can find examples of analytic functions that are regular and bounded everywhere in $|z| < 1$, that are not regular at any point of $|z| = 1$, and which even so have just a single boundary value at every point of $|z| = 1$. Thus Fatou's theorem (*cf.* § 310) holds here not only for approach within a sector to a point of $|z| = 1$ but also for any arbitrary approach to the point.

Remark. If we wish to make use of the theory of Fourier Series, we can expand the mapping function $w = f(z)$ of a Jordan region in a series of the form

$$f(r\, e^{i\vartheta}) = \sum_{n=0}^{\infty} a_n\, r^n\, e^{in\vartheta},$$

which for $r = 1$ becomes a trigonometric series

$$f(e^{i\vartheta}) = \sum_{n=0}^{\infty} a_n (\cos n\,\vartheta + i \sin n\,\vartheta).$$

This series need not converge, but by a well-known result of L. Fejér it is summable. Therefore every Jordan curve can be represented by means of a Fourier series.

346. We still have to prove a result which we have already made use of in § 345, namely the fact that any two points A and B of the frontier γ of a Jordan region G can be joined by means of a cross cut of G. It clearly suffices to show that any point O in G can be joined to any given frontier point A by means of a Jordan arc all of whose points, with the exception of A, are in G.

To this end, let the curve γ be given by means of parametric equations

$$x = x(\varphi), \ y = y(\varphi),$$

and let A be any point of this curve, which we may without loss of generality assume to correspond to the value $\varphi = 0$ of the parameter. The function

$$\varrho(\varphi) = \sqrt{(x(\varphi) - x(0))^2 + (y(\varphi) - y(0))^2}, \tag{346.1}$$

which represents the distance between the point A and a variable point of γ, is continuous and positive in the interval $-\pi \leq \varphi < \pi$ and has its only zero at $\varphi = 0$. If r is a positive number that is $\leq \max \varrho(\varphi)$, then there are certain values of φ in the above interval for which

$$\varrho(\varphi) = r \tag{346.2}$$

holds. The l.u.b. of the moduli of these values of φ is a non-zero positive number $\delta(r)$ that decreases monotonically as r does.

Let $m(r)$ be the minimum of the function $\varrho(\varphi)$ in the intervals

$$-\pi \leq \varphi \leq -\delta(r)$$

and

$$\delta(r) \leqq \varphi < \pi$$

Then the number $m(r)$ cannot exceed r; the function $m(r)$ is positive, non-zero, and decreases monotonically as r does. If $\varkappa(r)$ is the circle of radius r whose center is at A, then by § 344 there is a least one cross cut of G that is an arc of $\varkappa(r)$. In general, there will be several or even perhaps infinitely many arcs of $\varkappa(r)$ that are cross cuts of G, say $\beta_1, \beta_2, \dots$. Each of these arcs β_k divides G into two subregions G_k' and G_k''. We reserve the symbol G_k'' for that one of these two subregions whose frontier consists of the arc β_k together with a part of the Jordan curve γ on which $|\varphi| \geqq \delta(r)$ holds. Hence the distance from the point A to the subregion G_k'' is at least equal to $m(r)$. From this it follows that the points P of G for which the distance AP is less than $m(r)$ must all lie in the subregion G_k'.

Now let P and Q be two (interior) points of G whose distances from A are both less than $m(r)$; we join P to Q by a polygonal train σ wholly within G. If there are points on σ whose distance from A exceeds r, then σ must intersect some of the arcs $\beta_1, \beta_2, \dots$ and must have at least two points in common with each of the arcs that it intersects. There can be only a finite number of such arcs β_{ν_j}, since each of the finitely many segments that make up σ cuts the circle $\varkappa(r)$ in at most two points.

Let M_j be the first and N_j the last of the points in which σ meets β_{ν_j} as σ is traversed from P to Q. We replace the part of σ that goes from M_j to N_j by the appropriate sub-arc of β_{ν_j}. After doing this for each of the finitely many j involved, we obtain a path that lies within G, joins P to Q, and has all of its points within distance r (or less) of A. Thus we have the following result:

Any two points of G whose distance from A is less than $m(r)$ can be joined to each other by a path that lies wholly in G and has all of its points within distance r (or less) of A.

Now let $r_1, r_2, \dots$ be an infinite sequence of positive numbers for which $r_n > r_{n+1}$ and $\lim r_n = 0$. Also, let $P_1, P_2, \dots$ be a sequence of points of G whose distances from A satisfy the conditions $\varrho_n < m(r_n)$, $n = 1, 2, \dots$. Since $m(r)$ decreases with r, we have $m(r_{n+1}) \leqq m(r_n)$ and hence also $\varrho_{n+1} < m(r_n)$. Now if O is any (interior) point of G, let us join O to P_1 by a path wholly within G; next we join P_1 to P_2 by a path in G that lies within distance r_1 of A; then we join P_2 to P_3 by a path in G that lies within distance r_2 of A; more generally, we join each P_n to P_{n+1} by a path in G that lies within distance r_n of A.

The curve $OP_1P_2\dots$ constructed in this way may of course have double points; we can avoid this by simply eliminating certain portions of the curve. The resulting curve is then a Jordan arc that joins O to A and lies in G (except for its end-point A), and this is what we had set out to obtain.

The Concept of Free Boundary Arc (§§ 347-348)

347. A point A of the frontier of a region G_w of the w-plane is said to be *accessible* if it can be joined to an interior point of G_w by a Jordan arc (by a *free cut*; cf. § 113, Vol. I, p. 105). There are regions not all of whose frontier points are accessible. For example, consider a square in which we delete all of the points of an infinite number of free cuts that accumulate toward the segment AE of the side AD (see Fig. 64). Then it is not possible to join the

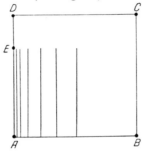

Fig. 64

vertex A to any interior point of the resulting region G by means of a continuous curve lying in G.

On the other hand, the frontier of G certainly contains points that can be joined to interior points of G by means of free cuts. In special cases, these free cuts may even be straight-line segments.

Returning to a general region G_w, let A be a frontier point that is joined to an interior point O by a free cut, and consider any sequence of points $w_1, w_2, \ldots$ of the free cut that converge to the point A. Then if G_w is mapped conformally onto the disc $|z| < 1$, the images $z_1, z_2, \ldots$ of $w_1, w_2, \ldots$ must converge to a definite point A_1 of $|z| = 1$; the proof of this fact, with the aid of Fatou's theorem (cf. §§ 310-311), is similar to the proof of the analogous theorem for Jordan curves in § 343 ff. above. But in contrast to the results for Jordan curves, it is here not necessarily true that the images of two convergent sequences on two *different* free cuts joining O to A are the same point of $|z| = 1$. There are even cases in which the set of points of $|z| = 1$ that is obtained from a set of different cross cuts all ending at A has the cardinality of the continuum, as is shown by the following example (see Fig. 65 below).

Consider the half-disc $y > 0$, $x^2 + y^2 < 1$, and for every rational number p/q with $0 < p < q$, where p and q are relatively prime, lay off the line-segment of length $1/q$ that emanates from the origin O and forms the angle $p\pi/q$ with the positive real axis. Our region G_w will be the open half-disc minus all of the points that lie on any of these segments. Consider any

sequence of points converging to O that lies on a radius whose angle of in-
clination is πa, where a is irrational. These points lie on a free cut of G_w,
and their images under the mapping onto $|z| < 1$ lie on a free cut of $|z| < 1$.
But between any two such free cuts of G_w there lies at least one of the above

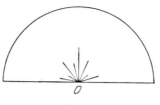

Fig. 65

segments, with an angle $p\pi/q$, that is part of the frontier of G_w. This implies
that the images of the points of two convergent sequences on the two free cuts
converge to two distinct points of $|z| = 1$.

348. By a *free (or accessible) arc* of the frontier of G_w we shall mean a
Jordan arc γ_w' that has the following properties: 1. Every point of γ_w' is an
accessible frontier point of G_w (i.e. a frontier point that can be joined to an
interior point of G_w by a free cut). 2. If O is any (interior) point of G_w and
if P and Q are any two points of γ_w', then we can draw two free cuts OP and
OQ in such a way that these two free cuts together with a sub-arc PQ of γ_w'

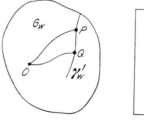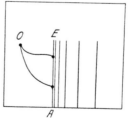

γ_w' is here the line-segment AE

Fig. 66

form a (closed) Jordan curve $OPQO$ whose interior is a subregion of G_w.
(See for instance Fig. 66.)

We now wish to prove that under a conformal mapping of the disc $|z| < 1$
onto the region G_w, there corresponds to any given free arc γ_w' of the frontier
of G_w, with end-points A and B, at least one circular arc A_1B_1 of $|z| = 1$,
and this correspondence between the arcs γ_w' and A_1B_1 is one-to-one and
continuous.

To prove this statement, let us consider the Jordan region $OPQO$ used in the above definition of free arc, P and Q being any points of γ_w', and let us denote this Jordan region by G_w'. If $w = f(z)$ is the function that gives the mapping of the disc $|z| < 1$ onto the region G_w, then the pre-image of G_w' under $w = f(z)$ is a subregion G_z' of the disc $|z| < 1$. The frontier of G_z' consists of two free cuts $O_1 P_1$ and $O_1 Q_1$ of the disc $|z| < 1$ together with the circular arc $P_1 Q_1$ (unless P_1 and Q_1 coincide). In any case, G_z' is a Jordan region whose frontier, by § 345, is mapped one-to-one and continuously onto the frontier of G_w'. Therefore P_1 and Q_1 cannot coincide, since their images P and Q are distinct. We now let P and Q converge to A and B, and our statement is proved.

Reflection in Analytic Curves (§ 349)

349. The Reflection Principle of §§ 341-342 can be generalized so as to apply to "reflections" in arbitrary analytic curves. Let a real analytic curve in the z-plane ($z = x + iy$) be given, either by an equation of the form

$$F(x, y) = 0 \tag{349. 1}$$

or by means of parametric equations

$$x = \varphi(t), \quad y = \psi(t) \qquad (t \text{ real}) \tag{349. 2}$$

where the functions $F(x, y)$, $\varphi(t)$ and $\psi(t)$ are assumed to be represented in a certain neighborhood of a point of the curve by power series with real coefficients. Throughout this neighborhood, we assume at least one of the two partial derivatives F_x and F_y, or at least one of the two derivatives φ' and ψ', to be non-zero.

We consider the function

$$z = f(t) = \varphi(t) + i \psi(t) \tag{349. 3}$$

as an analytic function of the complex variable t defined in a neighborhood of a real point t_0. Our assumptions imply that $f'(t_0) \neq 0$, so that there exists a disc $|t - t_0| < r$ that is mapped by (349.3) one-to-one and conformally onto a neighborhood of the point $z_0 = f(t_0)$. One of the diameters of this disc is a segment of the real axis of the t-plane, and this diameter is mapped by (349.3) onto a certain arc of the curve (349.2) in the z-plane. Now the following definition was given by H. A. Schwarz:

Two points z and z^* are said to be reflections (or inverses) of each other relative to the curve (349.2) if they are the images under (349.3) of two points t and $\bar{t}$ of the disc $|t - t_0| < r$ that are each other's reflections in the real axis of the t-plane.

Hence if z satisfies (349.3) then z^* satisfies

$$z^* = \varphi(\bar{t}) + i\,\psi(\bar{t}). \tag{349.4}$$

Now let w be the complex conjugate of z^*. Since the coefficients in the Taylor expansions of $\varphi(t)$ and $\psi(t)$ are real numbers, we can write

$$w = \overline{z^*} = \varphi(t) - i\,\psi(t). \tag{349.5}$$

From (349.3) and (349.5) we obtain

$$x = \frac{z+w}{2}, \qquad y = \frac{z-w}{2i}. \tag{349.6}$$

Substitution of these expressions for x and y in (349.1) yields

$$F\left(\frac{z+w}{2}, \frac{z-w}{2i}\right) = 0. \tag{349.7}$$

From this relation we can calculate w as an analytic function of z, and it follows in particular that the operation of reflection in the curve (349.1) is independent of the choice of the parameter t. The calculation of the derivative dw/dz from (349.7) shows that there are singular points at which $dw/dz = 0$ or $= \infty$, except in the case of a circle or a straight line; but we shall not prove this here. At such points, the reflection is undefined.

Thus it should not be thought that if γ is a given analytic curve, any and all points of the complex plane can be reflected in γ. As an example of this, one might study the reflection in the ellipse—which is an analytic curve—given by

$$F(x, y) = \frac{x^2}{a^2} + \frac{y^2}{b^2} - 1 = 0.$$

The Mapping of the Frontier in the Neighborhood of a Free Analytic Boundary Arc (§ 350)

350. Let the function

$$w = f(z) \tag{350.1}$$

represent a mapping of the disc $|z| < 1$ onto a simply-connected region G_w whose frontier contains a free analytic arc γ_w'. If w_0 is an interior point of the arc γ_w', then by the preceding section there exists a subregion G_w' of G_w that is mapped by

$$w = \chi(t), \qquad t = \omega(w) \tag{350.2}$$

onto a region G_t', where $\chi(t)$ is regular in a neighborhood of $t_0 = \omega(w_0)$.

Let us assume, as we may, that G_t' lies in the upper half-plane and that γ_w' corresponds to a segment A^*B^* of the real axis of the t-plane. If

$$z = \varphi(w) \tag{350.3}$$

is the inverse function of (350.1), then G_w' is mapped by (350.3) onto a sub-

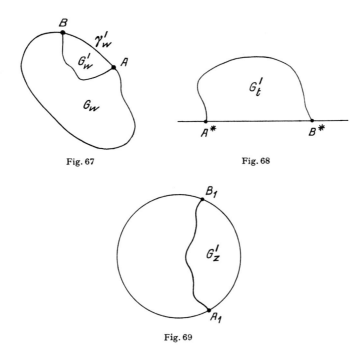

Fig. 67   Fig. 68

Fig. 69

region G_z' of the disc $|z| < 1$, and by § 348, the frontier of G_z' contains an arc A_1B_1 of $|z| = 1$.

Let us now apply the theorem of § 342 to the function

$$t = \omega(f(z)) = \lambda(z), \tag{350.4}$$

which is regular in the region G_z'; this yields the fact that the function (350.4) is regular on the arc A_1B_1. Then the function $f(z) = \chi(\lambda(z))$ is likewise regular on the arc A_1B_1, since by the preceding section the function (350.2) is regular on the line-segment A^*B^*. Hence the function $f(z)$ can be continued analytically across the arc A_1B_1, everywhere along that arc. In particular, if z is an interior point of G_z' and $z^* = 1/\overline{z}$ is its reflection in $|z| = 1$, then $f(z)$ is defined in the neighborhood of z^*, and the two points $w = f(z)$ and $w^* = f(z^*)$ are reflections of each other relative to the arc γ_w'.

The Mapping at a Corner (§§ 351-353)

351. Let G_w be a simply-connected region whose frontier contains a free Jordan arc MAN, and assume that at the point A the arc has two tangents AP and AQ that form an angle $\pi\alpha(0 < \alpha \leq 2)$. Let $w = f(z)$ represent a conformal mapping of $|z| < 1$ onto G_w. Then we shall prove that every free cut of G_w that ends at A and has a tangent at A which makes an angle

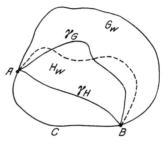

Fig. 70

.. $\vartheta\alpha\,(0 \leq \vartheta \leq 1)$ with AQ is the image of a free cut of $|z| < 1$ that meets the frontier $|z| = 1$ of that disc at the angle $\pi\vartheta$.

This result is almost obvious in the case that the parts AM and AN of the free Jordan arc are straight-line segments. For if we denote the point A by w_0, then the intersection of G_w with a suitable disc $|w - w_0| < \varrho$ is mapped by means of

$$u = (w - w_0)^{\frac{1}{\alpha}} \tag{351.1}$$

onto a half-disc. Now

$$u = (f(z) - w_0)^{\frac{1}{\alpha}} \tag{351.2}$$

maps this half-disc onto a subregion of $|z| < 1$, and by § 341, the diameter of the half-disc in the u-plane corresponds to a circular arc on $|z| = 1$ on which the function (351.2) is regular; in particular, therefore, it is regular at the point z_0 which corresponds to u_0. From this and from § 314 follows the truth of our statement in this special case.

352. The proof of the result in the general case requires the following preliminary proposition. Assume that the region G_w contains a subregion H_w and that the frontiers of these two regions have the free Jordan arc ACB in common (see Fig. 70 above). We map both G_w and H_w onto the interior of the same circle κ and we norm each of these two mappings in such a way that the end points A and B of the free Jordan arc ACB are mapped onto the points A_1 and B_1 of κ (see Fig. 71 below).

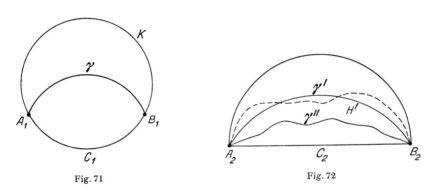

Fig. 71   Fig. 72

Now let γ be a cross cut of the interior of κ that joins A_1 to B_1 and is itself a circular arc. We denote the images of γ in the regions G_w and H_w by γ_G and γ_H, respectively. Then we shall show that γ_H lies in the (interior of the) Jordan region bounded by ACB and γ_G.

We map the open disc bounded by κ conformally onto the half-disc $|t| < 1$, $\Im t > 0$ of diameter A_2B_2, in such a way that A_2B_2 corresponds to the circular arc $A_1C_1B_1$. Under this mapping, γ is transformed into a circular arc γ' that joins A_2 to B_2 (see Fig. 72).

The half-disc may be regarded as the image of G_w; then γ' is the image of γ_G' and the image of H_w is a subregion H' of the half-disc. The same mapping transforms γ_H into an arc γ''. What we have to prove is that γ'' lies in the circular segment bounded by γ' and $A_2C_2B_2$.

Now the function that maps H' onto the upper half of the disc $|t| < 1$ and leaves the diameter $A_2C_2B_2$ fixed will map γ'' onto the circular arc γ'. By the Schwarz Reflection Principle (*cf.* § 341 above), this mapping function is regular on A_2B_2 and its Taylor expansion at $t = 0$ has real coefficients only. Thus we may apply the theorem of § 294, and our preliminary proposition is proved.

353. We now return to a corner of the frontier of G_w where the angle is πa, and we shall assume only one "side" AN of the corner A to be a straight-line segment (see Fig. 73 below). We construct two regions G_w' and G_w'' with the following properties: G_w' is to contain G_w, and its frontier is to contain two line segments AN and AM' that form an angle $\pi(\alpha + \varepsilon)$ at A. G_w'' is to be a subregion of G_w whose frontier shares with that of G_w the segment AN and contains a segment AM'' that forms an angle $\pi(\alpha - \varepsilon)$ with AN at A.

Now we consider three mapping functions that map the regions G_w', G_w, and G_w'', respectively, onto the interior of the same circle κ, each time in

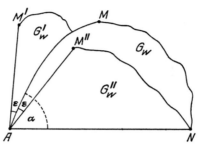

Fig. 73

such a way that the common frontier segment AN is mapped onto the same arc $A_1 N_1$ of the circle κ. Let γ_0 be a circular arc inside κ that joints A_1 to N_1 and meets the arc $A_1 N_1$ of κ at the angle $\pi \vartheta$ ($0 < \vartheta < 1$). The inverses of the three mapping functions map γ_0 onto curves γ', γ, and γ'', respectively, and by the preceding section γ lies between γ' and γ''. By § 351, γ' and γ'' have tangents at A that form with AN the angles $\pi \vartheta (\alpha + \varepsilon)$ and $\pi \vartheta (\alpha - \varepsilon)$, respectively. Since $\varepsilon > 0$ was arbitrary, γ must also have a tangent at A, and this tangent must form the angle $\pi \vartheta \alpha$ with AN. The result is therefore proved in the case that one side of the corner is a straight-line segment.

Finally, to settle the general case, let G_w have a corner MAN and let G_w' be a region that contains G_w and has the corner MAK with the straight side AK. If we map G_w' onto a half-plane, G_w is transformed into a subregion G_1 of the half-plane; the frontier of G_1 has a corner $M_1 A_1 N_1$, where $M_1 A_1$ is a straight-line segment. If G_1 is mapped in turn onto the interior of the unit circle, we have constructed altogether a mapping of G_w onto $|z| < 1$ in two steps each of which preserves the proportionality of the angles at the corner.

Every point A of the frontier at which a free arc has a single ordinary tangent can be regarded as a corner with the angle π. Our result thus implies that in this case the mapping is isogonal at A. Nevertheless, the mapping function may have a singularity at A and need not even possess an angular derivative at this point (cf. § 298).

Milloux's Theorem (§ 354)

354. We conclude this chapter with an application of the Koebe-Faber distortion theorem (*cf.* § 328), an application that is actually related to the material of the preceding chapter.

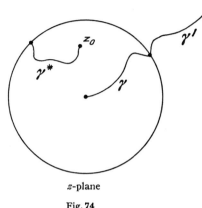

s-plane

Fig. 74

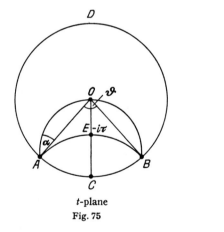

t-plane

Fig. 75

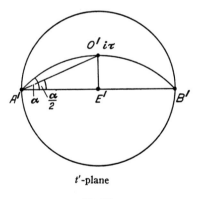

t'-plane

Fig. 76

We consider in the disc $|z| < 1$ a Jordan arc γ that joins $z = 0$ to a point of the frontier $|z| = 1$. If the image of γ under the reflection (inversion) in $|z| = 1$ is added to γ, we obtain a Jordan arc that we denote by γ'. By z_0 we shall denote a point of $|z| < 1$ that does not lie on γ.

We now cut the z-plane along γ', and we map the resulting region onto the disc $|\,t\,| < 1$ by means of a function

$$z = g(t), \tag{354.1}$$

where we assume that $g(0) = z_0$. By our construction, the circle $|\,z\,| = 1$ is a line of symmetry of the z-plane cut along γ'; hence its image in the t-plane is a non-Euclidean straight line if $|\,t\,| < 1$ is taken to represent a non-Euclidean plane, say the non-Euclidean line that passes through the point $-i\tau$ $(\tau > 0)$ and is perpendicular to the line joining $t = 0$ to $t = -i\tau$.

We now wish to find a lower bound for τ that depends only on $|\,z_0\,|$ and is independent of the particular choice of the curve γ. To this end, we note first that the distance between γ and any point z of $|\,z\,| < 1$ never exceeds $|\,z\,|$, so that we may conclude from the Koebe-Faber distortion theorem—in particular from (328.4), adapted to our present notation—that

$$\left|\frac{dz}{dt}\right| \leqq \frac{4\,|z|}{1 - |t|^2}. \tag{354.2}$$

Now if we let t vary on the segment that joins $t = 0$ to $t = -i\tau$, and denote the image of this segment in the z-plane by γ^*, it follows from (354.2) that

$$\left.\begin{aligned}
\frac{1}{2}\,l\,\frac{1+\tau}{1-\tau} &= \int_0^\tau \frac{dt}{1-t^2} \geqq \int_{\gamma^*} \frac{|dz|}{4\,|z|} \geqq \int_{|z_0|}^1 \frac{d|z|}{4\,|z|} \\
&= -\frac{1}{4}\,l\,|z_0| = \frac{1}{2}\,l\,\frac{1}{\sqrt{|z_0|}}
\end{aligned}\right\} \tag{354.3}$$

and finally that

$$\frac{1+\tau}{1-\tau} \geqq \frac{1}{\sqrt{|z_0|}}, \qquad \tau \geqq \frac{1-\sqrt{|z_0|}}{1+\sqrt{|z_0|}}. \tag{354.4}$$

Fig. 76 is obtained from Fig. 75 by a translation of the non-Euclidean plane in the direction of the imaginary axis that takes E into $t' = 0$. From this it follows that

$$\tau = \operatorname{tg} \frac{\alpha}{2} = \operatorname{tg} \frac{\pi - \vartheta}{4}, \tag{354.5}$$

because $\vartheta = \pi - 2\alpha$; thus if we set $\sqrt{|z_0|} = \operatorname{tg} \beta$, then

$$\text{tg}\,\frac{\pi - \vartheta}{4} \geqq \frac{1 - \text{tg}\,\beta}{1 + \text{tg}\,\beta} = \text{tg}\left(\frac{\pi}{4} - \beta\right), \tag{354.6}$$

whence

$$\frac{\pi - \vartheta}{4} \geqq \frac{\pi}{4} - \arctan \sqrt{|z_0|}. \tag{354.7}$$

Let $\psi(t)$ be an analytic function that does not vanish anywhere in $|t| < 1$ and whose modulus equals $\mu\,(\mu < 1)$ on the arc BDA, equals unity on the interior arc AEB, and hence equals $1/\mu$ on the arc ACB (see Fig. 75 above). Then we have

$$\left. \begin{aligned} \Re l\,\psi(0) &= \frac{1}{2\pi}\left\{(2\pi - \vartheta)\,l\,\mu - \vartheta\,l\,\mu\right\} \\ &= \frac{\pi - \vartheta}{\pi}\,l\,\mu, \quad |\psi(0)| = \mu^{\frac{\pi - \vartheta}{\pi}}. \end{aligned} \right\} \tag{354.8}$$

Hence by (354.7),

$$|\psi(0)| \leqq \mu^{1 - \frac{4}{\pi}\,\arctan \sqrt{|z_0|}}. \tag{354.9}$$

Now let $f(z)$ be any function that is of bound one and regular in the disc $|z| < 1$ with a cut along γ; also, let μ be the l.u.b. of the modulus of the boundary values of $f(z)$ on γ. Then $f(g(t))$ is regular and of bound one in the non-Euclidean half-plane $AEBD$, and its modulus along the arc BDA of the frontier of this half-plane is $\leqq \mu$. Therefore the modulus of this function does not exceed $|\psi(t)|$, and we can write

$$|f(z_0)| = |f(g(0))| \leqq |\psi(0)| \leqq \mu^{1 - \frac{4}{\pi}\,\arctan \sqrt{|z_0|}}. \tag{354.10}$$

This is the content of *Milloux's theorem*. The equality sign holds in (354.10) if and only if the Jordan arc γ coincides with a radius of the disc $|z| < 1$ while z_0 lies on the opposite radius.

PART SEVEN

THE TRIANGLE FUNCTIONS AND PICARD'S THEOREM

CHAPTER ONE

FUNCTIONS OF SEVERAL COMPLEX VARIABLES

Definition of an Analytic Function of Two Variables (§§ 355-356)

355. We have already used analytic functions of several variables in a few places in this book, without bothering about a general definition of such functions. Since in the sequel we shall have to define certain analytic functions (of one complex variable) as solutions of certain differential equations, we must now acquaint ourselves with the simplest facts about functions of two complex variables.

Let us consider a complex function $F(x, y)$ of two complex variables x, y. The pair of variables $x = x_1 + ix_2$, $y = y_1 + iy_2$ may be considered as determining a point in a four-dimensional space. We define the *distance* (*écart*) between two such points (x', y') and (x'', y'') to be the non-negative real number

$$E(x', y'; x'', y'') = |x' - x''| + |y' - y''|. \tag{355.1}$$

A point (x, y) of this space will be considered an *interior point* of a point set $\mathfrak{A}$ if there exists a $\delta > 0$ which is such that, (x, y) being a point of $\mathfrak{A}$, $\mathfrak{A}$ contains all those points (x', y') for which $E(x, y; x', y') < \delta$ holds. A sequence $\{(x_\nu, y_\nu)\}$ of points of the space is said to *converge* to the point (x_0, y_0) if

$$\lim_{\nu = \infty} E(x_\nu, y_\nu; x_0, y_0) = 0$$

holds. Using (355.1), we can also formulate the concepts of point of accumulation and of frontier of a point set in the usual way. A *region* is then defined as an open and connected point set (*cf.* § 100, Vol. I, p. 97).

Among the more important types of regions of the (x, y)-space are the *bi-cylinders*, defined as follows. Consider two regions G_x and G_y, of the x-plane and y-plane respectively. The set of points (x, y) of our four-dimensional space $\mathfrak{R}_4$ for which both $x \in G_x$ and $y \in G_y$ is then called a *bi-cylinder*. Not every region of $\mathfrak{R}_4$ is a bi-cylinder; for example, the hypersphere

$$x_1^2 + x_2^2 + y_1^2 + y_2^2 \leqq \varrho^2, \quad (x = x_1 + i\,x_2,\, y = y_1 + i\,y_2)$$

is not a bi-cylinder. A detailed study of functions of several variables, and especially a study of their singularities, is made immensely more complicated by the necessity of dealing with general regions. For our purposes, however, we need only the beginnings of the theory, where everything can be done in terms of bi-cylinders.

356. We now set down a definition of analytic function that corresponds to our definition for the case of one variable in § 128, Vol I, p. 124.

DEFINITION: *A function $F(x, y)$ defined in a region $\mathfrak{G}$ of the space $\mathfrak{R}_4$ is said to be a regular analytic function in $\mathfrak{G}$ if the partial derivatives $\partial F/\partial x$ and $\partial F/\partial y$ exist at every (interior) point of $\mathfrak{G}$.*

F. Hartogs (1874-1943) was the first to prove that if $F(x, y)$ is a regular analytic function in a bi-cylinder

$$|x| \leqq R_x, \quad |y| \leqq R_y, \tag{356. 1}$$

then it can be expanded in a power series

$$\sum_{\mu, \nu = 0}^{\infty} a_{\mu\nu} x^\mu y^\nu \tag{356.2}$$

that converges absolutely and uniformly in every closed subregion of (356.1).

The difficulties that arise when one proceeds to prove Hartogs' theorem are due to the fact that the above definition only insures the continuity of $F(x, y)$ as a function of x, where y is held fixed, or as a function of y, where x is held fixed; thus one must first prove that $F(x, y)$ is continuous as a function of the four variables x_1, x_2, y_1, y_2. This kind of difficulty does not come up at all in the case of functions of a single complex variable. Hartogs' proof probably cannot be simplified much further; at least, all attempts at simplification have so far been unsuccessful. But in Hartogs' own arrangement of his proof, the main lines of thought are not brought out quite clearly; for one thing because—as was customary at the time (1905)—he attaches too great an importance to the uniform convergence of certain series that are best omitted altogether and for another, because he did not use Lebesgue measure and had a hard time getting through the set-theoretic parts of his proof.

Proof of Hartogs' Theorem for Bounded Functions (§§ 357-358)

357. The result of Hartogs stated in § 356 would be almost trivial if we were given also that a relation

$$|F(x, y)| < M \tag{357. 1}$$

holds everywhere in the bi-cylinder (356.1). For by the above definition of analytic function, $F(x, y)$ is a regular analytic function of y in the disc $|y| \leqq R_y$, for each separate value of x involved, so that it can be expanded in a series of the form

$$F(x, y) = f_0(x) + f_1(x) y + \cdots + f_\nu(x) y^\nu + \cdots. \tag{357.2}$$

Now if $|F(x, y)| < M$, then $F(x, y)$ may be regarded within $|x| \leqq R_x$ as a normal family of analytic functions of x that depends on the parameter y, whence it follows that $f_0(x)$ is analytic in the disc $|x| \leqq R_x$.

For every x in this disc, the function

$$\frac{F(x, y) - f_0(x)}{y} = f_1(x) + f_2(x) y + \cdots \tag{357.3}$$

is a regular analytic function of y in the disc $|y| \leqq R_y$. Hence the modulus of this function attains its maximum on the circle $|y| = R_y$, and we have

$$\left| \frac{F(x, y) - f_0(x)}{y} \right| \leqq \frac{|F(x, y)| + |f_0(x)|}{R_y} < \frac{2M}{R_y}.$$

We can therefore apply the above argument to the right-hand side of (357.3) and find that $f_1(x)$ is also a regular analytic function in $|x| \leqq R_x$. Continuing in this way, we find that all of the $f_\nu(x)$ have this property.

Now it follows from the inequality (209.3), Vol. I, p. 207, that

$$|f_\nu(x) y^\nu| < M \tag{357.4}$$

holds for $|y| \leqq R_y$, and if we represent $f_\nu(x)$ by a power series

$$f_\nu(x) = \sum_{\mu=0}^\infty a_{\mu\nu} x^\mu, \tag{357.5}$$

then it follows for the same reason that

$$|a_{\mu\nu} x^\mu y^\nu| < M \tag{357.6}$$

holds for $|x| \leqq R_x$, $|y| \leqq R_y$. This implies that the double series

$$\sum_{\mu,\nu=0}^\infty a_{\mu\nu} x^\mu y^\nu \tag{357.7}$$

converges absolutely and continuously in every closed subregion of the bicylinder, and this proves Hartogs' theorem in the case of bounded functions. In fact, if $|x| < \vartheta R_x$, $|y| < \vartheta' R_y$, where $0 < (\vartheta, \vartheta') < 1$, then

$$\sum_{\mu, \nu = 0}^{\infty} |a_{\mu\nu} x^\mu y_\nu| \leqq \frac{M}{(1 - \vartheta)(1 - \vartheta')} . \qquad (357.8)$$

358. Next, we wish to prove that if $F(x, y)$ is defined and has partial derivatives $\partial F / \partial x$ and $\partial F / \partial y$ in a closed bi-cylinder (356.1), then we can find subregions of this bi-cylinder in which the function is bounded. In particular, we shall prove that in every neighborhood

$$|y| < \varrho \qquad (358.1)$$

of the origin of the y-plane, there are regions G_y which are such that for every y of G_y and every x of the disc $|x| \leqq R_x$, the function $|F(x, y)|$ remains below a finite bound.

To this end, we first assign to every point y of the disc $|y| \leqq R_y$ the maximum $\mu(y)$ of $|F(x, y)|$ on the circle $|x| = R_x$, and we note that $\mu(y)$ is finite at every point of (358.1).

We denote by N_k $(k = 1, 2, \ldots)$ that part of (358.1) on which $\mu(y) < k$. By Osgood's theorem $(cf. \S 193, \text{Vol. I, p. 191})$, there exists at least one region G_y and a number k_0 for which N_{k_0} is everywhere dense in G_y. For otherwise we could find in the disc (358.1) a nested sequence of closed discs $\kappa_1, \kappa_2, \ldots$ which are such that at every point y of κ_n the inequality $\mu(y) \geqq n$ would hold; but the discs κ_j all have at least one point y_0 in common, and at this point $\mu(y_0) = \infty$ would have to hold, and this, as we noted above, is impossible. Therefore there exists at least one disc

$$|y - a| < \varrho^* \qquad (358.2)$$

contained in (358.1), in which N_{k_0} is everywhere dense. Then for every y in N_{k_0} and for every x in $|x| \leqq R_x$, we have $|F(x, y)| \leqq k_0$, and since $F(x, y)$ is a continuous function of y, this inequality is also valid at all points of the bi-cylinder

$$|x| < R_x, \quad |y - a| < \varrho^* \quad (|a| + \varrho^* < \varrho). \quad (358.3)$$

Thus the statement made at the beginning of this section has been proved.

Proof of Hartogs' Theorem in the General Case (§§ 359-361)

359. The decisive steps in the proof are contained in the following lemma of Hartogs.

Let $F(x, y)$ be a regular analytic function in the bi-cylinder

$$|x| \leqq R_x, \quad |y| \leqq |y_0|. \tag{359.1}$$

Also, let $|F(x, y)| < M$ *for*

$$|x| \leqq |R_x|, \quad |y| \leqq |y_1| \quad (|y_1| < |y_0|). \tag{359.2}$$

Then $F(x, y)$ *is bounded in every bi-cylinder*

$$|x| \leqq r, \quad |y| \leqq |y_2|, \tag{359.3}$$

where r *is any number* $< R_x$, *and* $|y_2|$ *any number between* $|y_1|$ *and* $|y_0|$.

To prove this, we again represent $F(x, y)$ by a series

$$F(x, y) = f_0(x) + f_1(x) y + f_2(x) y^2 + \cdots \tag{359.4}$$

and note that by (359.2), the argument of § 357 can be used to show that the $f_\nu(x)$ are analytic functions. We can then determine a number R between r and R_x which is such that none of the (at most denumerably many) zeros of the functions $f_\nu(x)$ ($\nu = 0, 1, 2, \ldots$) lie on the circle $|x| = R$.

Everything now depends on obtaining bounds for the functions

$$|f_\nu(x) y_0^\nu| \qquad (\nu = 0, 1, 2, \ldots) \tag{359.5}$$

in the disc $|x| \leqq R$. We first have, by (359.2), that

$$\left| \frac{f_\nu(x)}{M} y_0^\nu \right| < \left| \frac{y_0}{y_1} \right|^\nu. \tag{359.6}$$

Now denote by P_ν the set of all arcs of the circle $|x| = R$ on which the left-hand side of (359.6) exceeds unity. Also, let x be a fixed point on this circle. Since the right-hand side of (359.4) converges for $y = y_0$, there is a number n_x for which $|f_\nu(x) y_0^\nu| < M$ for all $\nu > n_x$. This means that for all sufficiently large values of ν, the point x does not belong to the set P_ν and hence does not belong to the union $Q_\nu = P_\nu + P_{\nu+1} + \cdots$. The intersection of all of these open sets Q_ν, therefore, cannot contain the point x, and since x was an arbitrary point of the circle $|x| = R$, the intersection is empty. If $m\,Q_\nu$ denotes the *Lebesgue measure* of Q_ν, then by a well-known theorem[1] we have

$$\lim_{\nu = \infty} m\,Q_\nu = 0$$

and hence also

---

[1] C. Carathéodory, *Vorlesungen über reelle Funktionen*, 2nd ed. (Chelsea Pub. Co., New York 1948), § 265, Theorem 15.

$$\lim_{\nu = \infty} m \, P_\nu = 0. \tag{359.7}$$

360.   Now we consider the functions

$$h_\nu(r \, e^{i\vartheta}) = \frac{1}{\nu} \, l \left| \frac{f_\nu(x)}{M} \right| + l \, |y_0|, \quad (x = r \, e^{i\vartheta}, \; |x| < R, \; \nu = 1, 2, \ldots), \tag{360.1}$$

which are harmonic except for a finite number of singularities at the zeros of $f_\nu(x)$, and by means of the Poisson Integral we construct non-negative harmonic functions $g_\nu(r \, e^{i\vartheta})$ in the disc $|x| < R$ that are equal to $l \, |y_0/y_1|$ on the point-sets P_ν and that vanish at all the remaining points of the circle $|x| = R$.   A comparison of (359.6) with (360.1) then yields

$$g_\nu(r \, e^{i\vartheta}) \geqq h_\nu(r \, e^{i\vartheta}) \tag{360.2}$$

everywhere in the disc $|x| < R$.   This is the first application known to the author of the concept of harmonic measure, which was rediscovered and used with great success in recent times by R. Nevanlinna.   Now we can find bounds for $g_\nu(r \, e^{i\vartheta})$ as follows: First, we have by § 157, Vol. I, p. 153, that

$$g_\nu(r \, e^{i\vartheta}) \leqq g_\nu(0) \, \frac{R + r}{R - r}, \tag{360.3}$$

and second, we have

$$g_\nu(0) = l \left| \frac{y_0}{y_1} \right| \frac{m \, P_\nu}{2 \, \pi}, \tag{360.4}$$

whence it follows by (359.7) that the sequence of $g_\nu(x)$ converges to zero uniformly in the disc $|x| \leqq r$.   Thus for any given $\varepsilon > 0$, we have by (359.1) that for all sufficiently large ν, and for all x in $|x| \leqq r$,

$$\frac{1}{\nu} \, l \left| \frac{f_\nu(x)}{M} \right| + l \, |y_0| < \varepsilon$$

holds, so that

$$\left| f_\nu(x) \left(\frac{y_0}{e^\varepsilon} \right)^\nu \right| < M.$$

Finally, we can assign to every ε a positive number M_ε which is such that for all $\nu = 1, 2, \ldots,$

$$\left| f_\nu(x) \left(\frac{y_0}{e^\varepsilon} \right)^\nu \right| < M_\varepsilon \tag{360.5}$$

holds true.   The lemma of Hartogs then follows from the fact that for every y_2 with $|y_2| < |y_0|$, we can determine ε from the equation

$$|y_2| = \left| \frac{y_0}{e^\varepsilon} \right|.$$

(360.6)

361. We now combine Hartogs' lemma with the result of § 358 and conclude from this that $F(x, y)$ is bounded in the bi-cylinder

$$|x| \leqq r < R_x, \quad |y - a| < R_y - 2|a|,$$

(361.1)

and hence also in the bi-cylinder

$$|x| \leqq r, \quad |y| \leqq R_y - 3|a|.$$

(361.2)

But we had $|a| < \varrho$, and ϱ was any positive number of our choice. Therefore $F(x, y)$ must actually be bounded in every closed bi-cylinder that lies in $|x| < R_x$, $|y| < R_y$. Together with the result of § 357, this finally yields Hartogs' theorem, which we state once more, as follows:

If the complex function $F(x, y)$ is defined and has partial derivatives $\partial F/\partial x$ and $\partial F/\partial y$ everywhere in the bi-cylinder $|x| < R_x$, $|y| < R_y$, then it can be represented by a double series

$$F(x, y) = \sum_{\mu, \nu = 0}^{\infty} a_{\mu\nu} x^\mu y^\nu$$

(361.3)

that converges absolutely and continuously everywhere in the bi-cylinder.

Properties of the Function $F(x, y)$ (§§ 362-363)

362. From the representation of the function $F(x, y)$ as a double series it follows immediately that $F(x, y)$ is continuous as a function of its two variables, and it follows also that all of its partial derivatives of all orders exist. We see that each of the various partial derivatives is itself a regular analytic function and that all of the well-known formulas of the differential calculus, such as, for example,

$$\frac{\partial^2 F}{\partial x \, \partial y} = \frac{\partial^2 F}{\partial y \, \partial x},$$

(362.1)

are valid here. Also, if $x = \varphi(u, v)$ and $y = \psi(u, v)$ are two regular analytic functions, then

$$\Phi(u, v) = F(\varphi(u, v), \psi(u, v))$$

(362.2)

is itself a regular analytic function of (u, v), and the following relation (as well as various others like it) holds true:

$$\frac{\partial \Phi}{\partial u} = \frac{\partial F}{\partial x} \cdot \frac{\partial \varphi}{\partial u} + \frac{\partial F}{\partial y} \cdot \frac{\partial \psi}{\partial u}. \tag{362.3}$$

Moreover, by § 130, Vol. I, p. 128, we have

$$F(x, y) = \frac{1}{2\pi i} \int_{\gamma_x} \frac{F(\xi, y)}{\xi - x} \, d\xi = -\frac{1}{4\pi^2} \int\int_{\gamma_x \gamma_y} \frac{F(\xi, \eta)}{(\xi - x)(\eta - y)} \, d\xi \, d\eta. \tag{362.4}$$

363. The theory of normal families can likewise be applied to functions of two complex variables. The developments of §§ 174-181, Vol. I, pp. 173 ff., involving the concept of continuous convergence, apply to point functions generally and can therefore be applied immediately to functions of two variables.

Let us now consider a sequence $\{F_n(x, y)\}$ of uniformly bounded analytic functions defined in the bi-cylinder

$$|x| < R_x, \quad |y| < R_y. \tag{363.1}$$

Given $\varepsilon > 0$, we can assign to every point (x_0, y_0) of this bi-cylinder a neighborhood

$$|x - x_0| < \delta, \quad |y - y_0| < \delta \tag{363.2}$$

in such a way that for all n and for every fixed y in $|y - y_0| < \delta$, the functions $F_n(x, y)$ have an oscillation in the disc $|x - x_0| < \delta$ that does not exceed ε; this follows from Schwarz's Lemma. Since a similar statement holds with x and y interchanged, it follows that for any two points of (363.2), the inequality

$$|F_n(x', y') - F_n(x'', y'')| < 2\varepsilon \tag{363.3}$$

holds. Therefore the limiting oscillation of the sequence $\{F_n(x, y)\}$ vanishes at every point of (363.1), which implies that there exist subsequences that converge continuously in (363.1). The limit function $F(x, y)$ of such a subsequence is of course analytic, since it represents, for fixed values of y (or x), an analytic function of x (or of y, respectively).

Analytic Functions of More Than Two Variables (§§ 364-365)

364. The proof of Hartogs' theorem in §§ 357-361 can be extended to functions of more than two variables by means of mathematical induction; this yields the following theorem:

If the function

$$F(z_1, \ldots, z_n) \tag{364.1}$$

is defined in the poly-cylinder

$$|z_1| \leq R_1, \; |z_2| \leq R_2, \; \ldots, \; |z_n| \leq R_n \tag{364.2}$$

and has partial derivatives $\partial F / \partial z_j$ in this poly-cylinder, then the function can be represented at every interior point of (364.2) by an absolutely and continuously convergent multiple power series

$$\sum_{\nu_1, \ldots, \nu_n = 0}^{\infty} a_{\nu_1 \ldots \nu_n} z_1^{\nu_1} z_2^{\nu_2} \ldots z_n^{\nu_n}. \tag{364.3}$$

A function of this kind is called a regular analytic function.

We shall sketch the proof of this theorem for $n = 3$. Thus, let there be given a function

$$F(x, y, z), \tag{364.4}$$

defined in the tri-cylinder

$$|x| \leq R_x, \; |y| \leq R_y, \; |z| \leq R_z \tag{364.5}$$

and having the derivatives

$$\frac{\partial F}{\partial x}, \quad \frac{\partial F}{\partial y}, \quad \frac{\partial F}{\partial z}$$

in this tri-cylinder. By the theorem for two variables, we can expand the function (364.4) at every point x of the disc $|x| \leq R_x$ into a series

$$\sum_{\mu, \nu = 0}^{\infty} f_{\mu\nu}(x) \, y^{\mu} z^{\nu}. \tag{364.6}$$

If in the tri-cylinder (364.5) we have

$$|F(x, y, z)| < M,$$

then we can prove, just as in § 357 above, that all of the $f_{\mu\nu}(x)$ must be **regular** analytic functions and that the expansion

$$F(x, y, z) = \sum_{\lambda, \mu, \nu = 0}^{\infty} a_{\lambda\mu\nu} \, x^{\lambda} y^{\mu} z^{\nu} \tag{364.7}$$

has all of the required properties. We now assign to every point (y, z) of the bi-cylinder $|y| \leq R_y, |z| \leq R_z$ the maximum $\mu^*(y, z)$ of $|F(x, y, z)|$ on the circle $|x| = R_x$. Using the fact that $\mu^*(y, z)$ assumes only finite values, we can show as in § 358 above, with the aid of Osgood's theorem, that in every neighborhood of a point of (364.5) there exist six-dimensional subregions in which $F(x, y, z)$ is bounded.

365. The lemma of Hartogs (*cf.* § 359 above) can be extended just as easily. To this end we note first that we may assume, without loss of generality, that $R_y = R_z$ in (364.5). Then if η_0 and $\eta_1 < \eta_0$ are two positive numbers less than R_y (and R_z), we shall assume that $F(x, y, z)$ is analytic in the tri-cylinder

$$|x| \leq R_x, \quad |y| \leq \eta_0, \quad |z| \leq \eta_0 \tag{365.1}$$

and bounded in the tri-cylinder

$$|x| \leq R_x, \quad |y| \leq \eta_1, \quad |z| \leq \eta_1. \tag{365.2}$$

With this as a basis, we can prove that in the representation (364.6) all of the $f_{\mu\nu}(x)$ are analytic, and we then choose a number $R < R_x$ which is such that on the circle $|x| = R$, all of the $f_{\mu\nu}(x)$ are different from zero. This entails that the following relation holds at every point of the disc $|x| \leq R$:

$$\left| \frac{f_{\mu\nu}(x)}{M} \eta^{\mu+\nu} \right| < \left(\frac{\eta_0}{\eta_1} \right)^{\mu+\nu}. \tag{365.3}$$

Now if $P_{\mu\nu}$ denotes the set of all those arcs of $|x| = R$ on which the left-hand side of (365.3) exceeds unity, it follows as in § 359 above that for any given $\varepsilon > 0$ there are at most finitely many $P_{\mu\nu}$ for which

$$m P_{\mu\nu} > \varepsilon \tag{365.4}$$

holds.

For all μ, ν, we now form the harmonic functions

$$h_{\mu\nu}(r e^{i\theta}) = \frac{1}{\mu + \nu} l \left| \frac{f_{\mu\nu}(r e^{i\theta})}{M} \right| + l \eta_0 \tag{365.5}$$

and we assign to these by means of the Poisson Integral the functions

$$g_{\mu\nu}(r e^{i\theta}) \geq h_{\mu\nu}(r e^{i\theta}) \tag{365.6}$$

that have the value $l\eta_0/\eta_1$ on the point sets $P_{\mu\nu}$ and vanish at all other points of $|x| = R$. Then in every disc $|x| \leq r$ $(r < R)$, we have $(cf.\ \S\ 360)$ that

$$g_{\mu\nu}(x) \leq \varepsilon,$$

provided we take $\mu + \nu$ sufficiently large. The remainder of the proof follows the lines of §§ 360-361.

Some Theorems on Differential Equations (§§ 366-368)

366. Frequently an analytic function $w = f(z)$ is defined as being a solution of a differential equation of the form

$$\frac{dw}{dz} = F(z, w). \tag{366.1}$$

We shall make the assumptions

$$F(z, w) \text{ regular in } |z| \leq 2\,R,\ |w| \leq 2\,R, \tag{366.2}$$

$$|F(z, w)| \leq M \text{ in } |z| \leq 2\,R,\ |w| \leq 2\,R \tag{366.3}$$

and we shall prove that under these assumptions, equation (366.1) has a uniquely determined solution

$$w = f(z, a) \text{ with } f(0, a) = a \tag{366.4}$$

that depends on the parameter a. Here $f(z, a)$ denotes a regular analytic function of two complex variables that is defined in a bi-cylinder

$$|z| \leq r_0,\ |a| \leq R. \tag{366.5}$$

To prove our statement, we begin by considering any analytic function $\varphi(z, a)$ of two variables that is defined in a bi-cylinder

$$|z| \leq r < 2\,R,\ |a| \leq R \tag{366.6}$$

and satisfies the condition

$$|\varphi(z, a)| \leq 2\,R \tag{366.7}$$

in this bi-cylinder. Then $F(z, \varphi(z, a))$ is a regular analytic function of z and a in the bi-cylinder (366.6) and satisfies the condition

$$|F(z, \varphi(z, a))| \leq M$$

in the bi-cylinder. We shall now investigate the function

$$\psi(z, a) = a + \int_0^z F(z, \varphi(z, a)) \, dz. \tag{366.8}$$

At every point of the bi-cylinder (366.6), the function (366.8) is regular and satisfies the inequality

$$|\psi(z, a)| \leq |a| + M r \leq R + M r.$$

Now if we set

$$r = \min \left(2 R, \, \frac{R}{2 M} \right), \tag{366.9}$$

then we have

$$|\psi(z, a)| \leq \frac{3 R}{2},$$

so that $\psi(z, a)$ satisfies all of the conditions that we imposed on $\varphi(z, a)$.

Now we set, successively,

$$f_0(z, a) = a, \quad f_{n+1}(z, a) = a + \int_0^z F(z, f_n(z, a)) \, dz \qquad (n = 0, 1, 2, \ldots) \tag{366.10}$$

and we note that with r determined by (366.9), all of the functions $f_n(z)$ are regular in the closed bi-cylinder (366.6) and that

$$|f_n(z, a)| \leq \frac{3 R}{2} \qquad (n = 0, 1, 2, \ldots) \tag{366.11}$$

holds in (366.6).

The sequence of functions (366.11) is normal. We shall prove that in a certain neighborhood of the origin $(z, a) = (0, 0)$, the functions $f_n(z, a)$ converge continuously to a limit function $f(z, a)$.

367. To prove the last statement, we define by means of

$$\left. \begin{aligned} \Psi(z, w, w_0) &= \frac{F(z, w) - F(z, w_0)}{w - w_0} \qquad \text{for} \quad w \neq w_0, \\ \Psi(z, w, w_0) &= \frac{\partial}{\partial w} F(z, w) \bigg|_{w = w_0} \qquad \text{for} \quad w = w_0 \end{aligned} \right\} \tag{367.1}$$

a function of three complex variables that is seen to be defined and regular in the tri-cylinder

$$|z| < 2 R, \quad |w| < 2 R, \quad |w_0| < 2 R$$

Therefore $\Psi(z, w, w_0)$ is bounded in every smaller closed tri-cylinder, so that for, say,

$$|z| \leqq r, \quad |w| \leqq \frac{3R}{2}, \quad |w_0| \leqq \frac{3R}{2} \qquad (367.2)$$

we can write

$$|\Psi(z, w, w_0)| \leqq N. \qquad (367.3)$$

But by (367.1), the identity

$$\left. \begin{array}{l} F(z, f_n(z, a)) - F(z, f_{n-1}(z, a)) \\ = \Psi(z, f_n(z, a), f_{n-1}(z, a)) \cdot (f_n(z, a) - f_{n-1}(z, a)) \end{array} \right\} \qquad (367.4)$$

holds not only at the points of the bi-cylinder (366.3) at which

$$f_n(z, a) \neq f_{n-1}(z, a)$$

but also at those where

$$f_n(z, a) = f_{n-1}(z, a).$$

We obtain therefore from equations (366.10) that

$$f_{n+1}(z, a) - f_n(z, a) = \int_0^z \Psi(z, f_n(z, a), f_{n-1}(z, a)) \cdot (f_n(z, a) - f_{n-1}(z, a)) \, dz. \quad (367.5)$$

Now we set

$$\alpha_n = \max |f_n(z, a) - f_{n-1}(z, a)| \quad \text{for} \quad |z| \leqq r, |a| \leqq R, \qquad (367.6)$$

and we select r in such a way that all of the relations (366.11) hold. Then by (367.3) we also have

$$|\Psi(z, f_n(z, a), f_{n-1}(z, a))| \leqq N,$$

and from (367.5) we obtain

$$|f_{n+1}(z, a) - f_n(z, a)| \leqq N r \alpha_n,$$

so that

$$\alpha_{n+1} \leqq N r \alpha_n$$

holds. We now place an additional restriction on the size of r by setting

$$r = \min\left(2R, \frac{R}{2M}, \frac{1}{2N}\right), \qquad (367.7)$$

whence we obtain

$$\alpha_{n+1} \leqq \frac{\alpha_n}{2} \leqq \frac{\alpha_1}{2^{n+1}} .$$

Hence in the bi-cylinder of (367.6), with r further restricted by (367.7), the limit function

$$f(z, a) = \lim_{n=\infty} f_n(z, a)$$

exists, and the convergence is uniform. The last fact, incidentally, not only follows from the general theory but can also be gleaned directly from our formulas, since we can write

$$|f_n(z, a) - f(z, a)| \leqq |f_n - f_{n+1}| + |f_{n+1} - f_{n+2}| + \cdots \leqq 2\,\alpha_{n+1}. \quad (367.8)$$

Finally, to establish the fact that the function $f(z, a)$ just obtained is a solution of the differential equation (366.1), we need only observe that

$$f_{n+1}(z, a) = a + \int_0^z F(z, f(z, a))\, dz + \int_0^z \Psi(z, f_n(z, a), f(z, a)) \cdot (f_n(z, a) - f(z, a))\, dz ,$$

and that the modulus of the last term on the right-hand side goes to zero as n increases.

368. The function $w = f(z, a)$ that we have constructed above is the *only* function of z and the parameter a which satisfies both the differential equation (366.1) *and* the boundary condition $f(0, a) = a$. To prove this, let $g(z, a)$ be another function that depends on the parameter a and for which

$$g(z, a) = a + \int_0^z F(z, g(z, a))\, dz \qquad (368.1)$$

holds; we do not even have to assume that $g(z, a)$ is an analytic function of two variables, but merely that for every value of a from the disc $|a| < R$, the function $g(z, a)$ is a regular function of $|z|$ in some disc $|z| < \varrho$. In any case, it then follows that

$$f(z, a) - g(z, a) = \int_0^z \Psi(z, f(z, a), g(z, a)) \cdot (f(z, a) - g(z, a))\, dz. \quad (368.2)$$

For any fixed value of a, let us now denote the maximum of $|f(z, a) - g(z, a)|$ in the disc $|z| \leqq \varrho$ by $\omega(\varrho)$. This first implies, by (368.2), that

$$|f(z, a) - g(z, a)| \leqq N \varrho \, \omega(\varrho),$$

and hence also that

$$0 \leqq \omega(\varrho) \leqq N \varrho \, \omega(\varrho).$$

Thus if ϱ is selected in such a way that $N\varrho < 1$ holds, $\omega(\varrho)$ must vanish.

Systems of Differential Equations (§ 369)

369. The existence and uniqueness proofs, given in §§ 366-368, for the differential equation (366.1) with a boundary condition (366.4), carry over without any but obvious modifications to systems of first-order differential equations. The statement of the corresponding theorem is as follows:

If the functions

$$F_k(z; w_1, w_2, \ldots, w_n) \qquad (k = 1, \ldots, n) \quad (369.\,1)$$

are regular analytic functions in the poly-cylinder

$$|z| < R_z, \; |w_\nu| < R_\nu \qquad (\nu = 1, \ldots, n) \quad (369.\,2)$$

and if the point

$$z = z_0, \; w_\nu = Q_\nu \qquad (\nu = 1, \ldots, n) \quad (369.\,3)$$

lies in (the interior of) the region (369.2), then there exist a neighborhood $|z - z_0| < r$ *of* z_0 *and* n *functions* $f_\nu(z)$ $(\nu = 1, \ldots, n)$ *regular in this neighborhood that satisfy the following relations (where we set* $w_k = f_k(z)$, $k = 1, \ldots, n)$:

$$f_\nu(z_0) = Q_\nu \qquad\qquad (369.\,4)$$

and

$$\frac{dw_k}{dz} = F_k(z; w_1, \ldots, w_n) \qquad (k = 1, \ldots, n). \quad (369.\,5)$$

The functions $f_\nu(z)$ *are determined uniquely by the two conditions* (369.4) *and* (369.5).

The theorem and its proof can be extended to the case that the functions (369.1) also depend on p parameters $\lambda_1, \ldots, \lambda_p$ and are analytic in a poly-cylinder of the space of the variables $(z; w_1, \ldots, w_n; \lambda_1, \ldots, \lambda_p)$. It can be proved that in this case the solutions $f_\nu(z; a_1, \ldots, a_n; \lambda_1, \ldots, \lambda_p)$ are analytic functions of all $n + p + 1$ variables z, a_i, λ_j. This can be done, for instance, by showing that the approximating functions that occur in the course of the proof are themselves analytic and bounded in the $n + p + 1$ variables and therefore constitute a normal family.

As is well known, differential equations of higher orders, or systems of such equations, can be reduced to systems of first-order differential equations by the introduction of new variables, and to the latter systems the above results can be applied.

CHAPTER TWO

CONFORMAL MAPPING OF CIRCULAR-ARC TRIANGLES

The Schwarzian Derivative (§§ 370-374)

370. The aim of this chapter is the study of the mapping of arbitrary circular-arc triangles (i.e. regions whose frontier consists of three arcs of circles). We shall develop analytic expressions for the mapping functions, expressions that can also be used for the numerical calculation of these functions. What we shall present here is one of the most complete branches of analysis, to which many of the most outstanding mathematicians of the 19th century have contributed.

By the Riemann Mapping Theorem (*cf.* § 323), every circular-arc triangle can be mapped conformally onto the interior of a circle or onto a half-plane. We shall norm the mapping function

$$u = u(z) \tag{370.1}$$

in such a way that the three vertices of the triangle are the images of the three points $z = 0, 1$, and ∞. By a proper choice of the order of these vertices, we can also arrange for the interior of the triangle to correspond to the half-plane $\Im z > 0$. Now the Moebius transformation

$$w = \frac{a\,u + b}{c\,u + d} \tag{370.2}$$

transforms $u(z)$ into $w(z)$, where $w(z)$ also maps the half-plane $\Im(z) > 0$ onto either the interior or the exterior of a circular-arc triangle. The vertices of this new triangle are at the points $w(0)$, $w(1)$, and $w(\infty)$, and these three points can be made to coincide with any three pre-assigned points of the w-plane by a suitable choice of the coefficients in (370.2). We know from §§ 70-72, Vol. I, pp. 59 ff., that the shape of a circular-arc triangle is uniquely determined by its angles, which we shall always denote in the sequel by $\pi\lambda$, $\pi\mu$, and $\pi\nu$. Besides ordinary circular-arc triangles with non-zero angles we shall also study those having one or more cusps; however, we shall not consider triangles with re-entrant corners, although the theory can be extended to that type as well. Thus λ, μ, ν will be subject to the conditions

$$0 \leqq (\lambda, \mu, \nu) < 1. \tag{370.3}$$

129

H. A. Schwarz proposed and solved the problem of finding a relation among the functions u, w, and their derivatives that is independent of the coefficients a, b, c, d and hence independent of the position of the circular-arc triangle in the plane. The calculations that lead to a solution of this problem are as follows.

From (370.2) we obtain by successive differentiations that

$$w' = \frac{a\,d - b\,c}{(c\,u + d)^2}\, u', \qquad \frac{d}{dz}\, l\,w' = \frac{d}{dz}\, l\,u' - \frac{2\,c\,u'}{c\,u + d},$$

or, setting

$$\frac{d}{dz}\, l\,w' = W, \tag{370.4}$$

$$\frac{d}{dz}\, l\,u' = U, \tag{370.5}$$

that

$$W = U - \frac{2\,c\,u'}{c\,u + d}. \tag{370.6}$$

Another differentiation yields

$$U' - W' = \frac{2\,c\,u''}{c\,u + d} - \frac{2\,c^2\,u'^2}{(c\,u + d)^2}.$$

Now $u'' = u'\,U$, and by (370.6) we also have

$$\frac{c\,u'}{c\,u + d} = \frac{1}{2}\,(U - W).$$

We finally obtain

$$U' - W' = U\,(U - W) - \frac{1}{2}\,(U - W)^2 = \frac{1}{2}\,U^2 - \frac{1}{2}\,W^2.$$

This result may also be written as follows:

$$\frac{d^2}{dz^2}\, l\,w' - \frac{1}{2}\left(\frac{d}{dz}\, l\,w'\right)^2 = \frac{d^2}{dz^2}\, l\,u' - \frac{1}{2}\left(\frac{d}{dz}\, l\,u'\right)^2. \tag{370.7}$$

The two sides of this relation represent a differential invariant that is independent of the coefficients a, b, c, d, that is, invariant under the transformations (370.2). The left-hand side of (370.7) is called the *Schwarzian derivative* of w with respect to z, and following Cayley (1821-1895), it is usually denoted by the symbol $\{w, z\}$; thus

$$\{w, z\} = \frac{2\,w'\,w''' - 3\,w''^2}{2\,w'^2}. \tag{370.8}$$

371. If we substitute the mapping function $w(z)$ of a circular-arc triangle ABC into the formula for the Schwarzian derivative, we obtain a function

$$\{w, z\} = F(z). \tag{371.1}$$

Schwarz calculated this function $F(z)$ explicitly, and this is what we shall now proceed to do.

To begin with, $w(z)$ is regular at every point z_0 of $\Im(z) > 0$ and satisfies $w'(z_0) \neq 0$, so that by (371.1), $F(z)$ is likewise regular at z_0. By the Schwarz

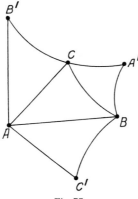

Fig. 77

Reflection Principle, $F(z)$ is regular on the real axis of the z-plane, except at the points $z = 0$ and $z = 1$ which correspond to two of the vertices of the triangle. The reflections (inversions) of the circular-arc triangle ABC in its three sides yield three new triangles $A'CB$, $B'AC$ and $C'BA$ (see Fig. 77 above). Since any two of these new triangles can be mapped onto each other by means of two successive reflections in circles, they are also the images of each other under a Moebius transformation (*cf.* § 51, Vol. I, p. 41). The mapping functions of the new triangles (i.e. the functions that map a half-plane of the z-plane onto these triangles) are obtained by analytic continuation of the function $w(z)$ across the segment $0 < x < 1$ and across the rays $1 < x$ and $x < 0$, respectively. In this way, we obtain three functions which when substituted in (371.1) always yield the same function $F(z)$. Thus $F(z)$ is a single-valued analytic function that has no singularities except possibly at $z = 0$ and $z = 1$.

372. We now wish to determine the expansion of $F(z)$ at $z = 0$, and to this end we first assume that the angle $\pi\lambda$ is > 0. We then use a Moebius transformation to map the vertex A of the triangle onto the origin and to map the sides AB and AC onto two straight-line segments the first of which lies on the real axis. This done, the mapping

$$v = w^{\frac{1}{\lambda}} \tag{372.1}$$

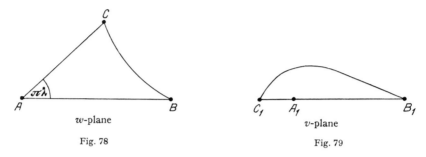

w-plane   v-plane

Fig. 78   Fig. 79

transforms Fig. 78 into Fig. 79; in the latter figure, the boundary in the neighborhood of $v = 0$ (i.e. near the point A_1) coincides with a segment of the real aixs of the v-plane. It follows that

$$w^{\frac{1}{\lambda}} = A_1 z + A_2 z^2 + \cdots, \qquad A_1 \neq 0$$

so that

$$w = z^\lambda (a_0 + a_1 z + \cdots), \qquad a_0 \neq 0 \tag{372.2}$$

and

$$w' = z^{\lambda-1}(b_0 + b_1 z + \cdots), \qquad b_0 \neq 0, \tag{372.3}$$

where the power series on the right-hand sides have a non-zero radius of convergence.

If the triangle ABC has a cusp at A, that is, if $\lambda = 0$, then we can map the point A onto the point at infinity by means of a suitable Moebius transformation that also takes the two sides AB and AC into two parallel rays whose distance from each other is π, and we can even arrange for one of these rays to be a part of the real axis of the v-plane. Hence we can write in this case

$$e^{i\pi w} = C_1 z + C_2 z + \cdots, \qquad C_1 \neq 0$$

and

$$w' = \frac{1}{\pi i} \cdot \frac{C_1 + 2 C_2 z + \cdots}{C_1 z + C_2 z^2 + \cdots} = z^{-1}(b_0 + b_1 z + \cdots), \qquad b_0 \neq 0. \tag{372.4}$$

We see that equation (372.4) has the same form as equation (372.3) if we set $\lambda = 0$ in the latter (but the numbers b_j are of course not the same in the two equations).

373. We therefore have in both cases that

$$\frac{d}{dz}\,l\,w' = \frac{\lambda - 1}{z} + c_0 + c_1 z + \cdots,$$
(373. 1)

$$\frac{d^2}{dz^2}\,l\,w' = \frac{1 - \lambda}{z^2} + \text{a regular function,}$$
(373. 2)

$$-\frac{1}{2}\left(\frac{d}{dz}\,l\,w'\right)^2 = -\frac{(1 - \lambda)^2}{2\,z^2} + c_0\,\frac{1 - \lambda}{z} + \text{a regular function.}$$
(373. 3)

This yields

$$F(z) = \{w, z\} = \frac{1 - \lambda^2}{2\,z^2} + \frac{h_1}{z} + \text{a regular function.}$$
(373. 4)

An entirely analogous procedure shows that in a neighborhood of $z = 1$ the expansion of $F(z)$ has the following form:

$$F(z) = \frac{1 - \mu^2}{2\,(1 - z)^2} + \frac{h_2}{1 - z} + \text{a regular function.}$$
(373. 5)

Finally, to investigate the behavior of $F(z)$ in the neighborhood of $z = \infty$, we first note that if we set $z = 1/t$, then in the neighborhood of $t = 0$ we have, by (373.4),

$$\{w, t\} = \frac{1 - \nu^2}{2\,t^2} + \frac{h_3}{t} + \text{a regular function.}$$
(373. 6)

Now in passing from z to t, we have

$$w' = \frac{dw}{dz} = -t^2\,\frac{dw}{dt},\qquad l\,w' = l\,\frac{dw}{dt} + 2\,l\,t + \pi\,i,$$

$$\frac{d}{dz}\,l\,w' = -t^2\,\frac{d}{dt}\left(l\,\frac{dw}{dt}\right) - 2\,t,$$

$$\frac{d^2}{dz^2}\,l\,w' = t^4\,\frac{d^2}{dt^2}\left(l\,\frac{dw}{dt}\right) + 2\,t^3\,\frac{d}{dt}\left(l\,\frac{dw}{dt}\right) + 2\,t^2,$$

$$-\frac{1}{2}\left(\frac{d}{dz}\,l\,w'\right)^2 = -\frac{t^4}{2}\,\frac{d}{dt}\left(l\,\frac{dw}{dt}\right) - 2\,t^3\,\frac{d}{dt}\left(l\,\frac{dw}{dt}\right) - 2\,t^2.$$

Hence we have

$$F(z) = \{w, z\} = t^4\,\{w, t\}$$
(373. 7)

and a comparison with (373.6) yields

$$F(z) = \frac{1 - \nu^2}{2\,z^2} + \frac{h_3}{z^3} + \frac{1}{z^4}\,\mathfrak{P}\left(\frac{1}{z}\right).$$
(373. 8)

Therefore the expression

$$F(z) - \frac{1-\lambda^2}{2\,z^2} - \frac{h_1}{z} - \frac{1-\mu^2}{2\,(1-z)^2} - \frac{h_2}{1-z} \tag{373.9}$$

is regular in the entire plane and converges to zero as z goes to ∞. Hence by Liouville's theorem (*cf.* § 167, Vol. I, p. 165), the expression (373.9) must vanish identically, so that

$$F(z) = \frac{1-\lambda^2}{2\,z^2} + \frac{h_1}{z} + \frac{1-\mu^2}{2\,(1-z)^2} + \frac{h_2}{1-z}. \tag{373.10}$$

It also follows from (373.8) that

$$\lim_{z=\infty} z\,F(z) = 0, \quad \lim_{z=\infty} z^2\,F(z) = \frac{1-\nu^2}{2}, \tag{373.11}$$

and this together with (373.10) yields the relations

$$\left. \begin{aligned} h_2 &= h_1, \\ \frac{1-\lambda^2}{2} + \frac{1-\mu^2}{2} - h_1 &= \frac{1-\nu^2}{2}, \end{aligned} \right\} \tag{373.12}$$

the latter because of

$$\frac{1}{z} + \frac{1}{1-z} = \frac{1}{z\,(1-z)}.$$

We have thus obtained the following final result:

$$F(z) = \frac{1-\lambda^2}{2\,z^2} + \frac{1-\mu^2}{2\,(1-z)^2} + \frac{1-\lambda^2-\mu^2+\nu^2}{2\,z\,(1-z)}. \tag{373.13}$$

374. The result expressed by (373.13) is due to Schwarz and may be stated as follows:

Let the half-plane $\Im z > 0$ be mapped conformally onto an arbitrary circular-arc triangle whose angles at its vertices A, B, and C are $\pi\lambda$, $\pi\mu$, and $\pi\nu$, and let the vertices A, B, C be the images of the points $z = 0$, 1, ∞, respectively. Then the mapping function $w(z)$ must be a solution of the third-order differential equation

$$\{w, z\} = \frac{w'\,w''' - 3\,w''^2}{w'^2} = \frac{1-\lambda^2}{2\,z^2} + \frac{1-\mu^2}{2\,(1-z)^2} + \frac{1-\lambda^2-\mu^2+\nu^2}{2\,z\,(1-z)}. \tag{374.1}$$

If $w_0(z)$ is any solution of (374.1) that satisfies $w_0'(z) \neq 0$ at all interior points of the half-plane, then by § 370 above, the function

$$w(z) = \frac{a \, w_0(z) + b}{c \, w_0(z) + d} \qquad (a \, d - b \, c \neq 0) \qquad (374.\,2)$$

is likewise a solution of (374.1). It follows from this that *every solution of the differential equation* (374.1) *that is regular and non-constant in the half-plane* $\Im z > 0$ *represents a mapping of this half-plane onto a circular-arc triangle with angles* $\pi\lambda$, $\pi\mu$, *and* $\pi\nu$.

The last two results together yield a theorem that we had already obtained in Chap. 3, Part I, Vol. I, to the effect that from any given circular-arc triangle with angles $\pi\lambda$, $\pi\mu$, and $\pi\nu$, we can obtain *all* other circular-arc triangles having the same angles by means of Moebius transformations. We have thus reduced the conformal mapping of circular-arc triangles to a problem of pure analysis; what remains to be done now is to actually carry out the integration (i.e. the solution) of the differential equation (374.1).

Reduction to the Hypergeometric Differential Equation (§§ 375-377)

375. We begin with the following observation: Every solution of a second-order linear homogeneous differential equation

$$u'' + p(z) \, u' + q(z) \, u = 0 \qquad (375.\,1)$$

can be represented as a linear combination of two particular solutions $u_1(z)$ and $u_2(z)$. For example, if z_0 is any point of the z-plane at which $p(z)$ and $q(z)$ are regular, we can select $u_1(z)$ and $u_2(z)$ as those solutions that satisfy at z_0 the initial conditions $u_1(z_0) = 1$, $u_1'(z_0) = 0$, and $u_2(z_0) = 0$, $u_2'(z_0) = 1$, respectively. Then every solution of (375.1) can be written in the form

$$u(z) = a \, u_1(z) + b \, u_2(z), \qquad (a = u(z_0), \ b = u'(z_0)) \qquad (375.\,2)$$

where a and b are finite constants.

Now it so happens that the Schwarzian derivative of the quotient

$$w = \frac{a \, u_1 + b \, u_2}{c \, u_1 + d \, u_2} \qquad (375.\,3)$$

can be expressed in terms of the coefficients $p(z)$ and $q(z)$. For if we set $v = u_2/u_1$, then we find that

$$v' = \frac{u_1\, u_2' - u_2\, u_1'}{u_1^2},$$

$$\frac{d}{dz}\, l\, v' = \frac{u_1\, u_2'' - u_2\, u_1''}{u_1\, u_2' - u_2\, u_1'} - 2\, \frac{u_1'}{u_1},$$

and since

$$u_1'' = -\, p\, u_1' - q\, u_1, \qquad u_2'' = -\, p\, u_2' - q\, u_2,$$

it follows that

$$\frac{d}{dz}\, l\, v' = -\, p - 2\, \frac{u_1'}{u_1},$$

$$\frac{d^2}{dz^2}\, l\, v' = -\, p' + 2\, p\, \frac{u_1'}{u_1} + 2\, q + 2\, \frac{u_1'^2}{u_1^2},$$

$$-\frac{1}{2} \left(\frac{d}{dz}\, l\, v' \right)^2 = -\frac{p^2}{2} - 2\, p\, \frac{u_1'}{u_1} - 2\, \frac{u_1'^2}{u_1^2}.$$

Therefore we finally have

$$\{v,\, z\} = 2\, q - p' - \frac{p^2}{2}. \tag{375.4}$$

376. Now if we determine the coefficients p and q in (375.1) in such a way that

$$2\, q - p' - \frac{p^2}{2} = \frac{1 - \lambda^2}{2\, z^2} + \frac{1 - \mu^2}{2\, (1 - z)^2} + \frac{1 - \lambda^2 - \mu^2 + \nu^2}{2\, z\, (1 - z)}, \tag{376.1}$$

then the quotient w of two arbitrary solutions of (375.1) yields the general solution of the differential equation (374.1). If we set, for instance,

$$p = \frac{a}{z} + \frac{b}{1 - z}, \tag{376.2}$$

where a and b are arbitrary, then we must have

$$2\, q = \frac{1 - \lambda^2 - 2\, a + a^2}{2\, z^2} + \frac{1 - \mu^2 + 2\, b + b^2}{2\, (1 - z)^2} + \frac{1 - \lambda^2 - \mu^2 + \nu^2 + 2\, a\, b}{2\, z\, (1 - z)}. \tag{376.3}$$

The expression for q is simplified if we choose $a = 1 - \lambda,\ -\, b = 1 - \mu$; for we find that in this case,

$$\left. \begin{aligned} p &= \frac{1 - \lambda}{z} - \frac{1 - \mu}{1 - z} = \frac{1 - \lambda - z\, (2 - \lambda - \mu)}{z\, (1 - z)}, \\ q &= -\, \frac{(1 - \lambda - \mu + \nu)\, (1 - \lambda - \mu - \nu)}{4\, z\, (1 - z)}. \end{aligned} \right\} \tag{376.4}$$

For this choice of p and q, equation (375.1) reduces to the celebrated *hypergeometric differential equation*

$$z(1-z)u'' + [\gamma - (\alpha + \beta + 1)z]u' - \alpha\beta u = 0, \qquad (376.5)$$

the study of which even goes back to Euler and Gauss. To make the two equations identical (with the choice (376.4)), we must also make the following identifications:

$$\lambda = 1 - \gamma, \quad \mu = \gamma - \alpha - \beta, \quad \nu = \alpha - \beta \qquad (376.6)$$

and hence

$$\alpha = \frac{1}{2}(1 - \lambda - \mu + \nu), \quad \beta = \frac{1}{2}(1 - \lambda - \mu - \nu), \quad \gamma = 1 - \lambda. \quad (376.7)$$

We also note that

$$\gamma - \beta = \frac{1}{2}(1 - \lambda + \mu + \nu). \qquad (376.8)$$

The hypergeometric equation (376.5) has the property of being transformed into an equation of the same form if the independent variable z is replaced by $1 - \eta$ or by $1/\zeta$; this expresses certain symmetry properties of the three points 0, 1, and ∞, which were to be foreseen from the method which we chose for deriving the differential equation (376.5).

377. The point $z = 0$ is a singular point of the hypergeometric differential equation, and the existence theorem of § 369 therefore does not apply in the neighborhood of this point. However, we can verify by a direct method that (376.5) has *one and only one* solution that is regular in the neighborhood of $z = 0$ and is represented by a series of the form

$$u = 1 + c_1 z + c_2 z^2 + \cdots + c_\nu z^\nu + \cdots. \qquad (377.1)$$

For if we form the series for u' and u'' on the basis of (377.1) and substitute them (as well as (377.1)) formally into (376.5), then the coefficient of z^ν in the expansion of the left-hand side of (376.5) becomes

$$\left.\begin{array}{l} (\nu + 1)\nu c_{\nu+1} - \nu(\nu - 1)c_\nu + \gamma(\nu + 1)c_{\nu+1} - (\alpha + \beta + 1)\nu c_\nu - \alpha\beta c_\nu \\ = (\nu + 1)(\gamma + \nu)c_{\nu+1} - (\alpha + \nu)(\beta + \nu)c_\nu. \end{array}\right\} \quad (377.2)$$

This coefficient vanishes for $\nu = 0, 1, 2, \ldots$ if and only if we set

$$c_1 = \frac{\alpha\,\beta}{\gamma}\,,$$

$$c_2 = \frac{\alpha\,(\alpha+1)\,\beta\,(\beta+1)}{1\cdot2\cdot\gamma\,(\gamma+1)}\,,$$

$$\cdots\cdots\cdots\cdots\cdots\cdots\cdots\cdots$$

$$c_\nu = \frac{\alpha\,(\alpha+1)\cdots(\alpha+\nu-1)\,\beta\,(\beta+1)\cdots(\beta+\nu-1)}{1\cdot2\cdots\nu\cdot\gamma\,(\gamma+1)\cdots(\gamma+\nu-1)}\,.$$

$$(377.3)$$

The series (377.1) satisfies our differential equation formally; it is known as Gauss's hypergeometric series

$$F(\alpha,\beta,\gamma;z) = 1 + \frac{\alpha\,\beta}{\gamma}\,z + \frac{\alpha\,(\alpha+1)\,\beta\,(\beta+1)}{1\cdot2\cdot\gamma\,(\gamma+1)}\,z^2 + \cdots. \qquad (377.4)$$

This series makes sense only if $\gamma \neq 0, -1, -2, \cdots$. It reduces to a polynomial if either α or β equals a negative integer. In all other cases we have

$$\frac{c_{\nu+1}}{c_\nu} = \frac{(\alpha+\nu)\,(\beta+\nu)}{(1+\nu)\,(\gamma+\nu)}\,, \qquad \lim_{\nu=\infty}\frac{c_{\nu+1}}{c_\nu} = 1\,, \qquad (377.5)$$

so that we see by § 207, Vol. I, p. 204 that the radius of convergence of the series is equal to unity. Thus we see that our formal operations were justified, and we have the following theorem:

In all but the exceptional cases listed above, Gauss's hypergeometric series (377.4) is a solution of the differential equation (376.5), and it is the only solution that is regular at the point $z = 0$ and assumes the value unity at this point.

The Hypergeometric Series (§§ 378-380)

378. In the problem that led us to the hypergeometric equation—the problem of determining the mapping functions of circular-arc triangles—the numbers γ, μ, ν are real and satisfy $0 \leq (\lambda,\mu,\nu) < 1$. Hence by relations (376.7) and (376.8), it will suffice to consider values of α, β, γ from the intervals

$$-1 < \alpha \leq 1, \quad -1 < \beta \leq 1, \quad 0 < \gamma < 1 \qquad (378.1)$$

and for which, also, $\gamma - \beta > 0$.

These restrictions enable us to find a very simple estimate of the remainder of the hypergeometric series and to give a bound for the error that is sufficiently practical to serve for numerical calculations. We need merely observe that, by (378.1), the coefficients c_ν all have the same sign and decrease monotonically as ν increases, because

$$0 < \frac{c_{\nu+1}}{c_\nu} = \frac{\alpha + \nu}{1 + \nu} \cdot \frac{\beta + \nu}{\gamma + \nu} \leq 1. \tag{378.2}$$

Hence if we set

$$R_\nu = c_{\nu+1} z^{\nu+1} + c_{\nu+2} z^{\nu+2} + \cdots , \tag{378.3}$$

we obtain the estimate

$$|R_\nu| < \left| \frac{c_{\nu+1} z^{\nu+1}}{1 - z} \right| . \tag{378.4}$$

379. In the case $\mu = \gamma - \alpha - \beta > 0$, the series for $F(\alpha, \beta, \gamma; z)$ converges also for $z = 1$ and therefore converges everywhere on its circle of convergence. We wish to derive a bound for

$$R_\nu = c_{\nu+1} + c_{\nu+2} + \cdots \tag{379.1}$$

in this case too. To this end, we shall need a sequence of positive numbers $c_1^*, c_2^*, \ldots$ whose sum is convergent and that have the property that for $\nu > \nu_0$,

$$\frac{c_{\nu+1}}{c_\nu} \leq \frac{c_{\nu+1}^*}{c_\nu^*} , \qquad \frac{c_{\nu+1}}{c_{\nu+1}^*} \leq \frac{c_\nu}{c_\nu^*}$$

holds. Then if we set

$$R_\nu^* = c_{\nu+1}^* + c_{\nu+2}^* + \cdots \tag{379.2}$$

and choose $\nu > \nu_0$, it follows that

$$\left. \begin{aligned} |R_\nu| &= |c_{\nu+1} + c_{\nu+2} + \cdots | = \left| c_{\nu+1}^* \frac{c_{\nu+1}}{c_{\nu+1}^*} + c_{\nu+2}^* \frac{c_{\nu+2}}{c_{\nu+1}^*} + \cdots \right| \\ &\leq \left| \frac{c_{\nu+1}}{c_{\nu+1}^*} \right| R_\nu^* \leq \left| \frac{c_{\nu_0+1}}{c_{\nu_0+1}^*} \right| R_\nu^* . \end{aligned} \right\} \tag{379.3}$$

For the terms c_ν^* of the comparison series, the numbers

$$c_\nu^* = \frac{1}{\nu^{1+\varrho}} , \tag{379.4}$$

with $\varrho > 0$, will do. To verify that they have the required property, we must show that

$$\frac{\alpha + \nu}{1 + \nu} \cdot \frac{\beta + \nu}{\gamma + \nu} \leq \frac{\nu^{1+\varrho}}{(1 + \nu)^{1+\varrho}} ,$$

that is, that

$$\left(1+\frac{1}{\nu}\right)^{\varrho} \leqq \frac{1+\frac{\gamma}{\nu}}{\left(1+\frac{\alpha}{\nu}\right)\left(1+\frac{\beta}{\nu}\right)} \tag{379.5}$$

holds. Thus we must choose $\varrho > 0$ in such a way that

$$\varrho\, l\left(1+\frac{1}{\nu}\right) \leqq l\left(1+\frac{\gamma}{\nu}\right) - l\left(1+\frac{\alpha}{\nu}\right) - l\left(1+\frac{\beta}{\nu}\right)$$

holds. But by relation (253.2), Vol. I, p. 262, we know that

$$\varrho\, l\left(1+\frac{1}{\nu}\right) < \frac{\varrho}{\nu}$$

and[1] $$l\left(1+\frac{\gamma}{\nu}\right) - l\left(1+\frac{\alpha}{\nu}\right) - l\left(1+\frac{\beta}{\nu}\right) > \frac{\gamma-\alpha-\beta}{\nu} - \frac{\gamma^2}{2\,\nu^2}.$$

Therefore it suffices to take

$$\varrho \leqq (\gamma - \alpha - \beta) - \frac{\gamma^2}{2\,\nu}. \tag{379.6}$$

If this inequality holds for a certain value of ν, then it also holds true for all larger values of ν. Now we have assumed at the beginning of this section that $\gamma - \alpha - \beta > 0$; hence if we select an integer ν_0 for which

$$\nu_0 > \frac{\gamma^2}{2\,(\gamma-\alpha-\beta)}$$

and if $\nu > \nu_0$, then we can determine a positive ϱ in such a way that for $\nu, \nu+1, \nu+2, \ldots$, the relation (379.6) holds. Hence by (258.4), Vol. I, p. 268, we have

$$R_\nu^* = \sum_{p=\nu+1}^{\infty} \frac{1}{p^{1+\varrho}} < \frac{1}{\varrho\,\nu^\varrho} \tag{379.7}$$

and by (379.3),

$$|R_\nu| \leqq \left|\frac{c_{\nu_0+1}}{c_{\nu_0+1}^*}\right| \frac{1}{\varrho\,\nu^\varrho}. \tag{379.8}$$

This implies that

$$\lim_{\nu=\infty} R_\nu = 0. \tag{379.9}$$

Thus we have proved the convergence of the series

---

[1] Note that the second inequality also holds for negative values of α and β, since we always have $l\left(1+\frac{x}{\nu}\right) \leqq \frac{x}{\nu}$.

$$F(\alpha, \beta, \gamma; z) = 1 + c_1 z + c_2 z^2 + \cdots$$

for $|z| = 1$, and we have at the same time obtained an estimate for the remainder on $|z| = 1$.

380. Let us take a closer look at the estimate (379.8) of the remainder R_ν. We note first that we can replace ν_0 by ν in (379.8). Second, we can use the gamma function to express c_ν, by (377.3), in the form

$$c_\nu = \frac{\Gamma(\alpha + \nu)}{\Gamma(\alpha)} \cdot \frac{\Gamma(\beta + \nu)}{\Gamma(\beta)} \cdot \frac{\Gamma(1)}{\Gamma(1 + \nu)} \cdot \frac{\Gamma(\gamma)}{\Gamma(\gamma + \nu)} \qquad (380.1)$$

Now we use Stirling's Formula (276.14), Vol. I, p. 293, to get bounds for the quantities in (380.1) that depend on ν, and we thus obtain

$$c_\nu = \frac{\Gamma(\gamma)}{\Gamma(\alpha)\,\Gamma(\beta)} \cdot \frac{1}{\nu^{1+\gamma-\alpha-\beta}}\, E_\nu \qquad (380.2)$$

with
$$\lim_{\nu=\infty} E_\nu = 1. \qquad (380.3)$$

This finally yields

$$\left| \frac{c_\nu}{c_\nu^*} \right| = \left| \frac{\Gamma(\gamma)}{\Gamma(\alpha)\,\Gamma(\beta)}\, E_\nu \right| \frac{1}{\nu^{(\gamma-\alpha-\beta)-\varrho}}. \qquad (380.4)$$

By using more terms of Stirling's series (cf. § 277, Vol. I, p. 293), we could of course secure still better bounds.

Calculation of $F(\alpha, \beta, \gamma; 1)$ (§ 381)

381. Two hypergeometric series $F(\alpha, \beta, \gamma; z)$ and $F(\alpha', \beta', \gamma'; z)$ are said to represent two *contiguous* functions (according to Gauss) if any two of the parameters of one function (for example, α and β) agree with the corresponding parameters (in the example, α' and β', respectively) of the other function, and if their third parameters (in the example, γ and γ') differ by ± 1. Gauss proved that a hypergeometric function F always enters with any two of its contiguous functions F_1 and F_{-1} into identities of the form

$$(A + B z) F + (C + D z) F_{-1} + (E + G z) F_1 = 0. \qquad (381.1)$$

Since a hypergeometric function F always has six contiguous functions, it follows that F enters altogether into $(6 \cdot 5)/2 = 15$ relations of the form (381.1). For example, if we set

$$F = F(\alpha, \beta, \gamma; z), \quad F_{-1} = F(\alpha, \beta, \gamma - 1; z) \quad \text{and} \quad F_1 = F(\alpha, \beta, \gamma + 1; z)$$

and once more use c_ν to denote the coefficient of z^ν in the expansion of F, then we can list as follows the coefficient of z^ν in the expansion of

$$z\,F: \qquad c_\nu \frac{\nu\,(\gamma + \nu - 1)}{(\alpha + \nu - 1)\,(\beta + \nu - 1)}$$

$$F_{-1}: \qquad c_\nu \frac{\gamma + \nu - 1}{\gamma - 1}$$

$$z\,F_{-1}: \qquad c_\nu \frac{\gamma + \nu - 1}{\gamma - 1} \cdot \frac{\nu\,(\gamma + \nu - 2)}{(\alpha + \nu - 1)\,(\beta + \nu - 1)}$$

$$F_1: \qquad c_\nu \frac{\gamma}{\gamma + \nu}$$

$$z\,F_1: \qquad c_\nu \frac{\gamma}{\gamma + \nu} \cdot \frac{\nu\,(\gamma + \nu)}{(\alpha + \nu - 1)\,(\beta + \nu - 1)}.$$

The coefficient of z^ν in the expansion of the left-hand side of (381.1) is then equal to the product of $c_\nu/[(\alpha + \nu - 1)\,(\beta + \nu - 1)]$ and a third-degree polynomial in ν, and we can determine the numbers $A, B, C, \ldots, G$ in such a way that the second factor vanishes for all values of ν. In this way we obtain

$$\gamma\,[\gamma - 1 - (2\,\gamma - \alpha - \beta - 1)\,z]\,F - \gamma\,(\gamma - 1)\,(1 - z)\,F_{-1}$$
$$+ (\gamma - \alpha)\,(\gamma - \beta)\,z\,F_1 = 0. \qquad\qquad \left.\right\} \quad (381.\,2)$$

Under the assumption $\gamma - \alpha - \beta > 1$, the three numbers

$$F(\alpha, \beta, \gamma; 1), \quad F(\alpha, \beta, \gamma + 1; 1), \quad F(\alpha, \beta, \gamma - 1; 1) \qquad (381.\,3)$$

are finite, and for $z = 1$ relation (381.2) takes on the form

$$\frac{F(\alpha, \beta, \gamma; 1)}{F(\alpha, \beta, \gamma + 1; 1)} = \frac{(\gamma - \alpha)\,(\gamma - \beta)}{\gamma\,(\gamma - \alpha - \beta)}. \qquad (381.\,4)$$

But this identity continues to hold true whenever

$$\gamma - \alpha - \beta > 0,$$

because the third of the three numbers (381.3) does not occur in (381.4). If we replace the parameter γ in (381.4) successively by

$$\gamma + 1, \gamma + 2, \ldots, \gamma + n$$

and multiply the resulting equations term by term, we are led to the relation

$$
\left.
\begin{aligned}
&\frac{F(\alpha, \beta, \gamma; 1)}{F(\alpha, \beta, \gamma + n + 1; 1)} \\
&= \frac{(\gamma - \alpha)(\gamma - \alpha + 1) \dots (\gamma - \alpha + n)}{\gamma(\gamma + 1) \dots (\gamma + n)} \cdot \frac{(\gamma - \beta) \dots (\gamma - \beta + n)}{(\gamma - \alpha - \beta) \dots (\gamma - \alpha - \beta + n)} \cdot
\end{aligned}
\right\} \quad (381.5)
$$

With the notation of § 271, Vol. I, p. 286, specifically (271.3), we can rewrite (381.5) in the form

$$
\frac{F(\alpha, \beta, \gamma; 1)}{F(\alpha, \beta, \gamma + n + 1; 1)} = \frac{\Gamma_n(\gamma)\, \Gamma_n(\gamma - \alpha - \beta)}{\Gamma_n(\gamma - \alpha)\, \Gamma_n(\gamma - \beta)} \cdot \quad (381.6)
$$

Noting that

$$
\lim_{n = \infty} F(\alpha, \beta, \gamma + n; 1) = 1
$$

holds, we finally obtain

$$
F(\alpha, \beta, \gamma; 1) = \frac{\Gamma(\gamma)\, \Gamma(\gamma - \alpha - \beta)}{\Gamma(\gamma - \alpha)\, \Gamma(\gamma - \beta)} \cdot \quad (381.7)
$$

All of the above calculations are due to Gauss.

Kummer's Differential Equation (§§ 382-383)

382. A given circular-arc triangle with angles $\pi\lambda$, $\pi\mu$, $\pi\nu$ can always be mapped by means of a Moebius transformation onto another such triangle that has the vertex A at $w = 0$ and whose sides AB and AC are straight-line segments, AB being, moreover, a segment of the positive real axis. By means of a different Moebius transformation, we could instead make the vertex B coincide with the origin, arrange for the sides BC and BA to be straight-line segments, and have BC lying along the positive real axis.

In the first case, the mapping function in the neighborhood of $z = 0$ must be of the form

$$
w = z^{\frac{1}{\lambda}}\, \mathfrak{P}_1(z), \quad (382.1)
$$

and in the second case, of the form

$$
w = (1 - z)^{\frac{1}{\mu}}\, \mathfrak{P}_2(1 - z). \quad (382.2)
$$

On the other hand, we have seen that w is always equal to the ratio u_2/u_1 of two solutions of the hypergeometric equation

$$z(1-z)u'' + [\gamma - (\alpha + \beta + 1)z]u' - \alpha\beta u = 0. \qquad (382.3)$$

The above suggests that we try

$$u = z^p(1-z)^q P(z) \qquad (382.4)$$

as a solution of (382.3), where p and q are any two constants and $P(z)$ is a suitable new function. The expression (382.4), as a possible solution of (382.3), was first tried out by E. E. Kummer (1810-1893). Kummer did not, however, introduce it in connection with conformal mapping, in fact, he was interested in real values of z only. He showed that the singularities of the solutions of (382.3) can be completely determined by setting up the solutions in the form (382.4), and that the general solution of the differential equation can then be determined by elementary calculations.

To begin with, if u is to be a solution of (382.3), then by formally substituting the right-hand side of (382.4) into (382.3) we see that $P(z)$ must satisfy a differential equation of the form

$$z^2(1-z)^2\frac{d^2P}{dz^2} + z(1-z)(A-Bz)\frac{dP}{dz} + (Lz^2 + Mz + N)P = 0. \qquad (382.5)$$

Here the coefficients A, B, L, M, N, and the quantity $S = L + M + N$ are constants which are related to p, q, α, β, and γ by the equations

$$\left.\begin{aligned} A &= 2p + \gamma \\ B &= 2p + 2q + \alpha + \beta + 1 \\ L &= (p + q + \alpha)(p + q + \beta) \\ N &= p(p - 1 + \gamma) \\ S &= L + M + N = q(q + \alpha + \beta - \gamma). \end{aligned}\right\} \qquad (382.6)$$

Now the connection between the solutions of the differential equation (382.3) on the one hand and (382.5) on the other hand is as follows. If u is a solution of (382.3) and if we set

$$P(z) = z^{-p}(1-z)^{-q}u,$$

then $P(z)$ is a solution of (382.5). Conversely, if $P(z)$ is a solution of (382.5) then the expression in (382.4) represents a solution u of (382.3), and this holds for all values of p and q provided only that these values satisfy the equations (382.6). If we set, in particular, $p = q = 0$, then by (382.6),

$$A = \gamma, \quad B = \alpha + \beta + 1, \quad L = -M = \alpha\beta, \quad N = 0, \quad S = 0. \quad (382.7)$$

In this case, the differential equations (382.3) and (382.5) differ only by the factor $z(1 - z)$.

Now let p', q', α', β', γ' be any set of constants that satisfy the system (382.6) when substituted for p, q, α, β, and γ respectively or—what is the same—that satisfy the equivalent system

$$\begin{rcases} p'^2 - (A - 1)\,p' + N = 0 \\ q'^2 - (B - A - 1)\,q' + S = 0 \\ (p' + q' + \alpha') + (p' + q' + \beta') = B - 1 \\ (p' + q' + \alpha')\,(p' + q' + \beta') = L \\ \gamma' = A - 2\,p'. \end{rcases} \quad (382.8)$$

Then by what we noted above, the function

$$z^{-p'}\,(1 - z)^{-q'}\,F(\alpha', \beta', \gamma'; z)$$

is a solution of (382.5), and if we choose the values of A, B, L, N, S as in (382.7) above, this function is also a solution of (382.3). Now the system of equations (382.8) has eight solutions, and these reduce to four solutions if the order of α and β is considered immaterial; these four solutions are as follows:

p'	0	0	$\gamma - 1$	$\gamma - 1$
q'	0	$\alpha + \beta - \gamma$	0	$\alpha + \beta - \gamma$
α'	α	$\gamma - \beta$	$\alpha + 1 - \gamma$	$1 - \alpha$
β'	β	$\gamma - \alpha$	$\beta + 1 - \gamma$	$1 - \beta$
γ'	γ	γ	$2 - \gamma$	$2 - \gamma$

We are thus led to the following four solutions of the hypergeometric differential equation (382.3):

$$
\left.
\begin{array}{ll}
\text{I} & F(\alpha, \beta, \gamma; z) \\[4pt]
\text{II} & (1 - z)^{\gamma - \alpha - \beta} F(\gamma - \alpha, \gamma - \beta, \gamma; z) \\[4pt]
\text{III} & z^{1 - \gamma} F(\alpha + 1 - \gamma, \beta + 1 - \gamma, 2 - \gamma; z) \\[4pt]
\text{IV} & z^{1 - \gamma} (1 - z)^{\gamma - \alpha - \beta} F(1 - \alpha, 1 - \beta, 2 - \gamma; z).
\end{array}
\right\}
\tag{382.9}
$$

We see immediately that both I and II can be expanded at $z = 0$ in power series whose constant term is unity. Therefore they represent one and the same solution, the hypergeometric equation having only one solution with the stated property. And the identity

$$
F(\alpha, \beta, \gamma; z) \equiv (1 - z)^{\gamma - \alpha - \beta} F(\gamma - \alpha, \gamma - \beta, \gamma; z)
$$

shows that III represents the same function as IV.

383. Kummer's differential equation enjoys the property of being transformed into an equation of the same form if the variable z is replaced by the new variable $\eta = 1 - z$ or by $\zeta = 1/z$. In fact, the transformed equations are

$$
\eta^2 (1 - \eta)^2 \frac{d^2 P}{d\eta^2} + \eta (1 - \eta) (A_1 - B_1 \eta) \frac{dP}{d\eta}
$$
$$
+ (L_1 \eta^2 + M_1 \eta + N_1) P = 0
\tag{383.1}
$$

with $A_1 = B - A$, $B_1 = B$, $L_1 = L$, $N_1 = S$, $S_1 = N$, and

$$
\zeta^2 (1 - \zeta)^2 \frac{d^2 P}{d\zeta^2} + \zeta (1 - \zeta) (A_2 - B_2 \zeta) \frac{dP}{d\zeta}
$$
$$
+ (L_2 \zeta^2 + M_2 \zeta + N_2) P = 0
\tag{383.2}
$$

with $A_2 = 2 - B$, $B_2 = 2 - A$, $L_2 = N$, $N_2 = L$, $S_2 = S$, where we have again set $S_1 = L_1 + M_1 + N_1$ and $S_2 = L_2 + M_2 + N_2$.

Now if the quantities $p_1, q_1, \alpha_1, \beta_1, \gamma_1$ and $p_2, q_2, \alpha_2, \beta_2, \gamma_2$ are solutions of the systems of equations

$$
\left.
\begin{array}{l}
p^2 - (A_1 - 1) p + N_1 = 0 \\[4pt]
q^2 - (B_1 - A_1 - 1) q + S_1 = 0 \\[4pt]
(p + q + \alpha) + (p + q + \beta) = B_1 - 1 \\[4pt]
(p + q + \alpha) (p + q + \beta) = L_1 \\[4pt]
\gamma = A_1 - 2 p
\end{array}
\right\}
\tag{383.3}
$$

and

$$p^2 - (A_2 - 1)\, p + N_2 = 0$$
$$q^2 - (B_2 - A_2 - 1)\, q + S_2 = 0$$
$$(p + q + \alpha) + (p + q + \beta) = B_2 - 1$$
$$(p + q + \alpha)\, (p + q + \beta) = L_2$$
$$\gamma = A_2 - 2\, p,$$

(383. 4)

respectively, then we know that (383.1) and (383.2) have integrals (i.e. solutions) of the form

$$\eta^{-p_1} (1 - \eta)^{-q_1} F(\alpha_1, \beta_1, \gamma_1; \eta),$$

$$\zeta^{-p_2} (1 - \zeta)^{-q_2} F(\alpha_2, \beta_2, \gamma_2; \zeta).$$

If we replace the numbers

$$A_1,\ B_1,\ L_1,\ N_1,\ S_1$$

in (383.3) and

$$A_2,\ B_2,\ L_2,\ N_2,\ S_2$$

in (383.4) by their expressions in terms of A, B, L, N, and S, and then substitute for the latter quantities their expressions in terms of p, q, α, β, γ from (382.6), we see that the systems (383.3) and (383.4) can be solved *rationally*, and we obtain for instance, as one of the possible solutions,

$$p_1 = q, \quad q_1 = p, \quad \alpha_1 = \alpha, \quad \beta_1 = \beta, \quad \gamma_1 = 1 - (\gamma - \alpha - \beta)$$

and

$$p_2 = -p - q - \alpha, \quad q_2 = q, \quad \alpha_2 = \alpha, \quad \beta_2 = 1 + \alpha - \gamma, \quad \gamma_2 = 1 + \alpha - \beta.$$

We see, therefore, that if the differential equation (382.5) has a solution of the form $z^{-p} (1 - z)^{-q} F(\alpha, \beta, \gamma; z)$, then the functions

$$\eta^{-p_1} (1 - \eta)^{-q_1} F(\alpha_1, \beta_1, \gamma_1; \eta) = z^{-p} (1 - z)^{-q} F(\alpha, \beta, \alpha + \beta + 1 - \gamma; 1 - z)$$

and

$$\zeta^{-p_2} (1 - \zeta)^{-q_2} F(\alpha_2, \beta_2, \gamma_2; \zeta)$$

$$= z^{-p-\alpha} (1 - z)^{-q} F\left(\alpha,\, 1 + \alpha - \gamma,\, 1 + \alpha - \beta;\, \frac{1}{z}\right)$$

are two more solutions of (382.5). The same is true of the hypergeometric differential equation (382.3), which is a special case of (382.5). Hence we may apply the transformations

$$\{p, q, \alpha, \beta, \gamma, z\} \to \{q, p, \alpha, \beta, 1 - (\gamma - \alpha - \beta), 1 - z\} \tag{383. 5}$$

and

$$\{p, q, \alpha, \beta, \gamma, z\} \to \left\{-p - q - \alpha, q, \alpha, 1 + \alpha - \gamma, 1 + \alpha - \beta, \frac{1}{z}\right\} \tag{383. 6}$$

to the integrals of (382.3) and may, in fact, apply them any number of times in succession, since each application amounts to transforming the differential equation (382.3) into an equivalent equation.

The Twenty-Four Integrals of Kummer (§ 384)

384. We are led in this way to a large number of new integrals of the equation (382.3). If we apply (383.5) to the integrals we have already listed in (382.9), we obtain

$$\left.\begin{array}{ll}
\text{V} & F(\alpha, \beta, \alpha + \beta + 1 - \gamma; 1 - z) \\[6pt]
\text{VI} & (1 - z)^{\gamma - \alpha - \beta} F(\gamma - \alpha, \gamma - \beta, \gamma + 1 - \alpha - \beta; 1 - z) \\[6pt]
\text{VII} & z^{1-\gamma} F(\alpha + 1 - \gamma, \beta + 1 - \gamma, \alpha + \beta + 1 - \gamma; 1 - z) \\[6pt]
\text{VIII} & z^{1-\gamma} (1 - z)^{\gamma - \alpha - \beta} F(1 - \alpha, 1 - \beta, \gamma + 1 - \alpha - \beta; 1 - z).
\end{array}\right\} \tag{384. 1}$$

If we set $1 - z = \zeta$ and apply the substitution (383.6) to the integrals (384.1), we find

$$\left.\begin{array}{ll}
\text{IX} & (1 - z)^{-\alpha} F\left(\gamma - \beta, \alpha, \alpha + 1 - \beta; \dfrac{1}{1-z}\right) \\[10pt]
\text{X} & (1 - z)^{-\beta} F\left(\gamma - \alpha, \beta, \beta + 1 - \alpha; \dfrac{1}{1-z}\right) \\[10pt]
\text{XI} & z^{1-\gamma} (1 - z)^{\gamma - \alpha - 1} F\left(\alpha + 1 - \gamma, 1 - \beta, \alpha + 1 - \beta; \dfrac{1}{1-z}\right) \\[10pt]
\text{XII} & z^{1-\gamma} (1 - z)^{\gamma - \beta - 1} F\left(\beta + 1 - \gamma, 1 - \alpha, \beta + 1 - \alpha; \dfrac{1}{1-z}\right).
\end{array}\right\} \tag{384. 2}$$

Application of (383.5) to (384.2) yields

XIII $\quad (1-z)^{-\alpha} F\left(\gamma - \beta, \alpha, \gamma; \dfrac{z}{z-1}\right)$

XIV $\quad (1-z)^{-\beta} F\left(\gamma - \alpha, \beta, \gamma; \dfrac{z}{z-1}\right)$

XV $\quad z^{1-\gamma} (1-z)^{\gamma-\alpha-1} F\left(\alpha + 1 - \gamma, 1 - \beta, 2 - \gamma; \dfrac{z}{z-1}\right)$

XVI $\quad z^{1-\gamma} (1-z)^{\gamma-\beta-1} F\left(\beta + 1 - \gamma, 1 - \alpha, 2 - \gamma; \dfrac{z}{z-1}\right).$

$$(384.3)$$

Finally, two more groups of solutions are obtained by using the transformations (383.5) and (383.6) once more, applying them this time to (384.3). It is desirable to multiply the resulting integrals by a constant of modulus unity so as to make their principal values real for sufficiently large negative real values of z; in this way we obtain

XVII $\quad (-z)^{\beta-\gamma} (1-z)^{\gamma-\alpha-\beta} F\left(\gamma - \beta, 1 - \beta, \gamma + 1 - \alpha - \beta; \dfrac{z-1}{z}\right)$

XVIII $\quad (-z)^{\alpha-\gamma} (1-z)^{\gamma-\alpha-\beta} F\left(\gamma - \alpha, 1 - \alpha, \gamma + 1 - \alpha - \beta; \dfrac{z-1}{z}\right)$

XIX $\quad (-z)^{-\alpha} F\left(\alpha + 1 - \gamma, \alpha, 1 + \alpha + \beta - \gamma; \dfrac{z-1}{z}\right)$

XX $\quad (-z)^{-\beta} F\left(\beta + 1 - \gamma, \beta, 1 + \alpha + \beta - \gamma; \dfrac{z-1}{z}\right)$

$$(384.4)$$

XXI $\quad (-z)^{\beta-\gamma} (1-z)^{\gamma-\alpha-\beta} F\left(\gamma - \beta, 1 - \beta, \alpha + 1 - \beta; \dfrac{1}{z}\right)$

XXII $\quad (-z)^{\alpha-\gamma} (1-z)^{\gamma-\alpha-\beta} F\left(\gamma - \alpha, 1 - \alpha, \beta + 1 - \alpha; \dfrac{1}{z}\right)$

XXIII $\quad (-z)^{-\alpha} F\left(\alpha + 1 - \gamma, \alpha, \alpha + 1 - \beta; \dfrac{1}{z}\right)$

XXIV $\quad (-z)^{-\beta} F\left(\beta + 1 - \gamma, \beta, \beta + 1 - \alpha; \dfrac{1}{z}\right).$

$$(384.5)$$

It is easy to verify that Kummer's method of algebraic transformations (i.e., (383.5) and (383.6)) yields no further integrals.

The Fundamental Solutions of the Hypergeometric Differential Equation (§ 385)

385. The twenty-four integrals of Kummer do not represent as many different functions. Thus, for example, the integrals I, II, XIII, and XIV all have a branch that is regular at $z = 0$ and assumes the value unity at this point. But we know that (382.3) has no more than one solution with this property.

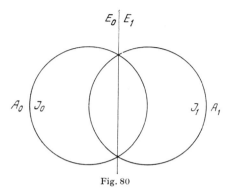

Fig. 80

Hence if we take the real branches of the powers $(1 - z)^{\gamma - \alpha - \beta}$ and $(1 - z)^{-\alpha}$ and $(1 - z)^{-\beta}$ on the segment $(0, 1)$, then

$$
\left.
\begin{aligned}
F(\alpha, \beta, \gamma; z) &= (1 - z)^{\gamma - \alpha - \beta} F(\gamma - \alpha, \gamma - \beta, \gamma; z) \\
&= (1 - z)^{-\alpha} F\left(\alpha, \gamma - \beta, \gamma; \frac{z}{z - 1}\right) \\
&= (1 - z)^{-\beta} F\left(\beta, \gamma - \alpha, \gamma; \frac{z}{z - 1}\right)
\end{aligned}
\right\}
\qquad (385.1)
$$

in the neighborhood of $z = 0$. Therefore these four expressions represent one and the same function, which we shall denote, for short, by φ_1.

With the aid of (385.1), we can verify that the remaining twenty integrals can be grouped into five sets of four integrals each, the four integrals in any given one of the sets having a branch in common. We obtain in this way the following six functions:

$$
\left.
\begin{array}{lcccc}
\varphi_1: & \text{I,} & \text{II,} & \text{XIII,} & \text{XIV} \\
\varphi_2: & \text{III,} & \text{IV,} & \text{XV,} & \text{XVI} \\
\varphi_3: & \text{V,} & \text{VII,} & \text{XIX,} & \text{XX} \\
\varphi_4: & \text{VI,} & \text{VIII,} & \text{XVII,} & \text{XVIII} \\
\varphi_5: & \text{XXIII,} & \text{XXI,} & \text{IX,} & \text{XI} \\
\varphi_6: & \text{XXIV,} & \text{XXII,} & \text{X,} & \text{XII.}
\end{array}
\right\}
\qquad (385.2)
$$

For each of the six functions φ_i we have four distinct representations. This is very useful, since it enables us to select in any situation that representation which converges the most rapidly under the given circumstances.

We introduce the following notation, which will be helpful to us in writing down the regions of convergence for the various functions under consideration: The interiors of the circles $|z| = 1$ and $|1 - z| = 1$ will be denoted by J_0 and J_1 respectively; the exterior regions of the same circles, by A_0 and A_1 respectively; finally, the half-planes $\Re z < 1/2$ and $\Re z > 1/2$ will be denoted by E_0 and E_1 respectively (see Fig. 80 above).

The hypergeometric series that appear in the integrals I-IV converge in J_0; those of V-VIII converge in J_1; IX-XII, in A_1; XIII-XVI, in E_0; XVII-XX, in E_1; and XXI-XXIV converge in A_0.

As to convergence *on* their circle of convergence, it takes place for

I,	III, XXIII, XXIV,	if	$\gamma - \alpha - \beta > 0$,	i.e. by	(376.6) $\mu > 0$,
II,	IV, XXI, XXII,	if	$\beta + \alpha - \gamma > 0$,	i.e. by	(376.6) $\mu < 0$,
V,	VI, IX, X,	if	$1 - \gamma > 0$,	i.e. by	(376.6) $\lambda > 0$,
VII, VIII,	XI, XII,	if	$1 - \gamma < 0$,	i.e. by	(376.6) $\lambda < 0$,
XIII, XV, XVII, XIX,		if	$\beta - \alpha > 0$,	i.e. by	(376.6) $\nu < 0$,
XIV, XVI, XVIII,	XX,	if	$\alpha - \beta > 0$,	i.e. by	(376.6) $\nu > 0$.

Since in our case (that is, in the study of the mapping of circular-arc triangles) the quantities λ, μ, ν are never negative, we can dispense with the solutions

$$\text{II,} \quad \text{IV,} \quad \text{XXI,} \quad \text{XXII}$$
$$\text{VII,} \quad \text{VIII,} \quad \text{XI,} \quad \text{XII}$$
$$\text{XIII,} \quad \text{XV,} \quad \text{XVII,} \quad \text{XIX}$$

because the remaining twelve contain everything we need.

The twelve solutions are listed in Table A below (after § 395). For each of the six regions $J_0, J_1, \ldots, E_1$, they yield two integrals of the hypergeometric differential equation that enable us to construct the general integral (general solution) for the region in question.

The Exceptional Cases and the Function $F^*(\alpha, \beta, \gamma; z)$ (§§ 386-388)

386. If one or more of the angles $\pi \lambda$, $\pi \mu$, $\pi \nu$ are zero, then certain of the functions $\varphi_1, \ldots, \varphi_6$ will coincide, and we must therefore look around, in this case, for new solutions of (376.5).

Thus, for instance, recalling that our mapping problem requires that $0 < \gamma \leqq 1$, we see that the functions

$$\varphi_1 = F(\alpha, \beta, \gamma; z)$$

and

$$\varphi_2 = z^{1-\gamma} F(\alpha + 1 - \gamma, \beta + 1 - \gamma, 2 - \gamma; z)$$

are the same in case $\gamma = 1$, that is, in case $\lambda = 1 - \gamma = 0$. To deal with the case $\lambda = 0$, we set $\gamma = 1 - \lambda$ and

$$\varphi_2(\lambda) = \varphi_1(\lambda) + \lambda \, \varphi_2^*(\lambda), \tag{386.1}$$

so that $\varphi_2^*(\lambda)$ stands for a function of z that is, for every $\lambda > 0$, a solution of the linear differential equation (376.5), being a linear combination of φ_1 and φ_2 with constant coefficients. We shall prove that

$$\varphi_2^* = \lim_{\lambda = 0} \varphi_2^*(\lambda) \tag{386.2}$$

is a solution of equation (376.5) for the special case $\lambda = 0$. We have

$$\varphi_2^* = \lim_{\lambda = 0} \frac{1}{\lambda} \left\{ z^\lambda F(\alpha + \lambda, \beta + \lambda, 1 + \lambda; z) - F(\alpha, \beta, 1 - \lambda; z) \right\}$$

or, expanding the expression in braces in powers of λ and then passing to the limit,

$$\varphi_2^* = F(\alpha, \beta, 1; z) \, l \, z + F^*(\alpha, \beta, 1; z), \tag{386.3}$$

where F^* is defined by

$$F^*(\alpha, \beta, \gamma; z) = \frac{\partial F}{\partial \alpha} + \frac{\partial F}{\partial \beta} + 2 \frac{\partial F}{\partial \gamma}, \quad (F = F(\alpha, \beta, \gamma; z)). \tag{386.4}$$

387. The function $F^*(\alpha, \beta, \gamma; z)$ can be calculated as follows. Since the partial sums of the power series $F(\alpha, \beta, \gamma; z) = \Sigma \, c_\nu \, z^\nu$ are uniformly bounded in a disc $|z| < r < 1$, they represent for every $|z| < 1$, and for any fixed values of β and γ, analytic functions of α; thus we have

$$\frac{\partial F}{\partial \alpha} = \sum_{\nu = 1}^{\infty} \frac{\partial c_\nu}{\partial \alpha} \, z^\nu. \tag{387.1}$$

But by (377.3),

$$\frac{\partial c_\nu}{\partial \alpha} = \left(\frac{1}{\alpha} + \frac{1}{\alpha+1} + \cdots + \frac{1}{\alpha+\nu-1}\right) c_\nu,$$ (387.2)

so that we obtain

$$\frac{\partial F}{\partial \alpha} = \sum_{\nu=1}^{\infty} \left(\frac{1}{\alpha} + \frac{1}{\alpha+1} + \cdots + \frac{1}{\alpha+\nu-1}\right) c_\nu z^\nu.$$ (387.3)

We can calculate $\partial F/\partial \beta$ and $\partial F/\partial \gamma$ in the same way and finally obtain

$$F^*(\alpha, \beta, \gamma; z) = \frac{\partial F}{\partial \alpha} + \frac{\partial F}{\partial \beta} + 2\frac{\partial F}{\partial \gamma} = \sum_{\nu=1}^{\infty} e_\nu c_\nu z^\nu,$$ (387.4)

where

$$\begin{aligned}
e_\nu &= \sum_{p=0}^{\nu-1} \left(\frac{1}{\alpha+p} + \frac{1}{\beta+p} - \frac{2}{\gamma+p}\right) \\
&= \sum_{p=0}^{\nu-1} \left(\frac{\gamma-\alpha}{(\alpha+p)(\gamma+p)} + \frac{\gamma-\beta}{(\beta+p)(\gamma+p)}\right), \\
e_1 &= \frac{1}{\alpha} + \frac{1}{\beta} - \frac{2}{\gamma}.
\end{aligned}\qquad(387.5)$$

The numbers e_ν converge to a finite limit as $\nu \to \infty$; therefore their absolute values $|e_\nu|$ have a finite l.u.b. $M(\alpha, \beta, \gamma)$. Hence the remainder of the series (387.4) is certainly less than $M(\alpha, \beta, \gamma) \cdot |R_\nu|$, where R_ν is given by (378.3).

Thus the function $F^*(\alpha, \beta, \gamma; z)$ is regular in the disc $|z| < 1$, and the series (387.4) converges *on* its circle of convergence if $\gamma - \alpha - \beta > 0$, by § 379.

In the above calculations we have implicitly assumed that the parameters α and β do not vanish. If one or both of them are zero, the calculations have to be modified somewhat; however, they lead to the same results.

388. Now it is easy to verify that φ_2^* is a solution of the equation

$$z(1-z)u'' + [1 - (\alpha+\beta+1)z]u' - \alpha\beta u = 0.$$

To do this, it suffices to show that the expression

$$\begin{aligned}
&2(1-z)F' - (\alpha+\beta)F + z(1-z)F^{*''} \\
&+ [1 - (\alpha+\beta+1)z]F^{*'} - \alpha\beta F^*,
\end{aligned}\qquad(388.1)$$

which represents a regular function in the neighborhood of $z = 0$, is identically equal to zero. (We recall that $F(\alpha, \beta, 1; z)$ is a solution of the above equation; F', $F^{*'}$ and $F^{*''}$ denote derivatives with respect to z.)

By (377.4), (387.4) and (387.5), we have

$$
\left.
\begin{aligned}
F(\alpha, \beta, 1; z) &= 1 + \sum_{\nu=1}^{\infty} c_\nu \, z^\nu \\
F^*(\alpha, \beta, 1; z) &= \sum_{\nu=1}^{\infty} e_\nu \, c_\nu \, z^\nu
\end{aligned}
\right\}
\tag{388.2}
$$

and

$$
\frac{c_{\nu+1}}{c_\nu} = \frac{(\alpha + \nu)\,(\beta + \nu)}{(1 + \nu)^2},
\tag{388.3}
$$

$$
e_{\nu+1} - e_\nu = \frac{1}{\alpha + \nu} + \frac{1}{\beta + \nu} - \frac{2}{1 + \nu}.
\tag{388.4}
$$

For $\nu \geqq 1$, the coefficient of z^ν in (388.1) equals

$$
2\,(\nu + 1)\, c_{\nu+1} - [(\alpha + \nu) + (\beta + \nu)]\, c_\nu
$$
$$
+ (\nu + 1)^2 \, c_{\nu+1}\, e_{\nu+1} - (\alpha + \nu)\,(\beta + \nu)\, c_\nu \, e_\nu
$$

or, if we express $c_{\nu+1}$ in terms of c_ν,

$$
c_\nu \left\{ \frac{2\,(\alpha + \nu)\,(\beta + \nu)}{1 + \nu} - (\alpha + \nu) - (\beta + \nu) + (\alpha + \nu)\,(\beta + \nu)\,(e_{\nu+1} - e_\nu) \right\},
$$

which is an expression that vanishes for every ν, by (388.4). We also see that the coefficient $(2\,c_1 - \alpha - \beta + c_1\, e_1)$, i.e. the term independent of z, is likewise equal to zero.

The function φ_2^* admits of a second representation which we can obtain by expressing φ_1 and φ_2 in (386.1) in terms of the integrals XIV and XVI, respectively. This yields

$$
\varphi_2^* = \lim_{\lambda = 0} \frac{1}{\lambda} \left\{ z^\lambda (1 - z)^{-\beta - \lambda} F\left(1 - \alpha, \beta + \lambda, 1 + \lambda; \frac{z}{z-1}\right) \right.
$$
$$
\left. - (1 - z)^{-\beta} F\left(1 - \alpha - \lambda, \beta, 1 - \lambda; \frac{z}{z-1}\right) \right\}
$$

or

$$
\varphi_2^* = (1 - z)^{-\beta} \left\{ F\left(1 - \alpha, \beta, 1; \frac{z}{z-1}\right) l \frac{z}{1-z} + F^*\left(1 - \alpha, \beta, 1; \frac{z}{z-1}\right) \right\}. \tag{388.5}
$$

Passing to the next special case, we see similarly that the solutions φ_4 and φ_3 coincide if $\mu = \gamma - \alpha - \beta$ vanishes. In this case, φ_4 can be replaced by a new solution that is defined by means of the equations

$$\varphi_4 = \varphi_3 + \mu\,\varphi_4^*(\mu)$$
$$\varphi_4^* = \lim_{\mu=0} \varphi_4^*(\mu).$$

(388. 6)

Finally if $\nu = \alpha - \beta = 0$, then we introduce the new solution φ_6^* defined by

$$\varphi_6 = \varphi_5 + \nu\,\varphi_6^*(\nu)$$
$$\varphi_6^* = \lim_{\nu=0} \varphi_6^*(\nu).$$

(388. 7)

We can calculate φ_4^* and φ_6^* by the above method and prove that they actually do satisfy the given differential equation. We are now ready to supplement Table A at the end of this chapter (p. 168) and are thus led to the construction of Table B.

Connecting Formulas (§§ 389-391)

389. The functions $\varphi_1, \ldots, \varphi_6$ defined in § 385 above give at least one pair of linearly independent solutions of the differential equation (376.5) at any

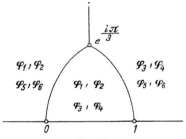

Fig. 81

given point of the complex plane.[1]

But since the points $z = 0, 1, \infty$ are branch points of the functions φ_2, φ_4, φ_6 (or of φ_2^*, φ_4^*, φ_6^*, if required), we cut the z-plane along its real axis, and we consider, to begin with, the *upper* half-plane only. Now we stipulate that φ_1, φ_2, φ_3, φ_4 (as well as φ_2^*, φ_4^*) are to be real and positive on the segment $0, 1$ while φ_5, φ_6 (as well as φ_6^*) are to be positive on the segment $-\infty, 0$ of the real axis; we are then dealing with well-defined single-valued branches of the functions $\varphi_1, \ldots, \varphi_6$ in the upper half-plane.

Now a more detailed study of our formulas reveals that at any interior point of any one of the three regions shown in Fig. 81, the formulas always define *two* pairs of functions. Since the functions $\varphi_1, \ldots, \varphi_6$ all are solutions of the

---

[1] However, in the case $\lambda = \mu = \nu = 0$ and in this case only, there exist two exceptional points, namely $z = e^{\pm \pi i/3}$, at which *none* of the series I-XXIV converges. This exceptional case must be treated separately (*cf.* § 408 below).

same second-order differential equation, any three of a set of four functions defined in a given region must be connected by linear relations with constant coefficients, relations that are preserved under analytic continuation of the functions.

390. For each of the three regions of Fig. 81, there are of course four linear relations as described above. As far as our mapping problem is concerned, it will suffice to determine explicitly the coefficients $a, b, \ldots$ in the equations

$$
\left.
\begin{aligned}
\varphi_1 &= a\,\varphi_3 + b\,\varphi_4 \\
\varphi_2 &= a'\,\varphi_3 + b'\,\varphi_4 \\
\varphi_1 &= c\,\varphi_5 + e\,\varphi_6 \\
\varphi_2 &= c'\,\varphi_5 + e'\,\varphi_6
\end{aligned}
\right\}
\tag{390.1}
$$

(and to do the same for the equations in which one or more of the functions $\varphi_2, \varphi_4, \varphi_6$ is replaced by one or more of the functions $\varphi_2^*, \varphi_4^*, \varphi_6^*$).

We shall first deal with the case that all three of the numbers λ, μ, ν are distinct from zero. If we substitute into the first equation of (390.1)

$$
\left.
\begin{aligned}
\varphi_1 &= F(\alpha, \beta, \gamma; z) \\
\varphi_3 &= F(\alpha, \beta, \alpha + \beta + 1 - \gamma; 1 - z) \\
\varphi_4 &= (1 - z)^{\gamma - \alpha - \beta} F(\gamma - \alpha, \gamma - \beta, \gamma + 1 - \alpha - \beta; 1 - z),
\end{aligned}
\right\}
\tag{390.2}
$$

as is indicated by Table A (see end of this chapter), then these formulas—which do apply on the segment $0 \leqq z \leqq 1$ of the real axis—yield for $z = 1$ that

$$
\varphi_1 = F(\alpha, \beta, \gamma; 1), \quad \varphi_3 = 1, \quad \varphi_4 = 0,
$$

hence

$$
a = F(\alpha, \beta, \gamma; 1),
$$

and for $z = 0$ that

$$
\varphi_1 = 1, \quad \varphi_3 = F(\alpha, \beta, \alpha + \beta + 1 - \gamma; 1), \quad \varphi_4 = F(\gamma - \alpha, \gamma - \beta, \gamma + 1 - \alpha - \beta; 1),
$$

hence

$$
1 = a\,F(\alpha, \beta, \alpha + \beta + 1 - \gamma; 1) + b\,F(\gamma - \alpha, \gamma - \beta, \gamma + 1 - \alpha - \beta; 1).
$$

We can solve the above relations for a and b. The resulting expressions for a and b become especially neat if we use formula (381.7) to evaluate F; in this way we obtain

$$a = \frac{\Gamma(\gamma - \alpha - \beta)\, \Gamma(\gamma)}{\Gamma(\gamma - \alpha)\, \Gamma(\gamma - \beta)}, \tag{390.3}$$

$$b \frac{\Gamma(\gamma - \alpha - \beta + 1)\, \Gamma(1 - \gamma)}{\Gamma(1 - \beta)\, \Gamma(1 - \alpha)} \tag{390.4}$$

$$= 1 - \frac{\Gamma(\gamma)\, \Gamma(\gamma - \alpha - \beta)}{\Gamma(\gamma - \alpha)\, \Gamma(\gamma - \beta)} \cdot \frac{\Gamma(\alpha + \beta + 1 - \gamma)\, \Gamma(1 - \gamma)}{\Gamma(\beta + 1 - \gamma)\, \Gamma(\alpha + 1 - \gamma)},$$

and hence, using the relation $\Gamma(x)\, \Gamma(1 - x) = \pi/\sin \pi x$ (*cf.* (272.5), Vol. I, p. 288),

$$b \frac{\Gamma(\gamma - \alpha - \beta + 1)\, \Gamma(1 - \gamma)}{\Gamma(1 - \beta)\, \Gamma(1 - \alpha)} \tag{390.5}$$

$$= \frac{\sin \pi \gamma \sin \pi (\gamma - \alpha - \beta) - \sin \pi (\gamma - \alpha) \sin \pi (\gamma - \beta)}{\sin \pi \gamma \sin \pi (\gamma - \alpha - \beta)}.$$

Now it follows from

$$2 \sin m \sin n = \cos (m - n) - \cos (m + n)$$

that

$$2 \sin \pi \gamma \sin \pi (\gamma - \alpha - \beta) = \cos \pi (\alpha + \beta) - \cos \pi (2\gamma - \alpha - \beta)$$

$$2 \sin \pi (\gamma - \alpha) \sin \pi (\gamma - \beta) = \cos \pi (\alpha - \beta) - \cos \pi (2\gamma - \alpha - \beta)$$

and hence that

$$\sin \pi \gamma \sin \pi (\gamma - \alpha - \beta) - \sin \pi (\gamma - \alpha) \sin \pi (\gamma - \beta)$$

$$= \frac{1}{2} \{ \cos \pi (\alpha + \beta) - \cos \pi (\alpha - \beta) \} = - \sin \pi \alpha \sin \pi \beta.$$

Passing again to the Gamma function, we obtain from (390.5) that

$$b = - \frac{\Gamma(\gamma)\, \Gamma(1 - \gamma)\, \Gamma(\gamma - \alpha - \beta)\, \Gamma(\alpha + \beta + 1 - \gamma)}{\Gamma(\alpha)\, \Gamma(1 - \alpha)\, \Gamma(\beta)\, \Gamma(1 - \beta)} \tag{390.6}$$

$$\times \frac{\Gamma(1 - \beta)\, \Gamma(1 - \alpha)}{\Gamma(1 - \gamma)\, \Gamma(\gamma - \alpha - \beta + 1)},$$

and finally, using $\Gamma(x + 1) = x\, \Gamma(x)$, that

$$b = \frac{\Gamma(\gamma)\, \Gamma(\alpha + \beta - \gamma)}{\Gamma(\alpha)\, \Gamma(\beta)}. \tag{390.7}$$

Therefore the first of the relations (390.1) becomes

$$\varphi_1 = \frac{\Gamma(\gamma)\, \Gamma(\gamma - \alpha - \beta)}{\Gamma(\gamma - \alpha)\, \Gamma(\gamma - \beta)}\, \varphi_3 + \frac{\Gamma(\gamma)\, \Gamma(\alpha + \beta - \gamma)}{\Gamma(\alpha)\, \Gamma(\beta)}\, \varphi_4. \tag{390.8}$$

An entirely analogous procedure yields the explicit form of the second of the relations (390.1), as follows:

$$\varphi_2 = \frac{\Gamma(2-\gamma)\,\Gamma(\gamma-\alpha-\beta)}{\Gamma(1-\alpha)\,\Gamma(1-\beta)}\,\varphi_3 + \frac{\Gamma(2-\gamma)\,\Gamma(\alpha+\beta-\gamma)}{\Gamma(\beta+1-\gamma)\,\Gamma(\alpha+1-\gamma)}\,\varphi_4. \quad (390.9)$$

In the third and fourth equations of (390.1), we must substitute, in accordance with Table A,

$$\varphi_1 = (1-z)^{-\beta}\,F\!\left(\beta,\gamma-\alpha,\gamma;\frac{z}{z-1}\right)$$

$$\varphi_2 = z^{1-\gamma}(1-z)^{\gamma-\beta-1}F\!\left(1-\alpha,\beta+1-\gamma,2-\gamma;\frac{z}{z-1}\right)$$

$$\varphi_5 = (1-z)^{-\alpha}\,F\!\left(\alpha,\gamma-\beta,\alpha+1-\beta;\frac{1}{1-z}\right)$$

$$\varphi_6 = (1-z)^{-\beta}\,F\!\left(\beta,\gamma-\alpha,\beta+1-\alpha;\frac{1}{1-z}\right),$$

all of which have expansions that are valid on the segment $-\infty,0$ of the real axis.

Because of its factor $z^{1-\gamma}$, the function φ_2 is not real-valued on this segment but is equal to the product of a real function by $e^{\pi i\,(1-\gamma)}$. Thus it is appropriate to write φ_2 in the form

$$\varphi_2 = e^{\pi i\,(1-\gamma)}\,(-z)^{1-\gamma}(1-z)^{\gamma-\beta-1}\,F\!\left(1-\alpha,\beta+1-\gamma,2-\gamma;\frac{z}{z-1}\right).$$

Finally, we have

$$(1-z)^{-\beta}\,F\!\left(\beta,\gamma-\alpha,\gamma;\frac{z}{z-1}\right)$$
$$= \quad c\,(1-z)^{-\alpha}\,F\!\left(\alpha,\gamma-\beta,\alpha+1-\beta;\frac{1}{1-z}\right)$$
$$+\,e\,(1-z)^{-\beta}\,F\!\left(\beta,\gamma-\alpha,\beta+1-\alpha;\frac{1}{1-z}\right)$$

and

$$e^{\pi i\,(1-\gamma)}\,(-z)^{1-\gamma}(1-z)^{\gamma-\beta-1}\,F\!\left(1-\alpha,\beta+1-\gamma,2-\gamma;\frac{z}{z-1}\right)$$
$$= \quad c'(1-z)^{-\alpha}\,F\!\left(\alpha,\gamma-\beta,\alpha+1-\beta;\frac{1}{1-z}\right)$$
$$+\,e'\,(1-z)^{-\beta}\,F\!\left(\beta,\gamma-\alpha,\beta+1-\alpha;\frac{1}{1-z}\right),$$

and hence also

$$F\left(\beta, \gamma - \alpha, \gamma; \frac{z}{z-1}\right)$$

$$= c \, (1 - z)^{\beta - \alpha} \, F\left(\alpha, \gamma - \beta, \alpha + 1 - \beta; \frac{1}{1-z}\right) + e \, F\left(\beta, \gamma - \alpha, \beta + 1 - \alpha; \frac{1}{z-1}\right),$$

$$e^{\pi i \,(1 - \gamma)} \left(\frac{z}{z-1}\right)^{1-\gamma} F\left(1 - \alpha, \beta + 1 - \gamma, 2 - \gamma; \frac{z}{z-1}\right)$$

$$= c' \, (1 - z)^{\beta - \alpha} \, F\left(\alpha, \gamma - \beta, \alpha + 1 - \beta; \frac{1}{1-z}\right)$$

$$+ e' \, F\left(\beta, \gamma - \alpha, \beta + 1 - \alpha; \frac{1}{1-z}\right).$$

These last equations are meaningful at $z = -\infty$ as well as at $z = 0$ and they therefore enable us to evaluate the constants c, e, c', e' in terms of the Gamma function. This yields

$$\varphi_1 = \frac{\Gamma(\gamma) \, \Gamma(\beta - \alpha)}{\Gamma(\gamma - \alpha) \, \Gamma(\beta)} \, \varphi_5 + \frac{\Gamma(\gamma) \, \Gamma(\alpha - \beta)}{\Gamma(\alpha) \, \Gamma(\gamma - \beta)} \, \varphi_6 \qquad (390.\,10)$$

and

$$\varphi_2 = \frac{\Gamma(2 - \gamma) \, \Gamma(\beta - \alpha)}{\Gamma(1 - \alpha) \, \Gamma(\beta + 1 - \gamma)} \, e^{\pi i \,(1 - \gamma)} \, \varphi_5$$

$$+ \frac{\Gamma(2 - \gamma) \, \Gamma(\alpha - \beta)}{\Gamma(\alpha + 1 - \gamma) \, \Gamma(1 - \beta)} \, e^{\pi i \,(1 - \gamma)} \, \varphi_6. \qquad (390.\,11)$$

391. In the limiting cases, that is, in the cases in which not all of the three numbers λ, μ, ν are distinct from zero so that some of the functions $\varphi_2, \varphi_4, \varphi_6$ must be replaced by the functions from Table B (after § 395 below), the most expedient way of obtaining the relations analogous to (390.1) is to go back to the definitions of the functions $\varphi_2^*, \varphi_4^*, \varphi_6^*$.

Consider first the case $\lambda = 0$, $\mu > 0$, $\nu > 0$. Here, relations (390.9) and (390.11) must be replaced by two others, of the form

$$\left.\begin{aligned} \varphi_2^* &= a^* \, \varphi_3 + b^* \, \varphi_4 \\ \varphi_2^* &= c^* \, \varphi_5 + e^* \, \varphi_6. \end{aligned}\right\} \qquad (391.\,1)$$

Now with $\gamma = 1 - \lambda$, we have

$$\varphi_2^* = \lim_{\lambda = 0} \frac{\varphi_2 - \varphi_1}{\lambda},$$

and hence by (390.1),

$$a^* = \lim_{\lambda=0} \frac{a'-a}{\lambda}, \qquad b^* = \lim_{\lambda=0} \frac{b'-b}{\lambda},$$

$$c^* = \lim_{\lambda=0} \frac{c'-c}{\lambda}, \qquad e^* = \lim_{\lambda=0} \frac{e'-e}{\lambda}.$$

By (390.8) and (390.9), the first of the last four equations can be written in the form

$$a^* = \lim_{\lambda=0} \frac{1}{\lambda} \left\{ \frac{\Gamma(1+\lambda)\,\Gamma(1-\alpha-\beta-\lambda)}{\Gamma(1-\alpha)\,\Gamma(1-\beta)} - \frac{\Gamma(1-\lambda)\,\Gamma(1-\alpha-\beta-\lambda)}{\Gamma(1-\alpha-\lambda)\,\Gamma(1-\beta-\lambda)} \right\}$$

or, expanding in powers of λ inside the braces and then setting $\lambda = 0$,

$$a^* = \frac{\Gamma(1-\alpha-\beta)}{\Gamma(1-\alpha)\,\Gamma(1-\beta)} \left\{ 2\frac{\Gamma'(1)}{\Gamma(1)} - \frac{\Gamma'(1-\alpha)}{\Gamma(1-\alpha)} - \frac{\Gamma'(1-\beta)}{\Gamma(1-\beta)} \right\}.$$

The coefficients b^*, c^*, and e^* can be calculated in the same way, and we finally obtain

$$\left. \begin{aligned} \varphi_2^* &= \frac{\Gamma(1-\alpha-\beta)}{\Gamma(1-\alpha)\,\Gamma(1-\beta)} \left\{ 2\frac{\Gamma'(1)}{\Gamma(1)} - \frac{\Gamma'(1-\alpha)}{\Gamma(1-\alpha)} - \frac{\Gamma'(1-\beta)}{\Gamma(1-\beta)} \right\} \varphi_3 \\ &+ \frac{\Gamma(\alpha+\beta-1)}{\Gamma(\alpha)\,\Gamma(\beta)} \left\{ 2\frac{\Gamma'(1)}{\Gamma(1)} - \frac{\Gamma'(\alpha)}{\Gamma(\alpha)} - \frac{\Gamma'(\beta)}{\Gamma(\beta)} \right\} \varphi_4, \end{aligned} \right\} \quad (391.2)$$

$$\left. \begin{aligned} \varphi_2^* &= \frac{\Gamma(\beta-\alpha)}{\Gamma(1-\alpha)\,\Gamma(\beta)} \left\{ 2\frac{\Gamma'(1)}{\Gamma(1)} - \frac{\Gamma'(1-\alpha)}{\Gamma(1-\alpha)} - \frac{\Gamma'(\beta)}{\Gamma(\beta)} + \pi i \right\} \varphi_5 \\ &+ \frac{\Gamma(\alpha-\beta)}{\Gamma(1-\beta)\,\Gamma(\alpha)} \left\{ 2\frac{\Gamma'(1)}{\Gamma(1)} - \frac{\Gamma'(1-\beta)}{\Gamma(1-\beta)} - \frac{\Gamma'(\alpha)}{\Gamma(\alpha)} + \pi i \right\} \varphi_6. \end{aligned} \right\} \quad (391.3)$$

Next we consider the case $\mu = 0$, $\lambda > 0$, $\nu > 0$, which we deal with by setting $\gamma = \alpha + \beta + \mu$ and $\varphi_4 = \varphi_3 + \mu\,\varphi_4^*(\mu)$ in (390.8) and (390.9) and then passing to the limit $\mu = 0$. This yields first

$$\varphi_1 = \frac{\Gamma(\alpha+\beta+\mu)\,\Gamma(\mu)}{\Gamma(\beta+\mu)\,\Gamma(\alpha+\mu)} \varphi_3 + \frac{\Gamma(\alpha+\beta+\mu)\,\Gamma(-\mu)}{\Gamma(\alpha)\,\Gamma(\beta)} (\varphi_3 + \mu\,\varphi_4^*(\mu)).$$

Then as μ is allowed to go to zero, we use the relations $\Gamma(\mu) = [\Gamma(1+\mu)]/\mu$ and $\Gamma(-\mu) = -[\Gamma(1-\mu)]/\mu$, obtaining

$$\varphi_1 = \frac{\Gamma(\alpha+\beta)}{\Gamma(\alpha)\,\Gamma(\beta)} \left\{ 2\frac{\Gamma'(1)}{\Gamma(1)} - \frac{\Gamma'(\alpha)}{\Gamma(\alpha)} - \frac{\Gamma'(\beta)}{\Gamma(\beta)} \right\} \varphi_3 - \frac{\Gamma(\alpha+\beta)}{\Gamma(\alpha)\,\Gamma(\beta)} \varphi_4^*. \quad (391.4)$$

Analogous calculations lead to the relations for φ_2, φ_3, φ_4^* and to those for φ_1, φ_2, φ_5, φ_6^* in the case $\nu = 0$ and $\beta = a$ (see Table C at the end of this chapter).

If λ and μ both vanish at the same time, there must exist a linear relation connecting φ_2^*, φ_3, φ_4^*; if λ and ν both vanish, there must be a relation involving φ_2^*, φ_5, φ_6^*. To obtain, for instance, the last-mentioned relation, we set in (391.3) $\beta = a - \nu$ and $\varphi_6 = \varphi_5 + \nu\, \varphi_6^*(\nu)$, which yields

$$\varphi_2^* = -\frac{\Gamma(1-\nu)}{\nu\,\Gamma(1-\alpha)\,\Gamma(\alpha-\nu)} \left\{ 2\,\frac{\Gamma'(1)}{\Gamma(1)} - \frac{\Gamma'(1-\alpha)}{\Gamma(1-\alpha)} - \frac{\Gamma'(\alpha-\nu)}{\Gamma(\alpha-\nu)} + \pi i \right\} \varphi_5$$

$$+ \frac{\Gamma(1+\nu)}{\nu\,\Gamma(1-\alpha+\nu)\,\Gamma(\alpha)} \left\{ 2\,\frac{\Gamma'(1)}{\Gamma(1)} - \frac{\Gamma'(1-\alpha+\nu)}{\Gamma(1-\alpha+\nu)} - \frac{\Gamma'(\alpha)}{\Gamma(\alpha)} + \pi i \right\} (\varphi_5 + \nu\,\varphi_6^*(\nu)).$$

As ν is now allowed to go to zero, the coefficient of φ_5 becomes

$$\left\{ 2\,\frac{\Gamma'(1)}{\Gamma(1)} - \frac{\Gamma'(1-\alpha)}{\Gamma(1-\alpha)} - \frac{\Gamma'(\alpha)}{\Gamma(\alpha)} + \pi i \right\} \frac{d}{d\nu} \left\{ \frac{\Gamma(1+\nu)}{\Gamma(\alpha)\,\Gamma(1-\alpha+\nu)} - \frac{\Gamma(1-\nu)}{\Gamma(1-\alpha)\,\Gamma(\alpha-\nu)} \right\}_{\nu=0}$$

$$+ \frac{1}{\Gamma(\alpha)\,\Gamma(1-\alpha)} \cdot \frac{d}{d\nu} \left\{ \frac{\Gamma'(\alpha-\nu)}{\Gamma(\alpha-\nu)} - \frac{\Gamma'(1-\alpha+\nu)}{\Gamma(1-\alpha+\nu)} \right\}_{\nu=0},$$

which because of the identity

$$\left. \frac{d}{d\nu}\, f(\alpha-\nu) \right|_{\nu=0} = -\frac{d}{d\alpha}\, f(\alpha)$$

can be written in the form

$$\frac{1}{\Gamma(\alpha)\,\Gamma(1-\alpha)} \left[\left\{ 2\,\frac{\Gamma'(1)}{\Gamma(1)} - \frac{\Gamma'(\alpha)}{\Gamma(\alpha)} - \frac{\Gamma'(1-\alpha)}{\Gamma(1-\alpha)} + \pi i \right\} \right.$$

$$\times \left\{ 2\,\frac{\Gamma'(1)}{\Gamma(1)} - \frac{\Gamma'(\alpha)}{\Gamma(\alpha)} - \frac{\Gamma'(1-\alpha)}{\Gamma(1-\alpha)} \right\}$$

$$\left. + \frac{d}{d\alpha} \left\{ \frac{\Gamma'(1-\alpha)}{\Gamma(1-\alpha)} - \frac{\Gamma'(\alpha)}{\Gamma(\alpha)} \right\} \right].$$

Now it follows from $\Gamma(\alpha)\,\Gamma(1-\alpha) = \pi/\sin \pi \alpha$ that

$$\frac{\Gamma'(\alpha)}{\Gamma(\alpha)} - \frac{\Gamma'(1-\alpha)}{\Gamma(1-\alpha)} = -\frac{\pi}{\operatorname{tg} \pi \alpha},$$

$$\frac{d}{d\alpha} \left\{ \frac{\Gamma'(\alpha)}{\Gamma(\alpha)} - \frac{\Gamma'(1-\alpha)}{\Gamma(1-\alpha)} \right\} = \frac{\pi^2}{\sin^2 \pi \alpha},$$

so that we finally obtain

$$
\begin{aligned}
\varphi_2^* = \frac{\sin \pi \alpha}{\pi} & \left[\left\{ 2 \frac{\Gamma'(1)}{\Gamma(1)} - \frac{\Gamma'(\alpha)}{\Gamma(\alpha)} - \frac{\Gamma'(1-\alpha)}{\Gamma(1-\alpha)} + \pi i \right\} \right. \\
& \left. \times 2 \left\{ \frac{\Gamma'(1)}{\Gamma(1)} - \frac{\Gamma'(\alpha)}{\Gamma(\alpha)} - \frac{\Gamma'(1-\alpha)}{\Gamma(1-\alpha)} \right\} - \frac{\pi^2}{\sin^2 \pi \alpha} \right] \varphi_5 \\
& + \frac{\sin \pi \alpha}{\pi} \left\{ 2 \frac{\Gamma'(1)}{\Gamma(1).} - \frac{\Gamma'(\alpha)}{\Gamma(\alpha)} - \frac{\Gamma'(1-\alpha)}{\Gamma(1-\alpha)} + \pi i \right\} \varphi_6^*.
\end{aligned} \tag{391.5}
$$

These and similar results are summarized in Table C (pp. 169 ff.).

Explicit Calculation of the Mapping Function of a Circular-Arc Triangle (§ 392)

392. If we wish to determine the mapping function $w = f(z)$ of a given circular-arc triangle of the w-plane having the angles $\pi \lambda$, $\pi \mu$ and πv, we

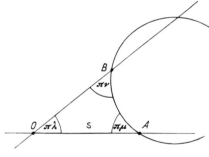

Fig. 82

need only determine the mapping function of *any* circular-arc triangle having the same angles, since we can always map the latter triangle onto the former by means of a suitable Moebius transformation. If the three angles are all $\neq 0$, we may therefore assume our triangle to be in the special position where the vertex with the angle $\pi \lambda$ is at the origin $w = 0$ while the two neighboring sides are straight-line segments, and one of them may be taken to be a segment of the real axis (see Fig. 82).

If we wish the upper half-plane $\Im z > 0$ to be mapped onto the (interior of the) triangle in such a way that the vertices O, A, B of the triangle correspond to the points $z = 0, 1, \infty$, then it follows from our previous results that we must set

$$w = C \frac{\varphi_2}{\varphi_1} = C \frac{F(\alpha + 1 - \gamma, \beta + 1 - \gamma, 2 - \gamma; z)}{F(\alpha, \beta, \gamma; z)} z^{1-\gamma}. \qquad (392.1)$$

Here, the numbers α, β, γ are given by

$$\alpha = \frac{1}{2}(1 - \lambda - \mu + \nu), \qquad \beta = \frac{1}{2}(1 - \lambda - \mu - \nu), \qquad \gamma = 1 - \lambda$$

in accordance with (376.7). Denoting the side OA of the triangle by s and using the formulas (cf. § 381)

$$F(\alpha, \beta, \gamma; 1) = \frac{\Gamma(\gamma)\, \Gamma(\alpha - \beta)}{\Gamma(\gamma - \alpha)\, \Gamma(\gamma - \beta)},$$

$$F(\alpha + 1 - \gamma, \beta + 1 - \gamma, 2 - \gamma; 1) = \frac{\Gamma(2 - \gamma)\, \Gamma(\gamma - \alpha - \beta)}{\Gamma(1 - \alpha)\, \Gamma(1 - \beta)},$$

we obtain by (392.1) that

$$C = \frac{\Gamma(\gamma)\, \Gamma(1 - \alpha)\, \Gamma(1 - \beta)}{\Gamma(2 - \gamma)\, \Gamma(\gamma - \alpha)\, \Gamma(\gamma - \beta)}\, s. \qquad (392.2)$$

By the results of §§ 72-74, Vol. I, pp. 61 ff., our triangle is spherical, Euclidean, or non-Euclidean according to whether $\lambda + \mu + \nu > 1$, $= 1$ or < 1. Since $\lambda + \mu + \nu = 1 - 2\beta$, these conditions may also be written in the form

$$\beta < 0, \quad \beta = 0, \quad \beta > 0.$$

If in particular, $\lambda + \mu + \nu < 1$, that is, if $\beta > 0$, we can norm the triangle in such a way that the circular arc AB is orthogonal to the circle $|w| = 1$. Then by the formulas of non-Euclidean trigonometry,

$$s = \operatorname{tgh} \frac{a_1}{2}$$

and by (75.1), Vol. I, p. 65,

$$s^2 = \frac{\sin \dfrac{\pi}{2}(1 - \lambda - \mu - \nu) \sin \dfrac{\pi}{2}(1 - \lambda - \mu + \nu)}{\sin \dfrac{\pi}{2}(1 - \lambda - \nu + \mu) \sin \dfrac{\pi}{2}(1 - \lambda + \mu + \nu)}, \qquad (392.3)$$

which we can also write in the form

$$s^2 = \frac{\Gamma(\gamma - \alpha)\, \Gamma(1 + \alpha - \gamma)\, \Gamma(\gamma - \beta)\, \Gamma(1 + \beta - \gamma)}{\Gamma(\beta)\, \Gamma(1 - \beta)\, \Gamma(\alpha)\, \Gamma(1 - \alpha)}, \qquad (392.4)$$

and this together with (392.2) yields C.

The Derivative of the Mapping Function (§ 393)

393. The derivative of the mapping function is frequently of use; by (392.1), it is given by

$$\frac{dw}{dz} = C\, \frac{\varphi_1\,\varphi_2' - \varphi_2\,\varphi_1'}{\varphi_1^2}. \tag{393.1}$$

We set

$$v = \varphi_1\,\varphi_2' - \varphi_2\,\varphi_1' \tag{393.2}$$

and hence obtain

$$v' = \varphi_1\,\varphi_2'' - \varphi_2\,\varphi_1''. \tag{393.3}$$

Now since φ_1 and φ_2 both are solutions of a differential equation of the form

$$u'' + p\,u' + q\,u = 0,$$

it follows that

$$v' = -\,p\,v, \tag{393.4}$$

whence

$$\frac{d}{dz}\,l\,v = -\,p. \tag{393.5}$$

But in our case,

$$-\,p = \frac{(\alpha + \beta + 1)\,z - \gamma}{z\,(1 - z)}$$

and hence

$$\frac{d}{dz}\,l\,v = \frac{-\gamma\,(1 - z) + (\alpha + \beta + 1 - \gamma)\,z}{z\,(1 - z)},$$

and an integration now yields

$$l\,v = -\,\gamma\,l\,z - (\alpha + \beta + 1 - \gamma)\,l\,(z - 1) + \text{const.} \tag{393.6}$$

Thus our final result for v is as follows:

$$\varphi_1\,\varphi_2' - \varphi_2\,\varphi_1' = v = \frac{A}{z^{\gamma}\,(1 - z)^{\alpha + \beta + 1 - \gamma}} = \frac{A}{z^{1 - \lambda}\,(1 - z)^{1 - \mu}}. \tag{393.7}$$

To determine the constant A, we expand the left-hand side of (393.7) in the neighborhood of $z = 0$, and after a simple calculation obtain

$$A = 1 - \gamma = \lambda. \tag{393.8}$$

Hence we finally have

$$\frac{dw}{dz} = \frac{C\,\lambda}{z^{1-\lambda}\,(1-z)^{1-\mu}\,\varphi_1^2}.$$

(393. 9)

The Case $\lambda = 0$ (§ 394)

394. We now turn to the mapping of triangles that have at least one cusp, i.e. for which, say, $\lambda = 0$. In the sequel we shall only be interested in tri-

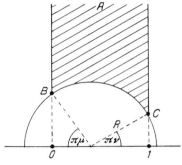

Fig. 83

angles for which $\lambda + \mu + \nu < 1$. Every such triangle can be brought into the position shown in **Fig. 83**.

Here, the sides AB and AC lie along the imaginary axis and along the straight line $\Re w = 1$, respectively, while the side BC is an arc of a circle whose center is located on the real axis of the w-plane. If we denote the radius of this circle by R, we can see from Fig. 83 that the following equations hold true:

$$\left.\begin{array}{c} R\,(\cos \pi\,\mu + \cos \pi\,\nu) = 1, \\[2mm] \overline{OB} = R \sin \pi\,\mu = \dfrac{\sin \pi\cdot\mu}{\cos \pi\,\mu + \cos \pi\,\nu}, \\[3mm] \overline{1\,C} = R \sin \pi\,\nu = \dfrac{\sin \pi\,\nu}{\cos \pi\,\mu + \cos \pi\,\nu}. \end{array}\right\}$$

(394. 1)

We shall prove that the mapping function under which the triangle of Fig. 83 corresponds to the half-plane $\Im z > 0$ is of the form

$$w = a\,\frac{\varphi_2^{*}}{\varphi_1} + b$$

(394. 2)

with suitably chosen constants a and b. In fact, the formulas of Table B (following § 395) show that

$$w = a\left(l\,z + \frac{F^*}{F}\right) + b = \frac{1}{\pi i}\cdot\frac{\varphi_2^*}{\varphi_1} + b. \tag{394.3}$$

From this we see immediately that $z=0$ corresponds to $w=\infty$ and that the intervals $0 < z < 1$ and $-\infty < z < 0$ are mapped onto the sides AB and AC, respectively, if we choose $a = 1/\pi i$.

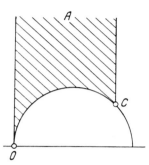

Fig. 84

In order to determine b we shall locate the image of the point $z=1$. For this point we have $\varphi_3=1$ and $\varphi_4=0$, hence by $\gamma=1$ from Table C (following § 395),

$$\varphi_1 = \frac{\Gamma(1-\alpha-\beta)}{\Gamma(1-\alpha)\,\Gamma(1-\beta)},$$

$$\varphi_2^* = \frac{\Gamma(1-\alpha-\beta)}{\Gamma(1-\alpha)\,\Gamma(1-\beta)}\left\{2\,\frac{\Gamma'(1)}{\Gamma(1)} - \frac{\Gamma'(1-\alpha)}{\Gamma(1-\alpha)} - \frac{\Gamma'(1-\beta)}{\Gamma(1-\beta)}\right\},$$

so that

$$\frac{\varphi_2^*}{\varphi_1} = 2\,\frac{\Gamma'(1)}{\Gamma(1)} - \frac{\Gamma'(1-\alpha)}{\Gamma(1-\alpha)} - \frac{\Gamma'(1-\beta)}{\Gamma(1-\beta)}.$$

From this, together with (394.1), we obtain

$$b = -\frac{1}{\pi i}\left\{2\,\frac{\Gamma'(1)}{\Gamma(1)} - \frac{\Gamma'(1-\alpha)}{\Gamma(1-\alpha)} - \frac{\Gamma'(1-\beta)}{\Gamma(1-\beta)}\right\} + i\,\frac{\sin\pi\mu}{\cos\pi\mu + \cos\pi\nu},$$

and we finally see, going back to (394.3), that the mapping function is given by

$$w = \frac{1}{\pi i}\left[\frac{\varphi_2^*}{\varphi_1} - \left\{2\,\frac{\Gamma'(1)}{\Gamma(1)} - \frac{\Gamma'(1-\alpha)}{\Gamma(1-\alpha)} - \frac{\Gamma'(1-\beta)}{\Gamma(1-\beta)}\right\}\right] + i\,\frac{\sin\pi\mu}{\cos\pi\mu + \cos\pi\nu}. \tag{394.4}$$

If $\lambda = \mu = 0$, then the vertex B of the triangle is at $w=0$ (see Fig. 84

above). We can verify easily that formula (394.4) remains valid in this case; besides $\gamma=1$, we must also set $\beta=1-\alpha$, and we note further that the last term on the right in (394.4) drops out because $\mu=0$. Thus (394.4) reduces in this case to

$$w = \frac{1}{\pi i}\left[\frac{\varphi_2^*}{\varphi_1} - \left\{2\frac{\Gamma'(1)}{\Gamma(1)} - \frac{\Gamma'(\alpha)}{\Gamma(\alpha)} - \frac{\Gamma'(1-\alpha)}{\Gamma(1-\alpha)}\right\}\right]. \qquad (394.5)$$

Calculation of the Derivative in the Case $\lambda=0$ (§ 395)

395. Differentiation of (394.4) with respect to z yields

$$\frac{dw}{dz} = \frac{1}{\pi i} \cdot \frac{\varphi_1 \varphi_2^{*\prime} - \varphi_2^* \varphi_1'}{\varphi_1^2}. \qquad (395.1)$$

For $\lambda > 0$, we again write, as in (386.1),

$$\varphi_2 = \varphi_1 + \lambda \varphi_2^*(\lambda)$$

and obtain from (393.7) and (393.8) that

$$\frac{\lambda}{z^{1-\lambda}(1-z)^{1-\mu}} = \varphi_1 \varphi_2' - \varphi_2 \varphi_1' = \lambda (\varphi_1 \varphi_2^{*\prime} - \varphi_2^* \varphi_1'). \qquad (395.2)$$

Here we divide by λ, for $\lambda \neq 0$, and then pass to the limit as λ goes to zero. We thus obtain from (395.2) that

$$\frac{dw}{dz} = \frac{1}{\pi i} \cdot \frac{1}{z(1-z)^{1-\mu}} \frac{1}{\varphi_1^2}. \qquad (395.3)$$

This result holds for $\mu > 0$ as well as for $\mu=0$.

Tables for the Hypergeometric Differential Equation

Table A

I	$\varphi_1 =$	$F(\alpha, \beta, \gamma; z)$	J_0	$\mu > 0$
XIV		$(1-z)^{-\beta} F\left(\beta, \gamma-\alpha, \gamma; \dfrac{z}{z-1}\right)$	E_0	$\nu > 0$
III	$\varphi_2 =$	$z^{1-\gamma} F(\alpha+1-\gamma, \beta+1-\gamma, 2-\gamma; z)$	J_0	$\mu > 0$
XVI		$z^{1-\gamma}(1-z)^{\gamma-\beta-1} F\left(1-\alpha, \beta+1-\gamma, 2-\gamma; \dfrac{z}{z-1}\right)$	E_0	$\nu > 0$
V	$\varphi_3 =$	$F(\alpha, \beta, \alpha+\beta+1-\gamma; 1-z)$	J_1	$\lambda > 0$
XX		$z^{-\beta} F\left(\beta, \beta+1-\gamma, \alpha+\beta+1-\gamma; \dfrac{z-1}{z}\right)$	E_1	$\nu > 0$
VI	$\varphi_4 =$	$(1-z)^{\gamma-\alpha-\beta} F(\gamma-\alpha, \gamma-\beta, \gamma+1-\alpha-\beta; 1-z)$	J_1	$\lambda > 0$
XVIII		$z^{\alpha-\gamma}(1-z)^{\gamma-\alpha-\beta} F\left((1-\alpha, \gamma-\alpha, \gamma+1-\alpha-\beta; \dfrac{z-1}{z}\right)$	E_1	$\nu > 0$
XXIII	$\varphi_5 =$	$(-z)^{-\alpha} F\left(\alpha+1-\gamma, \alpha, \alpha+1-\beta; \dfrac{1}{z}\right)$	A_0	$\mu > 0$
IX		$(1-z)^{-\alpha} F\left(\alpha, \gamma-\beta, \alpha+1-\beta; \dfrac{1}{1-z}\right)$	A_1	$\lambda > 0$
XXIV	$\varphi_6 =$	$(-z)^{-\beta} F\left(\beta, \beta+1-\gamma, \beta+1-\alpha; \dfrac{1}{z}\right)$	A_0	$\mu > 0$
X		$(1-z)^{-\beta} F\left(\beta, \gamma-\alpha, \beta+1-\alpha; \dfrac{1}{1-z}\right)$	A_1	$\lambda > 0$

Table B

$\lambda = 0$ $\gamma = 1$	$\varphi_2^* =$	$F(\alpha, \beta, 1; z)\, l\, z + F^*(\alpha, \beta, 1; z)$	J_0	$\mu > 0$
		$(1-z)^{-\beta}\left\{F\left(1-\alpha, \beta, 1; \dfrac{z}{z-1}\right) l\, \dfrac{z}{1-z} + F^*\left(1-\alpha, \beta, 1; \dfrac{z}{z-1}\right)\right\}$	E_0	$\nu > 0$
$\mu = 0$ $\gamma = \alpha+\beta$	$\varphi_4^* =$	$F(\alpha, \beta, 1; 1-z)\, l\, (1-z) + F^*(\alpha, \beta, 1; 1-z)$	J_1	$\lambda > 0$
		$z^{-\beta}\left\{F\left(1-\alpha, \beta, 1; \dfrac{z-1}{z}\right) l\, \dfrac{1-z}{z} + F^*\left(1-\alpha, \beta, 1; \dfrac{z-1}{z}\right)\right\}$	E_1	$\nu > 0$
$\nu = 0$ $\alpha = \beta$	$\varphi_6^* =$	$(-z)^{-\alpha}\left\{F\left(\alpha, \alpha+1-\gamma, 1; \dfrac{1}{z}\right) l\, (-z) + F^*\left(\alpha, \alpha+1-\gamma, 1; \dfrac{1}{z}\right)\right\}$	A_0	$\mu > 0$
		$(1-z)^{-\alpha}\left\{F\left(\alpha, \gamma-\alpha, 1; \dfrac{1}{1-z}\right) l\, (1-z) + F^*\left(\alpha, \gamma-\alpha, 1; \dfrac{1}{1-z}\right)\right\}$	A_1	$\lambda > 0$

Table C

λ = 0, γ = 1:

$$\varphi_1 = \frac{\Gamma(\gamma)\,\Gamma(\gamma-\alpha-\beta)}{\Gamma(\gamma-\alpha)\,\Gamma(\gamma-\beta)}\,\varphi_3 + \frac{\Gamma(\gamma)\,\Gamma(\alpha+\beta-\gamma)}{\Gamma(\alpha)\,\Gamma(\beta)}\,\varphi_4$$

$$\varphi_2 = \frac{\Gamma(2-\gamma)\,\Gamma(\gamma-\alpha-\beta)}{\Gamma(1-\alpha)\,\Gamma(1-\beta)}\,\varphi_3 + \frac{\Gamma(2-\gamma)\,\Gamma(\alpha+\beta-\gamma)}{\Gamma(\alpha+1-\gamma)\,\Gamma(\beta+1-\gamma)}\,\varphi_4$$

$$\varphi_2^* = \frac{\Gamma(1-\alpha-\beta)}{\Gamma(1-\alpha)\,\Gamma(1-\beta)}\left\{2\,\frac{\Gamma'(1)}{\Gamma(1)} - \frac{\Gamma'(1-\alpha)}{\Gamma(1-\alpha)} - \frac{\Gamma'(1-\beta)}{\Gamma(1-\beta)}\right\}\varphi_3 + \frac{\Gamma(\alpha+\beta-1)}{\Gamma(\alpha)\,\Gamma(\beta)}\left|2\,\frac{\Gamma'(1)}{\Gamma(1)} - \frac{\Gamma''(\alpha)}{\Gamma(\alpha)} - \frac{\Gamma'(\beta)}{\Gamma(\beta)}\right\}\varphi_4$$

μ = 0, γ = α + β:

$$\varphi_1 = \frac{\Gamma(\alpha+\beta)}{\Gamma(\alpha)\,\Gamma(\beta)}\left\{2\,\frac{\Gamma'(1)}{\Gamma(1)} - \frac{\Gamma'(\alpha)}{\Gamma(\alpha)} - \frac{\Gamma'(\beta)}{\Gamma(\beta)}\right\}\varphi_3 - \frac{\Gamma(\alpha+\beta)}{\Gamma(\alpha)\,\Gamma(\beta)}\,\varphi_4^*$$

$$\varphi_2 = \frac{\Gamma(2-\alpha-\beta)}{\Gamma(1-\alpha)\,\Gamma(1-\beta)}\left\{2\,\frac{\Gamma'(1)}{\Gamma(1)} - \frac{\Gamma'(1-\alpha)}{\Gamma(1-\alpha)} - \frac{\Gamma'(1-\beta)}{\Gamma(1-\beta)}\right\}\varphi_3 - \frac{\Gamma(2-\alpha-\beta)}{\Gamma(1-\alpha)\,\Gamma(1-\beta)}\,\varphi_4^*$$

λ = μ = 0, γ = 1, β = 1 − α:

$$\varphi_2^* = \frac{\sin\pi\alpha}{\pi}\left[\left\{2\,\frac{\Gamma'(1)}{\Gamma(1)} - \frac{\Gamma'(\alpha)}{\Gamma(\alpha)} - \frac{\Gamma'(1-\alpha)}{\Gamma(1-\alpha)}\right\}^2 - \frac{\pi^2}{\sin^2\pi\alpha}\right]\varphi_3 - \frac{\sin\pi\alpha}{\pi}\left\{2\,\frac{\Gamma'(1)}{\Gamma(1)} - \frac{\Gamma'(\alpha)}{\Gamma(\alpha)} - \frac{\Gamma'(1-\alpha)}{\Gamma(1-\alpha)}\right\}\varphi_4^*$$

λ = 0, γ = 1:

$$\varphi_1 = \frac{\Gamma(\gamma)\,\Gamma(\beta-\alpha)}{\Gamma(\gamma-\alpha)\,\Gamma(\beta)}\,\varphi_5 + \frac{\Gamma(\gamma)\,\Gamma(\alpha-\beta)}{\Gamma(\alpha)\,\Gamma(\gamma-\beta)}\,\varphi_6$$

$$\varphi_2 = \frac{\Gamma(2-\gamma)\,\Gamma(\beta-\alpha)}{\Gamma(1-\alpha)\,\Gamma(\beta+1-\gamma)}\,e^{\pi i(1-\gamma)}\,\varphi_5 + \frac{\Gamma(2-\gamma)\,\Gamma(\alpha-\beta)}{\Gamma(\alpha+1-\gamma)\,\Gamma(1-\beta)}\,e^{\pi i(1-\gamma)}\,\varphi_6$$

$$\varphi_2^* = \frac{\Gamma(\beta-\alpha)}{\Gamma(\beta)}\left\{2\,\frac{\Gamma'(1)}{\Gamma(1)} - \frac{\Gamma'(1-\alpha)}{\Gamma(1-\alpha)} - \frac{\Gamma'(\beta)}{\Gamma(\beta)} + \pi i\right\}\varphi_5 + \frac{\Gamma(\alpha-\beta)}{\Gamma(\alpha)}\left\{2\,\frac{\Gamma'(1)}{\Gamma(1)} - \frac{\Gamma'(\alpha)}{\Gamma(\alpha)} - \frac{\Gamma'(1-\beta)}{\Gamma(1-\beta)} + \pi i\right\}\varphi_6$$

ν = 0, β = α:

$$\varphi_1 = \frac{\Gamma(\gamma)}{\Gamma(\alpha)\,\Gamma(\gamma-\alpha)}\left\{2\,\frac{\Gamma'(1)}{\Gamma(1)} - \frac{\Gamma'(\alpha)}{\Gamma(\alpha)} - \frac{\Gamma'(\gamma-\alpha)}{\Gamma(\gamma-\alpha)}\right\}\varphi_5 + \frac{\Gamma(\gamma)}{\Gamma(\alpha)\,\Gamma(\gamma-\alpha)}\,\varphi_6^*$$

$$\varphi_2 = \frac{\Gamma(2-\gamma)}{\Gamma(1-\alpha)\,\Gamma(\alpha+1-\gamma)}\left\{2\,\frac{\Gamma'(1)}{\Gamma(1)} - \frac{\Gamma'(1-\alpha)}{\Gamma(1-\alpha)} - \frac{\Gamma'(\alpha+1-\gamma)}{\Gamma(\alpha+1-\gamma)}\right\}e^{\pi i(1-\gamma)}\,\varphi_5 + \frac{\Gamma(2-\gamma)}{\Gamma(1-\alpha)\,\Gamma(\alpha+1-\gamma)}\,e^{\pi i(1-\gamma)}\,\varphi_6^*$$

Table C (continued)

$\lambda = \nu = 0$
$\gamma = 1$
$\beta = \alpha = \dfrac{1}{2}(1-\mu)$

$$\varphi_2^* = \frac{\sin \pi \alpha}{\pi} \left[\left\{ 2 \frac{\Gamma'(1)}{\Gamma(1)} - \frac{\Gamma'(\alpha)}{\Gamma(\alpha)} - \frac{\Gamma'(1-\alpha)}{\Gamma(1-\alpha)} \right\} \left\{ 2 \frac{\Gamma'(1)}{\Gamma(1)} - \frac{\Gamma'(\alpha)}{\Gamma(\alpha)} - \frac{\Gamma'(1-\alpha)}{\Gamma(1-\alpha)} + \pi i \right\} - \frac{\pi^2}{\sin^2 \pi \alpha} \right] \varphi_5$$
$$+ \frac{\sin \pi \alpha}{\pi} \left\{ 2 \frac{\Gamma'(1)}{\Gamma(1)} - \frac{\Gamma'(\alpha)}{\Gamma(\alpha)} - \frac{\Gamma'(1-\alpha)}{\Gamma(1-\alpha)} + \pi i \right\} \varphi_6^*$$

$$\left\{ \begin{aligned} \varphi_3 &= \frac{\Gamma(1-\gamma)\,\Gamma(\alpha+\beta+1-\gamma)}{\Gamma(\alpha+1-\gamma)\,\Gamma(\beta+1-\gamma)} \varphi_1 + \frac{\Gamma(\gamma-1)\,\Gamma(\alpha+\beta+1-\gamma)}{\Gamma(\alpha)\,\Gamma(\beta)} \varphi_2 \\[2mm] \varphi_4 &= \frac{\Gamma(1-\gamma)\,\Gamma(\gamma+1-\alpha-\beta)}{\Gamma(1-\alpha)\,\Gamma(1-\beta)} \varphi_1 + \frac{\Gamma(\gamma-1)\,\Gamma(\gamma+1-\alpha-\beta)}{\Gamma(\gamma-\alpha)\,\Gamma(\gamma-\beta)} \varphi_2 \end{aligned} \right.$$

$\mu = 0$
$\gamma = \alpha + \beta$

$$\varphi_4^* = \frac{\Gamma(1-\alpha-\beta)}{\Gamma(1-\alpha)\,\Gamma(1-\beta)} \left\{ 2 \frac{\Gamma'(1)}{\Gamma(1)} - \frac{\Gamma'(1-\alpha)}{\Gamma(1-\alpha)} - \frac{\Gamma'(1-\beta)}{\Gamma(1-\beta)} \right\} \varphi_1 + \frac{\Gamma(\alpha+\beta-1)}{\Gamma(\alpha)\,\Gamma(\beta)} \left\{ 2 \frac{\Gamma'(1)}{\Gamma(1)} - \frac{\Gamma'(\alpha)}{\Gamma(\alpha)} - \frac{\Gamma'(\beta)}{\Gamma(\beta)} \right\} \varphi_2$$

$\lambda = 0$
$\gamma = 1$

$$\left\{ \begin{aligned} \varphi_3 &= \frac{\Gamma(\alpha+\beta)}{\Gamma(\alpha)\,\Gamma(\beta)} \left\{ 2 \frac{\Gamma'(1)}{\Gamma(1)} - \frac{\Gamma'(\alpha)}{\Gamma(\alpha)} - \frac{\Gamma'(\beta)}{\Gamma(\beta)} \right\} \varphi_1 - \frac{\Gamma(\alpha+\beta)}{\Gamma(\alpha)\,\Gamma(\beta)} \varphi_2^* \\[2mm] \varphi_4 &= \frac{\Gamma(2-\alpha-\beta)}{\Gamma(1-\alpha)\,\Gamma(1-\beta)} \left\{ 2 \frac{\Gamma'(1)}{\Gamma(1)} - \frac{\Gamma'(1-\alpha)}{\Gamma(1-\alpha)} - \frac{\Gamma'(1-\beta)}{\Gamma(1-\beta)} \right\} \varphi_1 - \frac{\Gamma(2-\alpha-\beta)}{\Gamma(1-\alpha)\,\Gamma(1-\beta)} \varphi_2^* \end{aligned} \right.$$

$\lambda = \mu = 0$
$\gamma = 1,\ \beta = 1 - \alpha$

$$\varphi_4^* = \frac{\sin \pi \alpha}{\pi} \left[\left\{ 2 \frac{\Gamma'(1)}{\Gamma(1)} - \frac{\Gamma'(1-\alpha)}{\Gamma(1-\alpha)} - \frac{\Gamma'(\alpha)}{\Gamma(\alpha)} \right\}^2 - \frac{\pi^2}{\sin^2 \pi \alpha} \right] \varphi_1 - \frac{\sin \pi \alpha}{\pi} \left\{ 2 \frac{\Gamma'(1)}{\Gamma(1)} - \frac{\Gamma'(\alpha)}{\Gamma(\alpha)} - \frac{\Gamma'(1-\alpha)}{\Gamma(1-\alpha)} \right\} \varphi_2^*$$

$$\left\{ \begin{aligned} \varphi_3 &= \frac{\Gamma(\beta-\alpha)\,\Gamma(\alpha+\beta+1-\gamma)}{\Gamma(\beta)\,\Gamma(\beta+1-\gamma)} e^{-\pi i \alpha} \varphi_5 + \frac{\Gamma(\alpha-\beta)\,\Gamma(\alpha+\beta+1-\gamma)}{\Gamma(\alpha)\,\Gamma(\alpha+1-\gamma)} e^{-\pi i \beta} \varphi_6 \\[2mm] \varphi_4 &= \frac{\Gamma(\beta-\alpha)\,\Gamma(\gamma+1-\alpha-\beta)}{\Gamma(1-\alpha)\,\Gamma(\gamma-\alpha)} e^{-\pi i(\gamma-\beta)} \varphi_5 + \frac{\Gamma(\alpha-\beta)\,\Gamma(\gamma+1-\alpha-\beta)}{\Gamma(1-\beta)\,\Gamma(\gamma-\beta)} e^{-\pi i(\gamma-\alpha)} \varphi_6 \end{aligned} \right.$$

Table C (continued)

$\mu = 0$, $\gamma = \alpha + \beta$

$$\varphi_4^* = \frac{\Gamma(\beta-\alpha)}{\Gamma(\beta)\,\Gamma(1-\alpha)}\left\{2\frac{\Gamma'(1)}{\Gamma(1)} - \frac{\Gamma'(1-\alpha)}{\Gamma(1-\alpha)} - \frac{\Gamma'(\beta)}{\Gamma(\beta)} - \pi i\right\}e^{-\pi i \alpha}\,\varphi_5$$
$$+ \frac{\Gamma(\alpha-\beta)}{\Gamma(\alpha)\,\Gamma(1-\beta)}\left\{2\frac{\Gamma'(1)}{\Gamma(1)} - \frac{\Gamma'(\alpha)}{\Gamma(\alpha)} - \frac{\Gamma'(1-\beta)}{\Gamma(1-\beta)} - \pi i\right\}e^{-\pi i \beta}\,\varphi_6$$

$\nu = 0$, $\alpha = \beta$

$$\varphi_3 = \frac{\Gamma(2\alpha+1-\gamma)}{\Gamma(\alpha)\,\Gamma(\alpha+1-\gamma)}\left\{2\frac{\Gamma'(1)}{\Gamma(1)} - \frac{\Gamma'(\alpha)}{\Gamma(\alpha)} - \frac{\Gamma'(\alpha+1-\gamma)}{\Gamma(\alpha+1-\gamma)} + \pi i\right\}e^{-\pi i \alpha}\,\varphi_5 + \frac{\Gamma(2\alpha+1-\gamma)}{\Gamma(\alpha)\,\Gamma(\alpha+1-\gamma)}\,e^{-\pi i \alpha}\,\varphi_6^*$$

$$\varphi_4 = \frac{\Gamma(\gamma+1-2\alpha)}{\Gamma(1-\alpha)\,\Gamma(\gamma-\alpha)}\left\{2\frac{\Gamma'(1)}{\Gamma(1)} - \frac{\Gamma'(1-\alpha)}{\Gamma(1-\alpha)} - \frac{\Gamma'(\gamma-\alpha)}{\Gamma(\gamma-\alpha)} - \pi i\right\}e^{-\pi i(\gamma-\alpha)}\,\varphi_5 + \frac{\Gamma(\gamma+1-2\alpha)}{\Gamma(1-\alpha)\,\Gamma(\gamma-\alpha)}\,e^{-\pi i(\gamma-\alpha)}\,\varphi_6^*$$

$\mu = \nu = 0$, $\gamma = 2\alpha$, $\beta = \alpha$

$$\varphi_1^* = \frac{\sin\pi\alpha}{\pi}\left[\left\{2\frac{\Gamma'(1)}{\Gamma(1)} - \frac{\Gamma'(\alpha)}{\Gamma(\alpha)} - \frac{\Gamma'(1-\alpha)}{\Gamma(1-\alpha)}\right\}^2 - \frac{\pi^2}{\mathrm{tg}^2\pi\alpha}\right]e^{-\pi i \alpha}\,\varphi_5$$
$$+ \frac{\sin\pi\alpha}{\pi}\left\{2\frac{\Gamma'(1)}{\Gamma(1)} - \frac{\Gamma'(\alpha)}{\Gamma(\alpha)} - \frac{\Gamma'(1-\alpha)}{\Gamma(1-\alpha)} - \pi i\right\}e^{-\pi i \alpha}\,\varphi_6^*$$

$$\varphi_5 = \frac{\Gamma(1-\gamma)\,\Gamma(\alpha+1-\beta)}{\Gamma(1-\beta)\,\Gamma(\alpha+1-\gamma)}\,\varphi_1 + \frac{\Gamma(\gamma-1)\,\Gamma(\alpha+1-\beta)}{\Gamma(\alpha)\,\Gamma(\gamma-\beta)}\,e^{-\pi i(1-\alpha)}\,\varphi_2$$

$$\varphi_6 = \frac{\Gamma(1-\gamma)\,\Gamma(\beta+1-\alpha)}{\Gamma(1-\alpha)\,\Gamma(\beta+1-\gamma)}\,\varphi_1 + \frac{\Gamma(\gamma-1)\,\Gamma(\beta+1-\alpha)}{\Gamma(\beta)\,\Gamma(\gamma-\alpha)}\,e^{-\pi i(1-\alpha)}\,\varphi_2$$

$$\varphi_6^* = -\frac{\Gamma(1-\gamma)}{\Gamma(1-\alpha)\,\Gamma(\alpha+1-\gamma)}\left\{2\frac{\Gamma'(1)}{\Gamma(1)} - \frac{\Gamma'(1-\alpha)}{\Gamma(1-\alpha)} - \frac{\Gamma'(\alpha+1-\gamma)}{\Gamma(\alpha+1-\gamma)}\right\}\varphi_1$$
$$- \frac{\Gamma(\gamma-1)}{\Gamma(\alpha)\,\Gamma(\gamma-\alpha)}\left\{2\frac{\Gamma'(1)}{\Gamma(1)} - \frac{\Gamma'(\alpha)}{\Gamma(\alpha)} - \frac{\Gamma'(\gamma-\alpha)}{\Gamma(\gamma-\alpha)}\right\}e^{-\pi i(1-\gamma)}\,\varphi_2$$

$$\varphi_5 = \frac{\Gamma(\alpha+1-\beta)}{\Gamma(\alpha)\,\Gamma(1-\beta)}\left\{2\frac{\Gamma'(1)}{\Gamma(1)} - \frac{\Gamma'(1-\beta)}{\Gamma(1-\beta)} + \pi i\right\}\varphi_1 - \frac{\Gamma(\alpha+1-\beta)}{\Gamma(\alpha)\,\Gamma(1-\beta)}\,\varphi_2^*$$

$$\varphi_6 = \frac{\Gamma(\beta+1-\alpha)}{\Gamma(\beta)\,\Gamma(1-\alpha)}\left\{2\frac{\Gamma'(1)}{\Gamma(1)} - \frac{\Gamma'(\beta)}{\Gamma(\beta)} - \frac{\Gamma'(1-\alpha)}{\Gamma(1-\alpha)} + \pi i\right\}\varphi_1 - \frac{\Gamma(\beta+1-\alpha)}{\Gamma(\beta)\,\Gamma(1-\alpha)}\,\varphi_2^*$$

Table C (continued)

$$\varphi_6^* = -\frac{\sin\pi\alpha}{\pi}\left[\left\{2\frac{\Gamma'(1)}{\Gamma(1)} - \frac{\Gamma'(\alpha)}{\Gamma(\alpha)} - \frac{\Gamma'(1-\alpha)}{\Gamma(1-\alpha)} + \pi i\right\}\left\{2\frac{\Gamma'(1)}{\Gamma(1)} - \frac{\Gamma'(\alpha)}{\Gamma(\alpha)} - \frac{\Gamma'(1-\alpha)}{\Gamma(1-\alpha)}\right\} - \frac{\pi^2}{\sin^2\pi\alpha}\right]\varphi_1$$

$$+ \frac{\sin\pi\alpha}{\pi}\left\{2\frac{\Gamma'(1)}{\Gamma(1)} - \frac{\Gamma'(\alpha)}{\Gamma(\alpha)} - \frac{\Gamma'(1-\alpha)}{\Gamma(1-\alpha)}\right\}\varphi_2^*$$

ν = 0, β = α

$$\varphi_5 = \frac{\Gamma(\alpha+1-\beta)\,\Gamma(\gamma-\alpha-\beta)}{\Gamma(1-\beta)\,\Gamma(\gamma-\beta)}\,e^{\pi i\alpha}\,\varphi_3 + \frac{\Gamma(\alpha+1-\beta)\,\Gamma(\alpha+\beta-\gamma)}{\Gamma(\alpha)\,\Gamma(\alpha+1-\gamma)}\,e^{\pi i(\gamma-\beta)}\,\varphi_4$$

$$\varphi_6 = \frac{\Gamma(\beta+1-\alpha)\,\Gamma(\gamma-\alpha-\beta)}{\Gamma(1-\alpha)\,\Gamma(\gamma-\alpha)}\,e^{\pi i\beta}\,\varphi_3 + \frac{\Gamma(\beta+1-\alpha)\,\Gamma(\alpha+\beta-\gamma)}{\Gamma(\beta)\,\Gamma(\beta+1-\gamma)}\,e^{\pi i(\gamma-\alpha)}\,\varphi_4$$

$$\varphi_6^* = -\frac{\Gamma(\gamma-2\alpha)}{\Gamma(1-\alpha)\,\Gamma(\gamma-\alpha)}\left\{2\frac{\Gamma'(1)}{\Gamma(1)} - \frac{\Gamma'(\alpha)}{\Gamma(\alpha)} - \frac{\Gamma'(\gamma-\alpha)}{\Gamma(\gamma-\alpha)} + \pi i\right\}e^{\pi i\alpha}\,\varphi_3$$

$$- \frac{\Gamma(2\alpha-\gamma)}{\Gamma(\alpha)\,\Gamma(\alpha+1-\gamma)}\left\{2\frac{\Gamma'(1)}{\Gamma(1)} - \frac{\Gamma'(\alpha)}{\Gamma(\alpha)} - \frac{\Gamma'(\alpha+1-\gamma)}{\Gamma(\alpha+1-\gamma)} + \pi i\right\}e^{\pi i(\gamma-\alpha)}\,\varphi_4$$

μ = 0, γ = α + β

$$\varphi_5 = \frac{\Gamma(\alpha+1-\beta)}{\Gamma(\alpha)\,\Gamma(1-\beta)}\left\{2\frac{\Gamma'(1)}{\Gamma(1)} - \frac{\Gamma'(\alpha)}{\Gamma(\alpha)} - \frac{\Gamma'(1-\beta)}{\Gamma(1-\beta)} - i\pi\right\}e^{\pi i\alpha}\,\varphi_3 - \frac{\Gamma(\alpha+1-\beta)}{\Gamma(\alpha)\,\Gamma(1-\beta)}\,e^{\pi i\alpha}\,\varphi_4^*$$

$$\varphi_6 = \frac{\Gamma(\beta+1-\alpha)}{\Gamma(1-\alpha)\,\Gamma(\beta)}\left\{2\frac{\Gamma'(1)}{\Gamma(1)} - \frac{\Gamma'(1-\alpha)}{\Gamma(1-\alpha)} - \frac{\Gamma'(\beta)}{\Gamma(\beta)} - \pi i\right\}e^{\pi i\beta}\,\varphi_3 - \frac{\Gamma(\beta+1-\alpha)}{\Gamma(1-\alpha)\,\Gamma(\beta)}\,e^{\pi i\beta}\,\varphi_4^*$$

μ = ν = 0, β = α, γ = 2α

$$\varphi_6^* = -\frac{\sin\pi\alpha}{\pi}\left[\left\{2\frac{\Gamma'(1)}{\Gamma(1)} - \frac{\Gamma'(\alpha)}{\Gamma(\alpha)} - \frac{\Gamma'(1-\alpha)}{\Gamma(1-\alpha)}\right\}^2 - \frac{\pi^2}{\text{tg}^2\pi\alpha}\right]e^{\pi i\alpha}\,\varphi_3$$

$$+ \frac{\sin\pi\alpha}{\pi}\left\{2\frac{\Gamma'(1)}{\Gamma(1)} - \frac{\Gamma'(\alpha)}{\Gamma(\alpha)} - \frac{\Gamma'(1-\alpha)}{\Gamma(1-\alpha)} + \pi i\right\}e^{\pi i\alpha}\,\varphi_4^*.$$

CHAPTER THREE

THE SCHWARZ TRIANGLE FUNCTIONS AND THE MODULAR FUNCTION

Description of the Schwarz Triangles (§§ 396-400)

396. Starting with an equilateral triangle and applying successive reflections in its sides (and in the sides of the newly obtained triangles), we arrive at a complete triangulation of the plane, i.e. at a complete covering of the plane by

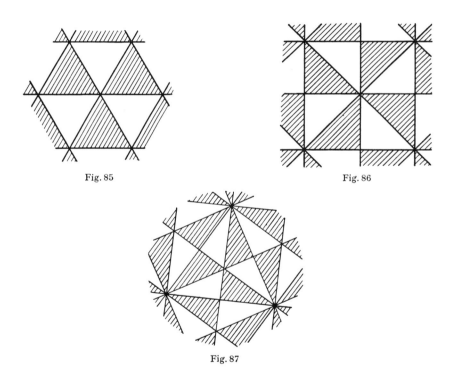

Fig. 85

Fig. 86

Fig. 87

means of equilateral triangles, which is such that no two triangles that occur in the triangulation have any interior points in common (see Fig. 85).

We arrive at similar triangulations if we start not with an equilateral but with an isosceles right triangle (see Fig. 86), or with a 30°-60°-90° triangle (see Fig. 87).

The three above-mentioned triangles have the property that all of their angles are of the form

$$\frac{\pi}{l}, \frac{\pi}{m}, \frac{\pi}{n} \tag{396.1}$$

where l, m, and n are natural numbers. Since the sum of the angles of a Euclidean triangle equals π, we must have

$$\frac{1}{l} + \frac{1}{m} + \frac{1}{n} = 1, \tag{396.2}$$

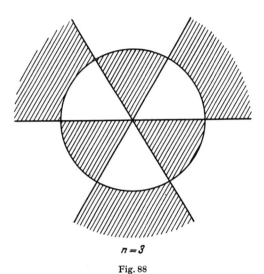

$n = 3$

Fig. 88

and it is easy to see that the only possible solutions of (396.2) are

$$\left. \begin{array}{l} l = 2, \quad m = n = 4; \\ l = 2, \quad m = 3, \quad n = 6; \\ l = m = n = 3; \end{array} \right\} \tag{396.3}$$

these yield the three triangles that we considered at the outset.

397. Spherical triangles have angles whose sum exceeds π. Hence if we wish the angles of such a triangle to be of the form (396.1), we are led to the condition

$$\frac{1}{l} + \frac{1}{m} + \frac{1}{n} > 1. \tag{397.1}$$

The only possible solutions of this condition are listed in the table below. To each of these solutions there corresponds a subdivision of the sphere into finitely many triangles all of which can be obtained from any fixed one of them by means of repeated reflections.

l	m	n
2	2	arbitrary
2	3	3
2	3	4
2	3	5

If we wish to construct the subdivision that corresponds, say to the first of the cases listed above, we can proceed by first dividing the equator into $2n$

Fig. 89

equal parts and then passing meridians through the points of division. The corresponding triangulation of the complex plane is now obtained by means of stereographic projection. A look at this triangulation (see Fig. 88 above for the case $n = 3$) immediately shows that its triangles are obtained, each from any other, by repeated reflections in their sides. This class of triangulations of the sphere is called the *dihedral class*.

In the remaining cases the construction proceeds as follows. We circumscribe one of the five regular polyhedra (tetrahedron, cube, octahedron, dodecahedron, icosahedron) about the Riemann sphere and project the edges of the polyhedron onto the (surface of the) sphere, using central projection from the center of the sphere. This yields a subdivision of the sphere into congruent regular spherical polygons. We join the center of each polygon to its vertices by arcs of great circles and we also draw the perpendiculars from the center onto the sides of the polygon. In this way we obtain a triangulation of the sphere which is such that any two neighboring triangles are the images of each other under reflection in their common side.

The angles of the triangles of any such triangulation always coincide with a triple of values as listed in the above table. For example, the surface of the

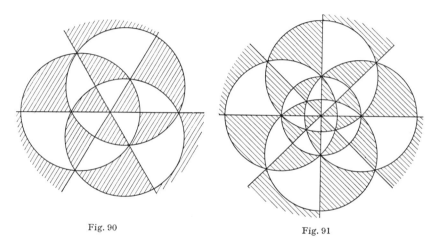

Fig. 90   Fig. 91

regular dodecahedron consists of twelve regular pentagons, and three of these meet at every vertex of the dodecahedron. The projection onto the sphere and the subsequent subdivision of the spherical pentagons, as described above, leads to ten triangles for each pentagon, so that the sphere is triangulated into $12 \cdot 10 = 120$ triangles each of which has the angles $\pi/2$, $\pi/3$, and $\pi/5$. The icosahedron leads to the same triangulation; of the twenty equilateral triangles that make up the surface of the icosahedron, five meet at every vertex, so that the resulting triangulation of the sphere contains $20 \cdot 6 = 120$ triangles, which are easily seen to be congruent to those resulting from the dodecahedron. The triangulation is for this reason said to belong to the *icosahedral class* (see Fig. 89 above).

In the same way, we find that the cube and the octahedron each leads to a triangulation involving forty-eight spherical triangles with the angles $\pi/2$, $\pi/3$, and $\pi/4$ (*octahedral class*; see Fig. 91), and that the tetrahedron leads to twenty-four triangles with the angles $\pi/2$, $\pi/3$, and $\pi/3$ (*tetrahedral class*; see Fig. 90).

We have thus seen that all possible regular subdivisions of the sphere into congruent triangles, or more generally into sets of triangles that are symmetric with respect to reflections .in the sides of their triangles, can be obtained either arithmetically, from (397.1), or geometrically, with the aid of the regular polyhedra.

398. Similar triangulations of a circular disc or of a half-plane lead to circular-arc triangles with the angles π/l, π/m, and π/n, where l, m, and n are three natural numbers for which

$$\frac{1}{l} + \frac{1}{m} + \frac{1}{n} < 1 \tag{398.1}$$

holds. In this case there are of course infinitely many admissible triples of values. However, the proof that there exists a corresponding triangulation of the disc or half-plane is not as simple here as for the cases of the sphere and the Euclidean plane.

To prove this, we note first that we can always construct non-Euclidean triangles in the disc $|w| < 1$ that have the given angles π/l, π/m, and π/n (cf. § 74, Vol. I, p. 64). Hence we can map the given triangle onto a triangle with the same angles in the non-Euclidean plane $|w| < 1$ by means of a Moebius transformation. Starting with the latter triangle, we then construct non-Euclidean triangles obtained by repeated reflections in their sides. All of the triangles constructed in this way are either congruent to the initial non-Euclidean triangle (in the non-Euclidean metric) or else symmetric to it with respect to reflection in one of its sides. What we wish to prove is that this construction leads to a net of triangles that will cover the whole non-Euclidean plane as the construction is carried out indefinitely.

To this end, we may assume without loss of generality that the vertex A of the initial triangle, with the angle π/l, is at $w = 0$, while the vertex B lies on the positive real axis. Then the sides AB and AC are straight-line segments (in the Euclidean sense). By means of a cyclic sequence of reflections in sides all of which are anchored at the point A, we can cover a neighborhood of $w = 0$ with $2l$ triangles which together form a non-Euclidean polygon P_1. We shall call the triangles constructed so far, triangles of the first order. Each vertex of P_1 is a common vertex of two first-order triangles that are the images of each other under the reflection in their common side.

The above special position of the vertex A was chosen only to make the construction easier to visualize. The cyclic reflection process just described can also be applied to the vertices other than A of the first-order triangles; this yields an even number of new triangles no two of which have any interior points in common unless they coincide. Also, we are led in this way to a polygon P_2 that is triangulated by means of all of the triangles that have just been constructed. P_2 contains P_1 in its interior. The triangles of P_2 which do not belong to P_1 will be called triangles of the second order. We shall show that this construction can be continued indefinitely and yields at each step a set of triangles of the next higher order, and that the totality of triangles obtainable in this way constitutes a net that covers the non-Euclidean plane completely and simply.

399. To prove the first part of the last statement, it suffices to show that for every natural number k, the triangles of order k do not overlap the triangles of lower order (if any) nor each other. We shall assume first that the numbers l, m, and n are all $\geqq 3$; the case of a right angle occurring in our circular-arc triangle will be treated separately further on.

Let us assume then, as an induction hypothesis, that the first part of the statement is established for the triangles of all orders up to and including $(k-1)$. Then the triangles of order $(k-1)$ are deployed like a wreath around the polygon P_{k-2}. They form an annular region bounded by P_{k-2} and P_{k-1}. Fig. 92 below exhibits the triangles $\varDelta_1, \varDelta_2, \ldots$ of order $(k-1)$ that

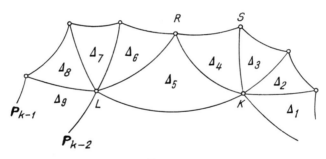

Fig. 92

have among their vertices two consecutive vertices L and K of P_{k-2}. Any vertex of a triangle $\varDelta_j$ that is not already a vertex of P_{k-2} will be counted as a vertex of P_{k-1}.

Any such vertex R of P_{k-1} is common to a certain number r of triangles $\varDelta_j$. If one of these triangles shares a side KL with the polygon P_{k-2}, then $r=3$. If S, on the other hand, is a vertex of P_{k-1} such that the triangles meeting at S have only a vertex in common with P_{k-2}, then $r=2$. Since we are assuming the numbers l, m, and n to be $\geqq 3$, all of the angles of P_{k-1} are $\leqq \pi$, and this implies, just as in the Euclidean case, that P_{k-1} is convex.

From the convexity of P_{k-1} it follows that each side RS of this polygon lies on a non-Euclidean line of support $MRSM'$ of the polygon (see Fig. 93).

Therefore one of the two half-planes $MM'N'$ and $MM'N$, say the former, is wholly exterior to P_{k-1}. Hence if RS and ST are two consecutive sides of the polygon, then the interior of P_{k-1} lies within the angle $MSNK$.

The k-th order triangles of the net that are obtained by cyclic reflections about the point S must all lie outside the angle $MSNK$; we can easily see this with the aid of a non-Euclidean motion that moves S to the origin O and transforms MS and NS into Euclidean straight lines. This proves the first part of the result stated at the end of § 398 above (in case l, m, n are all ≥ 3), to the effect that for any k we can construct triangles of order k lying entirely outside the region covered by the triangles of lower orders.

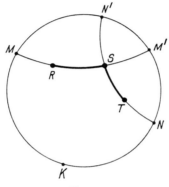

Fig. 93

To show that the k-th order triangles do not overlap each other either, we begin by subdividing the set of these triangles into two classes: The ones having two vertices on P_{k-1} we denote by $Z_1, Z_2, \ldots$, the others (i.e. those having only one vertex on P_{k-1}) we denote by $E_1, E_2, \ldots$ (see Fig. 94). Now we join the origin O to all of the vertices of P_{k-1} by straight-line segments. If one of these segments leads to a vertex at which two triangles of order $(k-1)$ meet, then the segment forms with each of the two adjacent sides of P_{k-1} an angle that is $\leq 2\pi/3$. If a segment leads to a vertex of P_{k-1} at which $r = 3$, we assume as an induction hypothesis that this segment likewise forms angles $\leq 2\pi/3$ with the two adjacent sides of P_{k-1}, and we refer to the paragraph after the next for the completion of the induction proof of this particular fact. Assuming this fact for the present, let us consider a side RS of P_{k-1} and the triangle Z_1 having RS as one of its sides (see Fig. 94); then it follows from l, m, $n \geq 3$ that the triangle Z_1 lies between the two consecutive lines OR and OS. This in turn implies that no two of the triangles $Z_1, Z_2, \ldots$ can overlap.

Next we consider any two consecutive triangles Z_i, say Z_1 and Z_2, with the common vertex R (see Fig. 95), as well as the triangles $E_1, E_2, \ldots$ lying between Z_1 and Z_2 which are obtained by continued reflections in sides issuing from R and which are not triangles of order $(k-1)$. All of the interior angles of the non-Euclidean polygon $OTUV\ldots T_1O$ are $< \pi$, so that the polygon is convex; hence all of the triangles $E_1, E_2, \ldots$ lie between OT and OT_1. Applying these considerations to all of the k-th order triangles, we see that these triangles form a closed wreath around P_{k-1} whose outer boundary is the polygon P_k. They cover the part of the non-Euclidean plane between P_{k-1} and P_k simply and completely.

It still remains to show that the above induction hypothesis on P_{k-1} implies the corresponding fact for P_k. The triangle Z_1 lies wholly between the lines OR and OS, so that the segment OT must pass through Z_1. Now Z_1 is the middle one of three k-th order triangles meeting at T, and hence each of the

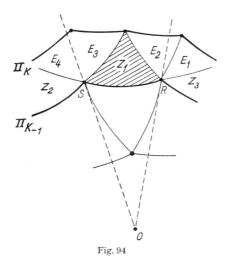

Fig. 94

two angles between OT and the two sides of the polygon emanating from T is $\leq 2\pi/3$. Thus we can proceed with our construction to determine the triangles of order $(k+1)$ and the polygon P_{k+1}, and so forth.

400. Finally, we must prove that the triangular net thus obtained covers the entire non-Euclidean plane $|w| < 1$. To this end, we consider any triangle of the net, say the triangle ABC, and the polygon P^* whose interior consists of all those triangles of the net that share a side or a vertex with the triangle ABC. The non-Euclidean distance δ between the triangle ABC and the polygon P^* is independent of the choice of the triangle ABC, because all of the triangles of the net are either congruent or symmetric under a reflection (in the non-Euclidean metric). Since every point w_0 of the net is in the interior or on the boundary of a triangle of the net, it follows that the net always contains the non-Euclidean disc with center at w_0 and radius δ.

Now if G is the region that is the union of the interiors of all the polygons $P_1, P_2, \ldots$, then by what we have just observed, G cannot have any frontier points that lie in $|w| < 1$. Being entirely contained in $|w| < 1$, G must therefore coincide with $|w| < 1$, and the result announced in § 398 above has therefore been proved for the case $l, m, n \geqq 3$.

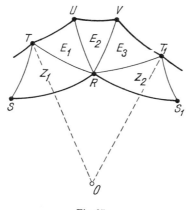

Fig. 95

Schwarz Triangles with a Right Angle (§ 401)

401. If one of the angles of a Schwarz triangle, say the angle λ, equals $\pi/2$, we must modify the construction of the sequence of polygons, and we shall have to deal first with the case in which the two remaining angles μ and ν are both $\leqq \pi/4$. We arrange for the triangles of the first order to have their right angles at the origin; if we did not take this precaution, it could happen that a vertex of P_2 would already be common to *four* triangles.

Even so, it will happen for certain polygons P_k, for instance already for P_2, that at least one of the triangles Z_i has a right angle at the vertex T that should be a vertex of P_k; as a consequence, P_k would have a re-entrant corner at T.

To avoid this, we add at T a new triangle H_1 which is the image of one of the triangles E_1 or E_2 (under reflection in a side); see Fig. 96.

With this modification, we can prove just as in §§ 399-400 above that no two of the k-th order triangles $Z_1, Z_2, \ldots, E_1, E_2, \ldots, H_1, H_2, \ldots$ overlap and that they are bounded by a convex polygon P_k (in addition to P_{k-1}). Since both μ and ν are $\leqq \pi/4$, the angle at a vertex of the polygon where three triangles meet is $\leqq 3\pi/4$. This fact simplifies our earlier proof for the present case, since it can be continued without the necessity of proving that the segment OT of Fig. 95 cuts through the middle one of the three triangles meeting at T. It then follows as before that the construction of the polygons can be continued indefinitely and that the resulting net of triangles covers the disc $|w| < 1$ simply and completely.

It only remains to deal with the case where $\lambda = \pi/2$, $\mu = \pi/3$, $\nu = \pi/n$ with

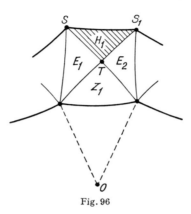

Fig. 96

$n > 6$. If a triangle ABC with these angles is reflected in its side AC, there is obtained a new triangle B_1BC with the angles $\pi/3$, $\pi/3$, and $2\pi/n < \pi/3$

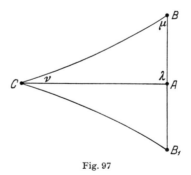

Fig. 97

(see Fig. 97). Now we can use the method of §§ 398-400 to generate a net of such "double" triangles, and once we have this net we need merely cut each of the double triangles into suitable halves to obtain the net that is actually desired. It is of no importance that the angle of the double triangle at C is a proper fraction of 2π but not necessarily of π, since the double triangle is isosceles and is therefore mapped onto congruent double triangles by the cyclic reflections about C.

Schwarz Triangles with Cusps (§ 402)

402. The construction of the net of Schwarz triangles can also be carried out in the cases that have thus far been excluded, namely the cases in which the triangles have one or more cusps. In each of these cases, it is again possible to construct, step by step, a sequence of nested convex polygons $P_1, P_2, \ldots$ whose union covers the whole non-Euclidean plane and each of which is triangulated into a finite number of triangles.

First, if λ, $\mu > 0$, $\nu = 0$, we perform reflections cyclically in the successive sides that issue from the vertex associated with the angle λ. The interior of

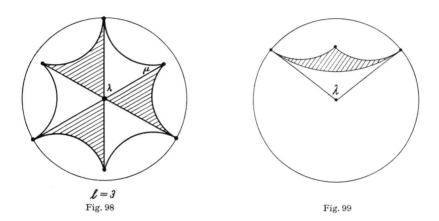

$$\ell = 3$$
Fig. 98   Fig. 99

the resulting polygon P_1 contains $2l$ triangles of the first order, and the polygon has l cusps located on $|w| = 1$, between any two of which it has another vertex (see Fig. 98). About each vertex between two cusps we apply cyclic reflections of the first-order triangles that meet at the vertex, obtaining in this way a number of non-overlapping new triangles which we call triangles of the second order. The second-order triangles lie between P_1 and the convex polygon P_2 which has $l(m-1)$ cusps plus the same number of non-cuspidal vertices. Continuing this process, we obtain the sequence of polygons P_k, one after the other. In the present case it is very easy to see that each polygon is made up of mutually non-overlapping triangles.

Let us fix our attention on any triangle ABC of the net and consider also all neighboring triangles of the net, i.e. all those that share a side or a vertex with the triangle ABC. Every point w_0 from the interior or the boundary of triangle ABC is the center of a certain maximal non-Euclidean disc $\kappa(w_0)$ that is covered by the configuration just described, consisting of ABC plus its neighbors. The radius of this disc converges to zero as w_0 is made to approach the cusp of the triangle ABC; but if we confine w_0 to a pre-assigned disc

$|w| \leqq r < 1$, then the g.l.b. $\delta(z)$ of the radii of the discs $\kappa(w_0)$—for all possible positions of the point w_0 *and* of the triangle ABC in which w_0 is chosen—is a fixed positive (non-zero) number. This implies that a finite number of triangles of the net will suffice to cover the disc $|w| \leqq r$, and since $r < 1$ was arbitrary, this in turn implies that the net of triangles covers the disc $|w| < 1$ completely.

Second, if $\lambda > 0$, $\mu = \nu = 0$, then certain sides of P_{k-1} connect two cusps of this polygon (in other words, there will be pairs of consecutive vertices of the polygon both of which are cusps). In this case, the $(k-1)$-st order triangle that contains the side in question must be reflected in this side as P_k is constructed (see Fig. 99). In all other respects the construction of the net proceeds just as before.

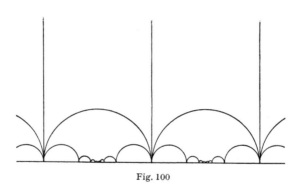

Fig. 100

The Modular Configuration (§ 403)

403. The third case, $\lambda = \mu = \nu = 0$, is of particular importance. It is studied most advantageously in the Poincaré half-plane $\Im w > 0$ (*cf.* § 84, Vol. I, p. 79). We start in this half-plane with a triangle having angles $0, 0, 0$ at its cusps $w = 0, 1, \infty$. We reflect this triangle in those two of its sides that are parallel to the imaginary axis, and we repeat this process indefinitely (see Fig. 100). This leads to a region G_1 whose frontier consists of congruent tangent semicircles of radius $1/2$. Now we reflect G_1 in each of these semi-circles and obtain a new region G_2 that contains G_1 in its interior and whose frontier consists of denumerably many tangent semicircles with periodically recurring points at which they accumulate (see Fig. 100). Then we reflect G_2 in each of the new semicircles, and we continue this process indefinitely. In this way we arrive at a net of triangles all of whose angles are zero, and this net covers the entire Poincaré half-plane; in fact, G_1 contains the half-plane $\Im w > 1/2$, G_2 contains $\Im w > 1/2^2$, and more generally, G_k contains $\Im w > 1/2^k$. Hence the union of the G_k is identical with the non-Euclidean plane.

Conformal Mapping of the Schwarz Triangle Nets (§ 404)

404. We map the half-plane $\Im z > 0$ onto a triangle with angles π/l, π/m, π/n, retaining the norming of the preceding chapter (*cf.* § 392), and we recall (*cf.* (392.1)) that the mapping function in the neighborhood of $z = 0$ is given by

$$w = C\,\frac{\varphi_2}{\varphi_1} = C\,z^{\frac{1}{l}}\,\frac{F(\alpha+1-\gamma,\,\beta+1-\gamma,\,2-\gamma;\,z)}{F(\alpha,\,\beta,\,\gamma;\,z)}. \qquad (404.1)$$

The inverse function can be written in the form

$$z = a_0\,w^l + a_1\,w^{l+1} + \cdots = \Omega(w) \qquad (a_0 \neq 0) \quad (404.2)$$

and is seen to be regular at the point $w = 0$; by the Schwarz Reflection Principle (*cf.* § 341), it maps the first-order triangles of the net alternately onto the half-planes $\Im z > 0$ and $\Im z < 0$. We join the appropriate specimens of these half-planes always along those parts of the real axis that correspond to the common sides of two neighboring triangles. We obtain in this way as the image of the interior of P_1 a Riemann surface of l sheets over the z-plane, with all of its boundary points lying on the real axis. By analytic continuation (*cf.* § 342, pp. 84-85) of (404.1), we obtain according to the formulas of the preceding chapter a relation of the form

$$w - w_B = (1 - z)^{\frac{1}{m}}\,(b_0 + b_1\,z + \cdots). \qquad (404.3)$$

Here, w_B is the value of w at the vertex B of the triangle ABC. The inverse of (404.3),

$$z = 1 + b'_0\,(w - w_B)^m + b'_1\,(w - w_B)^{m+1} + \cdots, \quad (b'_0 \neq 0) \quad (404.4)$$

is the analytic continuation of (404.2) and is regular at the point w_B. Continuing in this way, we see that the function $\Omega(w)$ of (404.2) can be continued analytically along any path that lies in the net of triangles derived from the initial triangle ABC, so that by the monodromy theorem (*cf.* § 232, Vol. I, p. 238), this function is single-valued and regular at every point covered by the net. Therefore the radius of convergence of the power series (404.2) is at least equal to unity.

This power series maps the open disc $|w| < 1$ onto a so-called *regular*, or *canonically branched*, *Riemann surface* over the z-plane. To every vertex of the net there corresponds a branch point over one of the three points $0, 1, \infty$. The multiplicity of the branch points over $z = 0$ is always equal to l, that of the branch points over $z = 1$ is equal to m and that of the branch points over $z = \infty$ is equal to n. The zeros of $\Omega(w)$ correspond to certain vertices of the net and have every point of $|w| = 1$ as a point of accumulation; the circle $|w| = 1$ is therefore a *natural boundary* of the function $\Omega(w)$, which is to say that this function is not regular at any point of the circle and hence cannot be continued anywhere beyond the circle (in the sense of § 232, Vol. I, pp. 236-238).

These properties of the function $z = \Omega(w)$ can be used to construct a new, analytic proof of the existence and properties of the Schwarz triangle nets. This proof, to be sure, is shorter than the geometric proof which we presented in §§ 396 ff. above; but the latter proof has the advantage that its constructions can be visualized geometrically and that it utilizes exclusively methods and results of the geometry of circles (inversive geometry) that are cognate to the matter at hand.

The Inverse Function $\Omega(w)$ as an Automorphic Function (§ 405)

405. The regular Riemann surface of the preceding section has a certain kinship with the Riemann surface (covering surface) which we studied in §§ 336-337 above. In fact, of any two neighboring triangles of our net in the w-plane, one is mapped conformally onto the upper half-plane and the other onto the lower half-plane of the z-plane; the circular-arc quadrangle formed by the two triangles thus constitutes a fundamental region, provided that we omit one of each pair of sides of the quadrangle that are mapped onto the same segment of the real axis of the z-plane.

For any pre-assigned point z_0 of the z-plane, each fundamental region contains one and only one point that corresponds to z_0. In this way we obtain sets of equivalent points in the w-plane. We have in the present case, just as we did earlier in § 332, non-Euclidean motions

$$w^* = \frac{\alpha\,w + \beta}{\gamma\,w + \delta} \qquad (\alpha\,\delta - \beta\,\gamma \neq 0) \quad (405.1)$$

of the plane $|w| < 1$ that permute the points of each set but leave the sets as such invariant. For any such motion (405.1), we always have the relation

$$\Omega(w) = \Omega(w^*) = \Omega\left(\frac{\alpha\, w + \beta}{\gamma\, w + \delta}\right). \tag{405.2}$$

The motions (405.1) constitute a group, whence it follows, by § 332, that the function $\Omega(w)$ is automorphic. The main difference between this function and the automorphic function $w = f(z)$ of § 332 lies in the fact that the group of motions of § 332 contained no non-Euclidean rotations, while in the present case the group may actually be generated by such rotations (having their fixed points at the vertices of the net). In addition to these rotations, the group (405.1) contains of course also motions that are not rotations. We need merely, for instance, consider two sides of triangles of the net that lie on two non-intersecting non-Euclidean lines; since each of these lines is an axis of symmetry (under reflection) of the net, the motion obtained from two consecutive reflections in these two lines is certainly not a rotation of the group.

Similar remarks apply if the triangle has one or two cusps, except that in this case, certain limiting rotations (cf. § 82, Vol. I, p. 78) have to be added to the above rotations in order that a complete set of generators for the group of congruence transformations of the net may be obtained.

The Modular Function (§§ 406-407)

406. For the mapping of a triangle with three cusps (a so-called *modular triangle*) onto a half-plane, the formulas of §§ 392-395 above must be specialized as follows. We have $\lambda = \mu = \nu = 0$ in this case, hence $\alpha = \beta = 1/2, \gamma = 1$. If we now write $F(z)$ as an abbreviation for the hypergeometric series $F(1/2, 1/2, 1; z)$, we have by (377.4) that

$$F(z) = F\left(\frac{1}{2}, \frac{1}{2}, 1; z\right) = 1 + \sum_{n=1}^{\infty} \left(\frac{1 \cdot 3 \cdots (2\,n-1)}{2 \cdot 4 \cdots 2\,n}\right)^2 z^n. \tag{406.1}$$

Similarly, if we write $F^*(1/2, 1/2, 1; z) = F^*(z)$ for short, then by (387.4),

$$F^*(z) = F^*\left(\frac{1}{2}, \frac{1}{2}, 1; z\right)$$

$$= 4 \sum_{n=1}^{\infty} \left(\frac{1 \cdot 3 \cdots (2\,n-1)}{2 \cdot 4 \cdots 2\,n}\right)^2 \left(1 - \frac{1}{2} \pm \cdots + \frac{1}{2\,n-1} - \frac{1}{2\,n}\right) z^n. \tag{406.2}$$

In the connecting formulas (cf. § 391) for this case, the expression

$$2\left(\frac{\Gamma'(1)}{\Gamma(1)} - \frac{\Gamma'\left(\frac{1}{2}\right)}{\Gamma\left(\frac{1}{2}\right)}\right) \tag{406.3}$$

occurs. This expression can be calculated numerically as follows: We differentiate logarithmically Legendre's identity (279.5) of Vol I, p. 297, i.e. the identity

$$\Gamma\left(\frac{x}{2}\right)\Gamma\left(\frac{x+1}{2}\right) = \frac{\sqrt{\pi}}{2^{x-1}}\,\Gamma(x)\,,$$

obtaining

$$\frac{1}{2}\cdot\frac{\Gamma'\left(\frac{x}{2}\right)}{\Gamma\left(\frac{x}{2}\right)} + \frac{1}{2}\cdot\frac{\Gamma'\left(\frac{x+1}{2}\right)}{\Gamma\left(\frac{x+1}{2}\right)} = \frac{\Gamma'(x)}{\Gamma(x)} - l\,2\,,$$

whence for $x = 1$,

$$2\left(\frac{\Gamma'(1)}{\Gamma(1)} - \frac{\Gamma'\left(\frac{1}{2}\right)}{\Gamma\left(\frac{1}{2}\right)}\right) = 4\,l\,2 = l\,16. \tag{406.4}$$

The functions $\varphi_1, \ldots, \varphi_6^*$ become in this case

$$\left.\begin{aligned}
\varphi_1 &= F(z) = \frac{1}{\sqrt{1-z}}\,F\left(\frac{z}{z-1}\right)\\[2mm]
\varphi_3 &= F(1-z) = \frac{1}{\sqrt{z}}\,F\left(\frac{z-1}{z}\right)\\[2mm]
\varphi_5 &= \frac{1}{\sqrt{-z}}\,F\left(\frac{1}{z}\right) = \frac{1}{\sqrt{1-z}}\,F\left(\frac{1}{1-z}\right)
\end{aligned}\right\} \tag{406.5}$$

and

$$\left.\begin{aligned}
\varphi_2^* &= F(z)\,l\,z + F^*(z) = \frac{1}{\sqrt{1-z}}\left\{F\left(\frac{z}{z-1}\right)l\,\frac{z}{1-z} + F^*\left(\frac{z}{z-1}\right)\right\}\\[2mm]
\varphi_4^* &= F(1-z)\,l\,(1-z) + F^*(1-z)\\[2mm]
&= \frac{1}{\sqrt{z}}\left\{F\left(\frac{z-1}{z}\right)l\,\frac{1-z}{z} + F^*\left(\frac{z-1}{z}\right)\right\}\\[2mm]
\varphi_6^* &= \frac{1}{\sqrt{-z}}\left\{F\left(\frac{1}{z}\right)l\,(-z) + F^*\left(\frac{1}{z}\right)\right\}\\[2mm]
&= \frac{1}{\sqrt{1-z}}\left\{F\left(\frac{1}{1-z}\right)l\,(1-z) + F^*\left(\frac{1}{1-z}\right)\right\}.
\end{aligned}\right\} \tag{406.6}$$

The connecting formulas of Table C (pp. 169 ff.) specialize as follows in the present case:

$$\varphi_1 = \frac{1}{\pi}\left\{\varphi_3\, l\, 16 - \varphi_4^*\right\}$$

$$\varphi_2^* = \frac{1}{\pi}\left\{((l\, 16)^2 - \pi^2)\, \varphi_3 - \varphi_4^*\, l\, 16\right\} = \varphi_1\, l\, 16 - \pi\, \varphi_3$$

$$\varphi_1 = \frac{1}{\pi}\left\{\varphi_5\, l\, 16 - \varphi_6^*\right\}$$

$$\varphi_2^* = \frac{1}{\pi}\left\{((l\, 16 + \pi\, i)\, l\, 16 - \pi^2)\, \varphi_5 + \varphi_6^*\, (l\, 16 + \pi\, i)\right\}$$

$$= \varphi_1\, (l\, 16 + \pi\, i) - \pi\, \varphi_5.$$

(406.7)

407. In order to calculate the mapping function $w = \tau(z)$ of the modular triangle, the *modular function*, we set $a = 1/2$ in (394.5) and obtain

$$\tau(z) = \frac{1}{\pi\, i}\left\{\frac{\varphi_2^*}{\varphi_1} - l\, 16\right\} = \frac{1}{\pi\, i}\left\{l\left(\frac{z}{16}\right) + \frac{F^*(z)}{F(z)}\right\}.$$

(407.1)

After a short calculation, we find that in the neighborhood of $z = 1$,

$$\tau(z) = \frac{\pi\, i}{l\, 16 - \dfrac{\varphi_4^*}{\varphi_3}} = -\frac{\pi\, i}{l\left(\dfrac{1-z}{16}\right) + \dfrac{F^*(1-z)}{F(1-z)}},$$

(407.2)

while in the neighborhood of $z = \infty$,

$$\tau(z) = \frac{1}{\pi\, i}\left\{(l\, 16 + \pi\, i) - \pi\,\frac{\varphi_5}{\varphi_1} - l\, 16\right\} = 1 + \frac{\pi\, i}{l\, 16 + \dfrac{\varphi_6^*}{\varphi_5}}.$$

(407.3)

For the derivative $d\tau/dz$, we obtain from (395.3) that

$$\frac{d\tau}{dz} = \frac{1}{\pi\, i}\cdot\frac{1}{z\,(1-z)\,\varphi_1^2}.$$

(407.4)

$d\tau/dz$ for $z = (1 \pm i\sqrt{3})/2$ (§§ 408-410)

408. We have already observed (see the footnote in § 389) that the points $z = (1 \pm i\sqrt{3})/2$ are the only points of the complex plane at which none of our hypergeometric power series converges. Towards calculating the modular function in the neighborhood of one of these points, we note that certain parts of the curves $|\tau| = 1$, $|\tau - 1| = 1$ and $\Re\tau = 1/2$ are axes of symmetry (under reflections) of the modular triangle of the Poincaré half-plane that has its vertices at $0, 1, \infty$; therefore the point of intersection $\tau = a_0 = (1 + i\sqrt{3})/2$

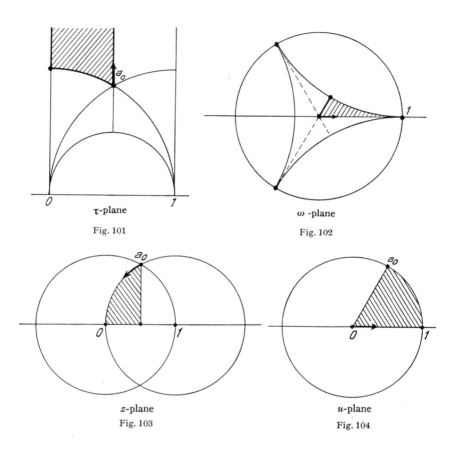

τ-plane

Fig. 101

ω -plane

Fig. 102

z-plane

Fig. 103

u-plane

Fig. 104

of these curves must be the image point of $z = a_0$.

Now the Moebius transformation

$$\tau = \bar{a}_0 \, \frac{\omega + \bar{a}_0}{\omega - 1}$$

(408.1)

maps the modular triangle $0, 1, \infty$ of the τ-plane (see Fig. 101) onto a triangle inscribed in the circle $|\omega| = 1$ (see Fig. 102), in such a way that the above-mentioned axes of symmetry are transformed into diameters of the circle. The axes of symmetry divide the modular triangle into six circular-arc triangles with the angles $\pi/3$, 0, and $\pi/2$. Under the conformal mapping onto the upper half of the z-plane, each of these six triangles is mapped onto a circular-arc triangle with the angles $\pi/3$, $\pi/2$, $\pi/2$ (see Fig. 103), as can be seen easily by an argument involving reflections. Thus we shall obtain the mapping function in the neighborhood of $z = a_0$ (or $\omega = 0$, or $\tau = a_0$) by mapping two corresponding circular-arc triangles (of the above sets of six in each plane) onto each other by means of series expansions that converge as rapidly as possible at the critical point in question; in this way we shall be able to determine $d\tau/dz$ at the critical point.

The Moebius transformation

$$u = \frac{\overline{a}_0}{a_0} \cdot \frac{z - a_0}{z - \overline{a}_0} \qquad (408.2)$$

maps the shaded triangle of the z-plane (Fig. 103) onto the circular-arc triangle of Fig. 104, in such a way that the point $z = a_0$ corresponds to the origin $u = 0$. We now wish to map this triangle of the u-plane onto the shaded triangle of the ω-plane (Fig. 102) in such a way that the vertex at $u = 0$ corresponds to the vertex at $\omega = 0$.

409. To this end, we introduce a parameter v and we map each of our two triangles, the one in the ω-plane with angles $\pi/3$, 0, $\pi/2$ and the one in the u-plane with angles $\pi/3$, $\pi/2$, $\pi/2$, onto the upper half-plane of the v-plane by means of the formulas developed in § 392. For the triangle in the ω-plane, we have

$$\alpha = \frac{7}{12}, \qquad \beta = \frac{1}{12}, \qquad \gamma = \frac{8}{12},$$

and for the triangle in the u-plane,

$$\alpha = \frac{4}{12}, \qquad \beta = -\frac{2}{12}, \qquad \gamma = \frac{8}{12}.$$

Relation (392.1) now yields the mapping functions $\omega = \omega(v)$ and $u = u(v)$ in the form

$$\omega = C \, v^{\frac{1}{3}} \, (1 + a_1 v + a_2 v^2 + \cdots), \qquad (409.1)$$

$$u = C^* \, v^{\frac{1}{3}} \, (1 + b_1 v + b_2 v^2 + \cdots). \qquad (409.2)$$

The constants C and C^* are obtained from (392.2), with $s = 1$, as follows:

$$C = \frac{\Gamma\left(\frac{8}{12}\right) \Gamma\left(\frac{5}{12}\right) \Gamma\left(\frac{11}{12}\right)}{\Gamma\left(\frac{16}{12}\right) \Gamma\left(\frac{1}{12}\right) \Gamma\left(\frac{7}{12}\right)}, \tag{409.3}$$

$$C^* = \frac{\Gamma\left(\frac{8}{12}\right) \Gamma\left(\frac{8}{12}\right) \Gamma\left(\frac{14}{12}\right)}{\Gamma\left(\frac{16}{12}\right) \Gamma\left(\frac{4}{12}\right) \Gamma\left(\frac{10}{12}\right)}. \tag{409.4}$$

From this we obtain, for $u = 0$,

$$\left. \frac{d\omega}{du} \right|_{u=0} = \lim_{u=0} \frac{\omega}{u} = \frac{C}{C^*} = \frac{\Gamma\left(\frac{5}{12}\right) \Gamma\left(\frac{11}{12}\right) \Gamma\left(\frac{4}{12}\right) \Gamma\left(\frac{10}{12}\right)}{\Gamma\left(\frac{1}{12}\right) \Gamma\left(\frac{7}{12}\right) \Gamma\left(\frac{8}{12}\right) \Gamma\left(\frac{14}{12}\right)}. \tag{409.5}$$

On the other hand, since $a_0 = (1 + i\sqrt{3})/2$ we find with the aid of (408.1) that

$$\left. \frac{d\tau}{d\omega} \right|_{\omega=0} = a_0 - \bar{a}_0 = i\sqrt{3},$$

and from (408.2) that

$$\left. \frac{du}{dz} \right|_{z=a_0} = -\frac{\bar{a}_0}{1 + \bar{a}_0} = -\frac{a_0}{i\sqrt{3}},$$

so that we finally have

$$\left. \frac{d\tau}{dz} \right|_{z=a_0} = \frac{d\tau}{d\omega} \cdot \frac{d\omega}{du} \cdot \frac{du}{dz} = -a_0 \frac{C}{C^*},$$

and hence

$$\left| \frac{d\tau}{dz} \right|_{z=a_0} = \frac{C}{C^*}. \tag{409.6}$$

Making use of the notation of § 280, Vol. I, p. 297, and of the relation

$$\Gamma\left(\frac{14}{12}\right) = \frac{1}{6} \Gamma\left(\frac{2}{12}\right),$$

we can write

$$\frac{C}{C^*} = \frac{x_5\, x_{11}\, x_4\, x_{10}}{x_1\, x_7\, x_2\, x_8} \cdot 6 = \frac{6\, x_4^2}{(x_1\, x_2\, x_7)^2} \cdot \frac{(x_1\, x_{11})\, (x_2\, x_{10})\, (x_5\, x_7)}{(x_4\, x_8)}. \tag{409.7}$$

Now according to the formulas of § 280,

$$x_1\, x_2\, x_7 = 2^{\frac{5}{6}} \sqrt{\pi}\; x_2^2 = 2^{\frac{5}{6}} \sqrt{\pi}\; \frac{(x_2\, x_8)^2}{(x_4\, x_8)^2}\; x_4^2 = \frac{3 \cdot 2^{\frac{1}{6}}}{\sqrt{\pi}}\; x_4^4,$$

so that

$$\frac{1}{(x_1\, x_2\, x_7)^2} = \frac{\pi}{3^2 \cdot 2^{\frac{1}{3}}\, x_4^8}.$$

This and relations (409.6) and (409.7), as well as § 280, finally yield the desired result in the form

$$\left|\frac{d\tau}{dz}\right|_{z=a_0} = \frac{1}{2^{\frac{1}{3}} \sqrt{3}} \left(\frac{\sqrt{2\,\pi}}{\Gamma\!\left(\frac{1}{3}\right)}\right)^6. \tag{409.8}$$

410. By § 405, the inverse function $z = \Omega(\tau)$ is an automorphic function regular in the half-plane $\Im\tau > 0$. It is periodic in this region with period 2. We set $\tau = s + it$, where s and t are real and $t > 0$. We denote by $\mu(t_0)$

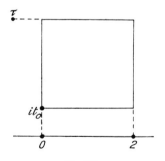

Fig. 105

the maximum of the function $|\,\Omega(s + it_0)\,|$ of s, for a fixed value t_0 of t. Because of the periodicity, we need determine this maximum only in the interval $0 \leq s < 2$. We wish to prove that if τ is any point of the upper half-plane for which $t > t_0$, then

$$|\,\Omega(\tau)\,| < \mu(t_0)$$

must hold.

To this end, we may assume without loss of generality, on account of the periodicity, that the real part of τ lies between 0 and 2. On the boundaries $\Re\tau = 0$, $\Re\tau = 2$, the function $\Omega(\tau)$ assumes real values, and because of the way in which we normed our mapping of the modular triangle, the modulus of this function decreases monotonically as t increases. As t goes to infinity, $|\Omega(\tau)|$ converges to zero within the strip. Hence in the closed half-strip $0 \leq \Re\tau \leq 2$, $\Im\tau \geq t_0$, the function $|\Omega(\tau)|$ attains its maximum on the line-segment $\Im\tau = t_0$, and this maximum is $\mu(t_0)$. This proves our statement above.

CHAPTER FOUR

THE ESSENTIAL SINGULARITIES AND PICARD'S THEOREMS

Landau's Theorem and Picard's First Theorem (§§ 411-413)

411. In § 166, Vol. I, p. 164, we proved a result that generalizes Weierstrass' theorem considerably, to the effect that those values which a function assumes infinitely often in any given neighborhood of an essential singularity constitute a set that is everywhere dense on the Riemann sphere. E. Picard (1856-1941) proved in 1879 the spectacular result that this set of values is not only everywhere dense but actually covers the entire sphere with the exception of two points at most. We need seek no further than the exponential function e^z, which has an essential singularity at the point $z = \infty$, to find an

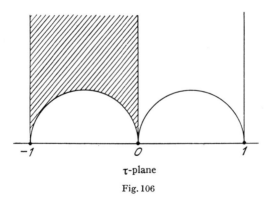

τ-plane

Fig. 106

example where two exceptional values occur, namely the values 0 and ∞. This remarkable state of affairs is related to the fact that the Riemann surface of the logarithm (*cf.* § 249, Vol. I, p. 258) can be mapped conformally onto the whole complex plane, while for the Riemann surface of the modular function, whose (logarithmic) branch points lie over three base points, an open circular disc or a half-plane will do as a conformal image. The most convenient approach to this whole class of questions is given by a theorem of E. Landau (1877-1938), a theorem which was discovered only in 1904 and to the exposition of which we shall now turn our attention.

We consider a power series

$$f(z) = a_0 + a_1 z + a_2 z^2 + \cdots \qquad (a_1 \neq 0), \qquad (411.\,1)$$

which we assume to be convergent in the disc $|z| < R$ and which we also assume to take on neither of the two values 0 and 1 in this disc. As a first consequence, we note that a_0 is neither $= 0$ nor $= 1$. Then the modular function $w = \tau(u)$, defined in § 407 above, has a branch for which $\tau(a_0)$ lies inside or on the circular-arc quadrangle with vertices at -1, 0, 1, ∞ (see Fig. 106), since this quadrangle is a fundamental region for the inverse function of $\tau(u)$. In a neighborhood of $z = 0$, therefore, the function

$$g(z) = \tau(f(z)) \qquad (411.\,2)$$

is regular. Moreover, from the assumption that $f(z)$ omits the values zero and unity in the disc $|z| < R$, it follows that $g(z)$ can be continued analytically along any path lying in this disc, and this in turn implies, by the monodromy theorem, that $g(z)$ is single-valued in the disc. We note further that $\Im g(z) > 0$ holds in $|z| < R$. Therefore the values assumed by the function

$$h(z) = \frac{g(z) - g(0)}{g(z) - \bar{g}(0)} \qquad (411.\,3)$$

in the disc $|z| < R$ must all be inside the unit circle, and Schwarz's Lemma applied to the function $h(Rv)$ yields

$$R\,|h'(0)| \leqq 1. \qquad (411.\,4)$$

Now

$$h'(0) = \frac{g(0) - \bar{g}(0)}{(g(0) - \bar{g}(0))^2}\, \tau'(a_0)\, a_1, \qquad (411.\,5)$$

from which it now follows that

$$R \leqq \frac{|\tau(a_0) - \bar{\tau}(a_0)|}{|a_1|\,|\tau'(a_0)|}. \qquad (411.\,6)$$

We denote the right-hand side of (411.6) by $R(a_0, a_1)$ and we call this quantity the *Landau radius*. It constitutes a bound for R which is the best possible, as the following argument will show. First, relation (411.3) yields

$$g(z) = \frac{\bar{g}(0)\, h(z) - g(0)}{h(z) - 1}.$$

Now if $h(z)$ is of bound one in the disc $|z| < R$, then $\Im g(z) > 0$, and

(411.2) can be solved for $f(z)$. With the notation of § 405, we obtain

$$f(z) = \Omega(g(z)) = \Omega\left(\frac{\bar{g}(0)\,h(z) - g(0)}{h(z) - 1}\right),$$

where Ω denotes the inverse function of τ. In particular, if

$$h(z) = \frac{z}{R}, \tag{411.7}$$

which entails

$$R\,|h'(0)| = 1,$$

then (411.5) implies the equality

$$R = \frac{2\,\Im\tau(a_0)}{|a_1|\,|\tau'(a_0)|}. \tag{411.8}$$

We have thus proved the following *theorem of Landau*:

If $f(z)$ is regular in the disc $|z| < R$ and omits the values zero and unity in this disc, then the first two coefficients a_0, a_1 and the radius of convergence R of the expansion

$$f(z) = a_0 + a_1 z + a_2 z^2 + \cdots \qquad (a_1 \neq 0) \tag{411.9}$$

satisfy the inequality

$$R \leq \frac{2\,\Im\tau(a_0)}{|a_1|\,|\tau'(a_0)|}. \tag{411.10}$$

There are certain functions $f(z)$ for which the equality sign holds in (411.10), so that the bound on R is the best bound possible.

We also restate this theorem in the following obverse formulation: *If the function*

$$f(z) = a_0 + a_1 z + a_2 z^2 + \cdots \qquad (a_0 \neq 0, 1; a_1 \neq 0)$$

is regular in the disc $|z| < R$ and if $R > \dot{R}(a_0, a_1)$, then $f(z)$ must assume one of the values zero or unity at least once in the disc $|z| < R$.

412. Toward the numerical calculation of the Landau radius, we substitute the values of $\tau(a_0)$ and $\tau'(a_0)$, obtainable from § 407 above, into (411.10). Specifically, we have

$$2\,\Im\tau(a_0) = \frac{1}{\pi}\left\{2\,l\,16 - \frac{\varphi_1\,\bar{\varphi}_2^{*} + \varphi_1\,\bar{\varphi}_2^{*}}{\varphi_1\,\bar{\varphi}_1}\right\}, \tag{412.1}$$

$$\frac{1}{|\tau'(a_0)|} = \pi\,|a_0\,(1 - a_0)|\,\varphi_1\,\bar{\varphi}_1. \tag{412.2}$$

$$z = a_0$$

This yields

$$R(a_0, a_1) = \frac{|a_0 (1 - a_0)|}{|a_1|} \left(2\, \varphi_1\, \bar{\varphi}_1\, l\, 16 - \varphi_1\, \bar{\varphi}_2^* - \bar{\varphi}_1\, \varphi_2^*\right). \qquad (412.3)$$

For $|a_0| < 1$ we find

$$R(a_0, a_1) = \frac{|a_0 (1 - a_0)|}{|a_1|} \left(2\, F\, \bar{F}\, l\, \frac{16}{|a_0|} - F\, \bar{F}^* - \bar{F}\, F^*\right), \quad z = a_0. \qquad (412.4)$$

To find convergent series in terms of which we can express $R(a_0, a_1)$ for a_0 not inside the unit circle, we must make use of the connecting formulas.

In the exceptional case treated in § 408, we have $2\,\Im\tau = \sqrt{3}$, so that by (409.8),

$$R\!\left(\frac{1}{2}\,(1 + i\sqrt{3}), a_1\right) = \frac{3 \cdot 2^{\frac{1}{3}}}{|a_1|} \left(\frac{\Gamma\,\dfrac{1}{3}}{\sqrt{2\,\pi}}\right)^{6} = \frac{1}{|a_1|} \cdot 5{,}6325 \ldots . \qquad (412.5)$$

The Landau radius can also be determined very easily in case $a_0 = 0$, i.e. if we are dealing with a regular function

$$f(z) = a_1 z + a_2 z^2 + \cdots$$

that omits the values zero and unity in the punctured disc $0 < |z| < R$. In this case we must replace the modular function $\tau(z)$ in the argument of the preceding section by the function

$$e^{i\pi\tau(z)} = \frac{z}{16}\, e^{\frac{F^*(z)}{F(z)}}. \qquad (412.6)$$

This function is regular at $z = 0$ and can be continued analytically along any path that starts at $z = 0$ and subsequently avoids the points $z = 0$ and $z = 1$. We have $\tau'(0) = 1/16$, so that the Landau radius is given in the present case by

$$R(0, a_1) = \frac{16}{|a_1|}. \qquad (412.7)$$

This yields the following theorem:

If the function $f(z)$ is regular in the disc $|z| < R$, satisfies $f(0) = 0$, but is not equal to zero or unity at any other point of the disc, then

$$R \leq \frac{16}{|a_1|} \qquad (412.8)$$

must hold. This bound is the best bound possible.

413. Let $f(z)$ be any non-constant integral function. Then there must certainly exist points z_0 of the complex plane for which $f(z_0) \neq 0$ or 1 and $f'(z_0) \neq 0$. If we set $a_0 = f(z_0)$, $a_1 = f'(z_0)$, then we know from the theorem of § 411 that in every disc $|z - z_0| < R$ with $R > R(a_0, a_1)$, the function $f(z)$ assumes one of the values 0 and 1 at least once.

Now let $g(z)$ be a function that is meromorphic in the entire complex plane and omits three distinct values a, b, and c. If we set

$$f(z) = \frac{c-a}{c-b} \cdot \frac{g(z) - b}{g(z) - a},$$

then $f(z)$ is an integral function which omits the values zero and unity and which must therefore be a constant. This leads to the following result, which greatly generalizes Liouville's theorem (cf. § 167, Vol. I, p. 165) and is known as *Picard's first theorem*:

If $g(z)$ is meromorphic in the whole complex plane and omits three distinct values a, b, and c, then $g(z)$ is a constant.

Schottky's Theorem (§§ 414-415)

414. Let the function

$$f(z) = a_0 + a_1 z + a_2 z^2 + \cdots \qquad (a_0 \neq 0, 1) \qquad (414.1)$$

be regular in the disc $|z| < 1$ and assume that it omits the values zero and unity in this disc. Then just as in § 411 above, the function

$$g(z) = \tau(f(z))$$

is regular in $|z| < 1$ and assumes values whose imaginary part is > 0. If $0 < \vartheta < 1$, then the values assumed by $g(z)$ in $|z| \leq \vartheta$ must by Pick's theorem lie in a non-Euclidean disc whose non-Euclidean center is at $\tau(a_0)$ and whose periphery is tangent to the straight line

$$t_0 = \Im \tau(a_0) \frac{1 - \vartheta}{1 + \vartheta}.$$

Here we have set $\tau = s + it$, as in § 410 above. Also by § 410, the values which $|f(z)| = |\Omega(g(z))|$ assumes in the closed disc $|z| \leq \vartheta$ do not exceed a finite number that we denoted by

$$\mu(t_0) = \mu\left(\Im\tau(a_0) \frac{1 - \vartheta}{1 + \vartheta}\right) = \mu(\vartheta, a_0). \qquad (414.2)$$

This result is known as *Schottky's theorem* and may be stated as follows:

Assume that

$$f(z) = a_0 + a_1 z + a_2 z^2 + \cdots \qquad (a_0 \neq 0, 1) \qquad (414.3)$$

is regular and omits the values zero and unity in the disc $|z| < 1$. *Also, let* $0 < \vartheta < 1$. *Then there exists a number* $\mu(\vartheta, a_0)$ *that depends only on* ϑ *and* a_0 *(not on* $a_1, a_2, \ldots$*) which is such that for* $|z| \leq \vartheta$,

$$|f(z)| \leq \mu(\vartheta, a_0) \qquad (414.4)$$

holds.

415. The proof of Schottky's theorem goes through independently of the particular branch of the modular function $\tau(u)$ into which $f(z)$ is substituted. To minimize the bound $\mu(t_0)$, we must choose that branch for which $\Im\tau(a_0)$ is as large as possible, i.e. we must choose $\tau(a_0)$ as lying in the fundamental region shown in Fig. 106.

We now consider in the u-plane a region $G(\varepsilon, \omega)$ that is defined by the relations

$$\left. \begin{array}{c} |u| > \varepsilon, \quad |u - 1| > \varepsilon, \quad |u| < \omega, \\[2mm] \varepsilon < \dfrac{1}{2}, \quad \omega > 2. \end{array} \right\} \qquad (415.1)$$

If a_0 is a point of this region and if $\tau(a_0)$ lies in the fundamental region just mentioned, there exists a number $\eta > 0$ for which $\Im\tau(a_0) > \eta$ always holds. For all points a_0 of the region $G(\varepsilon, \omega)$, we can use one and the same bound $\mu(t_0)$ in Schottky's theorem, for we need only set

$$t_0 = \eta \, \frac{1 - \vartheta}{1 + \vartheta}.$$

This generalization is also due to Schottky.

From Figs. 101 and 103 above we see that if the branch of $\tau(u)$ is chosen as indicated above, then

$$\Im\tau(a_0) > \frac{1}{2}\sqrt{3}$$

holds for $0 < |a_0| < 1/2$. Thus we have for these values of a_0 a bound $\mu^*(\vartheta)$ in Schottky's theorem that is independent of a_0.

If a_0 lies in the punctured disc $0 < |u - 1| < 1/2$, then it follows from the equation

$$f(z) - 1 = a_0 - 1 + a_1 z + a_2 z^2 + \cdots$$

that in $|z| \leq \vartheta$ we have

$$|f(z) - 1| \leq \mu^*(\vartheta),$$

and hence

$$|f(z)| \leq \mu^*(\vartheta) + 1. \tag{415.2}$$

Now if a_0 is any point of the doubly punctured disc

$$|u| < \omega, \quad u \neq 0, 1, \quad \omega > 2, \tag{415.3}$$

then a_0 lies in at least one of the three regions dealt with in this section, and we have therefore obtained the following theorem:

Let the function

$$f(z) = a_0 + a_1 z + a_2 z^2 + \cdots \tag{415.4}$$

be regular and $\neq 0, 1$ in the disc $|z| < 1$. Also, let $0 < \vartheta < 1$ and $|a_0| < \omega$. Then there exists a number $\bar{\mu} = \bar{\mu}(\vartheta, \omega)$, dependent only on ϑ and ω (not on $a_0, a_1, \ldots$) such that for $|z| \leq \vartheta$,

$$|f(z)| \leq \bar{\mu} \tag{415.5}$$

holds.

Montel's Theorem (§ 416)

416. Let G be any given region of the z-plane and let $\{f\}$ be a family of regular functions in G each of which omits the values zero and unity in G. Let z_0 be a point of G and $|z - z_0| \leq R$ a closed disc that lies wholly in G.

We divide $\{f\}$ into two subfamilies $\{g\}$ and $\{h\}$, where the former is to contain all functions of $\{f\}$ for which $|g(z_0)| \leq 1$ while the latter is to contain all the others, i.e. all functions of $\{f\}$ for which $|h(z_0)| > 1$.

By Schottky's theorem, the functions of the family $\{g\}$ are uniformly bounded in the small (*cf.* § 185, Vol. I, p. 184), since there are discs $|z - z_0| < \varrho$ within G for which $R/\varrho = \vartheta < 1$. Moreover, it follows from our assumptions that every function $1/h(z)$ is regular in G and omits the values zero and unity, and we also have

$$\frac{1}{|h(z_0)|} < 1.$$

This implies that each of the two families $\{g\}$ and $\{h\}$ is normal at the point z_0. Therefore by the criterion of § 183, Vol. I, p. 183, the union $\{f\}$ of these two normal families is itself a normal family at z_0. Since z_0 is any point of G, it follows that the family $\{f\}$ is normal in the whole region G. Thus we have obtained the following theorem: *The set of all functions that are regular and omit the values zero and unity in a region G constitutes a normal family in G.*

By combining this result with the theorem of § 197, Vol. I, p. 194, we obtain the following additional result: *If in a region G every function f of a family omits three distinct values a, b, c (which may depend on the function f), then the family $\{f\}$ is normal in G provided only that the product*

$$\chi(b, c) \cdot \chi(c, a) \cdot \chi(a, b)$$

of the chordal distances of these points is greater than a fixed positive number, for all functions of the family.

Picard's Second Theorem (§ 417)

417. We consider a function $f(z)$ that is regular and omits the three values $0, 1, \infty$ in the punctured disc

$$0 < |z| < \varrho \tag{417.1}$$

and we define a sequence of analytic functions by means of the equations

$$f_n(z) = f\left(\frac{z}{2^n}\right) \qquad (n = 0, 1, 2, \ldots). \tag{417.2}$$

In the circular annulus $\varrho/2 < |z| < \varrho$, each of these functions is regular and omits the values zero and unity. Hence by the preceding section, the set of functions (417.2) is a normal family in the annulus; it must therefore contain a subsequence

$$\{f_{n_j}(z)\} \qquad (j = 1, 2, \ldots) \tag{417.3}$$

that converges continuously in the annulus. By the last theorem of § 198, Vol. I, p. 195, the limit function is either regular in the annulus or it is the constant ∞.

Let us assume first that the limit function is regular. In this case, the functions of the sequence (417.3) are uniformly bounded on the circle $|z| = 3\varrho/4$. Equations (417.2) now imply that the disc $|z| < \varrho$ contains an infinite sequence of concentric circles whose radii converge to zero and on which $f(z)$ is bounded. Since $f(z)$, by our assumptions, has no poles, $f(z)$ is bounded in the punctured disc (417.1) and can therefore be extended, by Riemann's theorem of § 133, Vol. I, p. 131, to a function that is also regular at $z = 0$.

In the second case, where the limit function of the sequence (417.3) is the constant ∞, we simply replace $f(z)$ by $1/f(z)$, which reduces this case to the first case. We have thus proved a theorem that extends Riemann's theorem of § 133, Vol. I, p. 131 in the most remarkable way, as follows:

If in a neighborhood $0 < |z - z_0| < \varrho$ of a point z_0, the function $f(z)$ omits three distinct values a, b, and c, then $f(z)$ is continuous at z_0 in the chordal (spherical) metric and can be extended to a function analytic at z_0.

This theorem can also be restated as follows: *If the function $f(z)$ has an essential singularity at the point z_0 (which may also be the point at infinity), then in every neighborhood of z_0 the function $f(z)$ assumes every value, with the possible exception of at most two values, an infinite number of times.*

This theorem was discovered by Picard in the year 1879. The above proof is due to P. Montel (1916).

A Corollary of Montel's Theorem (§ 418)

418. Let $\{f\}$ be a family of functions that are regular and omit the values 0, 1 and ∞ in the punctured disc $0 < |z| < 1$. Then by Montel's theorem of § 416, the family $\{f\}$ is normal in the punctured disc. According to the theorem of the preceding section, each of the functions $f(z)$ can be extended to a function analytic at the point $z = 0$. We shall prove that the family of extended functions is normal at $z = 0$.

To this end, let $\{f_n(z)\}$ be any sequence from the family $\{f\}$. If infinitely many of the numbers $f_n(0)$ are distinct from all three of the values 0, 1, ∞, then by Montel's theorem we can select from the sequence $\{f_n(z)\}$ a subsequence that is normal in the whole disc $|z| < 1$. Thus we need only deal with the case that all of the $f_n(0)$ are $= 0$, since the remaining two cases can be reduced to this one by introducing the functions $f(z) - 1$ and $1/f(z)$, respectively.

We can select from the sequence of the $f_n(z)$ a subsequence $\{f_{n_j}(z)\}$ that converges continuously in the punctured interior of the unit circle. If the limit function $g(z)$ of this subsequence is not identically equal to infinity, there exists a circle $|z| = r < 1$ on which all of the $f_{n_j}(z)$ are uniformly bounded. They must have the same property in the disc $|z| \leq r$ and therefore constitute a normal family in this disc.

To assume that $g(z) \equiv \infty$ would lead to a contradiction, because there would exist in this case a disc $|z| < r < 1$ on the boundary of which $|f_{n_j}(z)| > 3$ for at least one of the functions of the convergent subsequence; then for the function $\varphi(z) = 1 - f_{n_j}(z)$, we would have $|\varphi(z)| > 2$ at every point of $|z| = r$ while at the same time $\varphi(0) = 1$, and thus by the result of § 138, Vol. I, p. 135, $\varphi(z)$ would have at least one zero z_0 at which $f_{n_j}(z_0) = 1$ would then hold, in contradiction to our assumptions. Thus we have obtained the following result:

If F is the frontier of the normal kernel of a family of functions all of which omit three values, then F cannot contain any isolated points.

A Generalization (§ 419)

419. The theorems of §§ 411ff. can be generalized by the substitution, in the appropriate places in the course of their proofs, of an arbitrary Schwarz triangle function for the modular function. Thus for instance, let l, m, n be three natural numbers for which

$$\frac{1}{l} + \frac{1}{m} + \frac{1}{n} < 1$$

holds, and let $f(z)$ be a function that is meromorphic in the disc $|z| < 1$ and for which the multiplicity with which it assumes the values 0, 1, and ∞ (i.e., the multiplicity of its zeros, "ones," and poles) is always divisible by l, m. and n, respectively. Let $f(z)$ be represented by

$$f(z) = a_0 + a_1 z + a_2 z^2 + \cdots \qquad (a_0 \neq 0, 1)$$

in the neighborhood of $z = 0$. The function (404.1) maps the point a_0 onto at least one point w_0 of the disc $|w| < 1$. We map w_0 onto the origin by means of a non-Euclidean motion of our net of triangles, and we obtain a function

$$\Psi(u) = \frac{a\,\varphi_1(u) + b\,\varphi_2(u)}{c\,\varphi_1(u) + d\,\varphi_2(u)},$$

which maps the upper half-plane $\Im u > 0$ onto a triangle of the net. It is easy to see that $g(z) = \Psi(f(z))$ is regular and of bound one in the disc $|z| < 1$, and vanishes at $z = 0$. From this it follows, by Schwarz's Lemma, that

$$|a_1| \leqq \frac{1}{|\Psi'(a_0)|}. \qquad (419.1)$$

This is the crucial inequality from which we can obtain, after a modification of the norming, the analogue of the result on the Landau radius.

The Essential Singularities of Meromorphic Functions (§§ 420-424)

420. We consider the function $z = \Omega(w)$ introduced in § 404 and we wish to determine the radii of the disc $|w| < 1$ on which

$$\lim_{r=1} \Omega(r\,e^{i\vartheta}) \tag{420.1}$$

exists. As the point w travels along such a radius, the corresponding point $\Omega(w)$ of the z-plane traverses a path γ_z whose interior points do not include $z = 0$, 1 and ∞. But the end point of this path, which exists by our assumption, always coincides with one of the three points just mentioned; no other point of the z-plane can be a boundary value of $\Omega(w)$, because the mapping is neighborhood-preserving.

Now if the path γ_z ends, say, at the point $z = 0$, we consider the part of γ_z that lies in a circular disc having its center at $z = 0$ and excluding $z = 1$ (say the disc $|z| < 1/2$); this part of γ_z is the image of a curve γ_w that passes through triangles of the modular configuration all of which have a cusp at a common vertex. Since by our assumption γ_w coincides with part of a radius of $|w| < 1$, it follows that this radius passes only through a finite number of triangles. This last condition however is met by no more than a denumerable number of radii of $|w| < 1$, since there are only denumerably many cusps of the modular net on $|w| = 1$. For all other radii, therefore, the limit (420.1) does not exist. Hence by the result of § 311, the boundary values of $\Omega(w)$ at any given point ζ of $|w| = 1$ must cover the entire Riemann sphere. Thus we see that the conclusion of Fatou's theorem does not hold for certain functions that omit three distinct values.

As long as we were dealing only with isolated frontier points of the domain of definition, we were able to extend results for bounded functions to functions that omit three values. This is one way of looking at the content of Picard's theorems. But our last considerations show that extensions of this kind may no longer be possible if the singularities of a function are not isolated. However, even in the latter case it is possible to arrive at certain results without too much difficulty.

421. Toward this end we first derive a lemma. We note that for a function $f(z)$ regular in the disc $|z| \leq 1$, equation (135.5), Vol. I, p. 132 can be written in the form

$$f(0) = \frac{1}{2\pi} \int_0^{2\pi} f(e^{i\vartheta})\,d\vartheta,$$

which admits of the following geometric interpretation. The right-hand side of this equation may be considered as representing the center of gravity of a certain positive mass distribution on the curve $w = f(e^{i\vartheta})$. Thus the equation implies that $f(0)$ must lie in the convex hull of this curve.

Now let $f(z)$ be regular and bounded in the disc $|z| < 1$, say

$$|f(z)| < M. \tag{421.1}$$

Let $\varDelta$ be an open subset of the circle $|z| = 1$ that consists of at most denumerably many subarcs whose lengths add up to ε, and assume that at every point ζ of $|z| = 1$ that is not on $\varDelta$, the limit

$$\lim_{r=1} f(r\,\zeta) \qquad\qquad (0 < r < 1) \tag{421.2}$$

exists and that the convergence in (421.2) is uniform for all ζ in question. We denote the set of all limits (421.2) by W and the convex hull of W by W^*.

For any given r with $0 < r < 1$, we denote by $\varDelta_r$ the projection of $\varDelta$ onto the circle $|z| = r$ under the central projection from the origin. In addition to the analytic function $f(r\,e^{i\vartheta})$ $(0 \leqq \vartheta < 2\,\pi)$, we introduce a continuous function $\varphi(r\,e^{i\vartheta})$ that is linear in ϑ on every subinterval of $\varDelta_r$ and coincides with $f(r\,e^{i\vartheta})$ at all other points of the circle $|z| = r$.

Then from the relations

$$f(0) = \frac{1}{2\,\pi} \int_0^{2\pi} f(r\,e^{i\vartheta})\,d\vartheta = \frac{1}{2\,\pi} \int_0^{2\pi} \varphi_r(\vartheta)\,d\vartheta + \frac{1}{2\,\pi} \int_0^{2\pi} (f(r\,e^{i\vartheta}) - \varphi_r(\vartheta))\,d\vartheta \tag{421.3}$$

and with the notation

$$\left.\begin{aligned} w_1 &= \lim_{r=1} \frac{1}{2\,\pi} \int_0^{2\pi} \varphi_r(\vartheta)\,d\vartheta \\[2mm] w_2 &= \lim_{r=1} \frac{1}{2\,\pi} \int_0^{2\pi} (f(r\,e^{i\vartheta}) - \varphi(\vartheta))\,d\vartheta \end{aligned}\right\} \tag{421.4}$$

it follows that

$$f(0) = w_1 + w_2. \tag{421.5}$$

Now w_1 belongs to the convex hull W^*, and

$$|w_2| \leqq 2\,\varepsilon\,M, \tag{421.6}$$

since

$$|f(r\,e^{i\vartheta}) - \varphi_r(\vartheta)| < 2\,M$$

holds true. We shall make use of these inequalities to prove the following lemma:

Let $f(z)$ be a regular and bounded function in the disc $|z| < 1$. Assume that the limit

$$\lim_{r=1} f(r\,\zeta)$$

exists at every point ζ, except on a set e_z of measure zero, of an arc AB of the circle $|z| = 1$, and that these limits lie in a point set W of the w-plane. Then every boundary value of $f(z)$ at any interior point ζ_0 of the arc AB is a point of the interior or the frontier of the convex hull W^* of W.

To complete the proof of this lemma, let z_0 be any point of the disc $|z| < 1$. The Moebius transformation

$$z = \frac{z_0 - u}{1 - \bar{z}_0\, u}$$

represents a one-to-one mapping of the two closed discs $|z| \leqq 1$ and $|u| \leqq 1$ onto each other and maps the arc AB onto an arc $A_1 B_1$ whose length we denote by

$$2\,\pi - \frac{\varepsilon}{2}.$$

The set e_z of measure zero on the arc AB corresponds to a set e_u of measure zero on the arc $A_1 B_1$. We introduce the function

$$h(u) = f\left(\frac{z_0 - u}{1 - \bar{z}_0\, u}\right).$$

The point set e_u and the complement of the arc $A_1 B_1$ on $|u| = 1$ can be covered by a sequence Δ of intervals of total length ε; this set Δ then satisfies the assumptions at the beginning of this section, so that we can write, in accordance with (421.5),

$$f(z_0) = h(0) = w_1 + w_2,$$

where w_1 is a point of W^* while w_2 satisfies the inequality

$$|w_2| \leqq 2\,\varepsilon\, M.$$

The lemma now follows if we note that ε goes to zero if $|\zeta_0 - z_0|$ does. Incidentally, the assumption that $f(z)$ is bounded in the whole disc $|z| < 1$

can be replaced by the weaker assumption that $f(z)$ is bounded in a neighborhood of ζ_0, with the aid of the method of § 348.

422. Next we consider an arbitrary analytic function $f(z)$ meromorphic in the disc $|z| < 1$. We wish to derive a characterization of the set W of boundary values assumed by $f(z)$ at a point ζ_0 of the unit circle in terms of the radial limits

$$\lim_{r=1} f(r\,e^{i\vartheta})$$

in the neighborhood of ζ_0 (to the extent to which these limits exist).

To this end, we cover the Riemann sphere by a normal sequence of open discs[1]

$$K_1, K_2, K_3, \ldots \tag{422.1}$$

that is by a denumerable set of open discs having the property that to every disc к on the Riemann sphere with center at P, and no matter how small, we can assign at least one disc K_ν of the sequence (422.1) that lies in к and covers P.

To each disc K_ν of the sequence (422.1) we now assign a subset A_ν of the circle $|z| = 1$ consisting of all points ζ of the circle for which the limit

$$\lim_{r=1} f(r\,\zeta) \qquad (0 < r < 1) \tag{422.2}$$

either fails to exist or exists and coincides with a point of K_ν.

We also define on the circle $|z| = 1$ a nested sequence of subarcs

$$\delta_1 \succ \delta_2 \succ \delta_3 \succ \cdots \tag{422.3}$$

that have a common interior point ζ_0 and whose lengths converge to zero.

For every ν, we form the sequence of intersections

$$A_\nu\,\delta_1,\ A_\nu\,\delta_2,\ A_\nu\,\delta_3, \ldots \qquad (\nu = 1, 2, \ldots) \tag{422.4}$$

and we denote by

$$n_j \qquad (j = 1, 2, \ldots) \tag{422.5}$$

those natural numbers (if any) for which at least one of the sets

$$A_{n_j}\,\delta_p\ (p = 1, 2, \ldots)$$

is of linear measure zero.

---

[1] *Cf.* C. Carathéodory, *Reelle Funktionen*, Vol. I (Chelsea Publishing Co., New York 1946), § 85, p. 71.

423. Having defined the n_j in this way, we consider the open set

$$U = K_{n_1} \dotplus K_{n_2} \dotplus K_{n_3} \dotplus \cdots \tag{423.1}$$

and its closed complement H.

The set U may be the empty set, in which case H coincides with the whole Riemann sphere. For example, for the function Ω introduced in § 404, the limit (422.2) exists according to § 420 only if it equals one of the three numbers 0, 1 and ∞, and this happens only if ζ coincides with one of the denumerably many cusps of the modular configuration that lie on the unit circle. Therefore in this case, the linear measure of $A_\nu \delta_p$ is positive for every ν and every p, so that the point set U is empty.

The point set H, on the other hand, cannot ever be empty. For if it were, there would exist a finite number of K_{n_j} whose union would cover the Riemann sphere, so that there would have to exist an arc δ_p in which the points ζ for which the limit (422.2) fails to exist, or exists and equals any number at all, would constitute a set of linear measure zero; but this is absurd.

Now we shall prove that every point ω of H must be a boundary value of $f(z)$ at the point ζ_0. To this end, consider a disc K_j of our covering sequence (422.1) that contains ω and is itself contained in a preassigned neighborhood of ω. Suppose that ω were not a boundary value of $f(z)$ at ζ_0. Then there would exist a neighborhood of ζ_0 in which

$$\frac{1}{f(z) - \omega}$$

would be bounded, and an arc δ_{p_0} on which the conclusion of Fatou's theorem holds true. On the other hand, the number ν is by assumption not a member of the sequence (422.5). Hence every arc δ_p for which $p \geqq p_0$ must contain at least one point ζ_p for which the limit

$$\lim_{r=1} f(r\, \zeta_p)$$

exists and is contained in K_ν. Therefore there exist boundary values of $f(z)$ at ζ_0 whose distance from ω is as small as we please. The set of boundary values of $f(z)$ at ζ_0 being a closed set, it would follow that the point ω is itself a boundary value at ζ_0 after all. Thus we have proved the above statement.

424. The complement U of H can always be represented as the union of at most denumerably many mutually disjoint regions G_i. If the number a is not a boundary value of $f(z)$ at ζ_0, then the point of the Riemann sphere that corresponds to a must lie in one of the regions G_i, say in G_1.

Let κ_0 be a closed disc lying in G_1 and having α as one of its boundary points. Since α is not a boundary value of $f(z)$ at ζ_0, the function

$$g(z) = \frac{1}{f(z) - \alpha}$$

is bounded in a certain neighborhood of ζ_0; therefore Fatou's theorem is applicable in this neighborhood.

By assumption, every point of κ_0 lies in one of the open discs K_{nj} of § 422, and by the Borel Covering Theorem, a finite number of these open discs suffice to cover κ_0. To each of these there corresponds, also by § 422, an arc δ_{nj} on which the radial limits exist, except on a set of measure zero, and are equal to values that do not belong to K_{nj}. On the intersection $\delta(\kappa_0)$ of all of these δ_{nj}, the radial limits likewise exist, except on a set of measure zero, and fall outside κ_0. We can therefore apply the theorem of § 421 to $g(z)$. The transformation

$$v = \frac{1}{w - \alpha}$$

maps the disc κ_0 onto a half-plane. The radial limits of $g(z)$, corresponding to those mentioned in the theorem of § 421, all lie in the complementary half-plane, as does also the convex hull of the set of these limits. From this we conclude that none of the boundary values of $f(z)$ at ζ_0 lies in the interior of κ_0. This result can be supplemented as follows.

If β is an arbitrary point of the region G_1, we can always find a chain of closed discs

$$\kappa_0, \kappa_1, \ldots, \kappa_m$$

all of which lie in G_1 and which are such that any two consecutive discs overlap while the points α and β lie on the boundary of the first disc κ_0 and in the last disc κ_m, respectively. This construction shows that none of the points of the region G_1 can be a boundary value of the function $f(z)$ at the point ζ_0.

We have thus proved the following theorem: *Let the analytic function $f(z)$ be meromorphic in the disc $|z| < 1$, and let ζ_0 be any point of the periphery $|z| = 1$. Then we can represent the Riemann sphere, by means of the construction of §§ 422 ff. above, as the union of mutually disjoint sets*

$$H + G_1 + G_2 + \ldots,$$

where H is closed and non-empty while the G_i (which may be absent entirely) are regions. For each of the regions G_i, either every point of G_i is a boundary value of $f(z)$ at ζ_0 or else none of the points of G_i has this property. Thus the set of boundary values of $f(z)$ at ζ_0 consists of the closed set H plus certain of the regions G_i, including in any case all those of the G_i which are multiply-connected.

The last statement, concerning the multiply-connected regions G_i, is a direct consequence of the fact that the set W of boundary values is always a continuum and that the complementary set of a continuum is always a union of disjoint simply-connected regions.

We note that the above theorem bears a certain resemblance to the theorem on isolated essential singularities of § 165, Vol. I, p. 163, if the latter is stated in the following form: *If a function $f(z)$ is single-valued and analytic at all points, other than z_0 itself, of a certain neighborhood of z_0, then the set of boundary values of $f(z)$ at z_0 either consists of a single point or else covers the entire Riemann sphere.*

This corresponds precisely to the case that the point set H consists of a single point.

An Application to the Reflection Principle (§ 425)

425. The result of the preceding section enables us to complement the theorem of § 348. Let $f(z)$ be meromorphic in the disc $|z| < 1$. Assume that to every point ζ of an arc AB of the periphery $|z| = 1$, with the exception of a fixed set e_0 of linear measure zero, we can assign at least one sequence of points z_ν of the disc that converges to ζ and whose points lie between two chords of the unit circle that meet at ζ, and which is such that $\lim f(z_\nu)$ exists and is real or infinite.

Now if ζ_0 is any point of the arc AB, the following two cases, and no others, are possible. Either the set W of boundary values of $f(z)$ at ζ_0 covers the whole Riemann sphere, or Fatou's theorem holds, by § 311, in a neighborhood of ζ_0. In the latter case, the radial limits must exist everywhere (except on a set of measure zero) and must be real or infinite. This implies that the point set H of § 423 must in the present case be a subset of the real axis. If H is not the entire real axis, the complementary set U of H is a single region none of whose points are boundary values of $f(z)$ at ζ_0. Then by § 348, the function $f(z)$ must either be regular at ζ_0 or have a pole at this point. But if H coincides with the entire real axis, then there are exactly two regions, G_1 and G_2, in the complement of H. Hence the theorem of the preceding section applied to the function $f(z)$ of the present section yields the following result:

For the function $f(z)$ introduced in the first paragraph of this section, the following three possibilities—and no others—exist at every point ζ_0 of the circular arc AB:

1. *The set W of boundary values of $f(z)$ at ζ_0 covers the entire extended complex plane. In this case, we call ζ_0 an essential singularity of the first kind.*

2. *The set W covers one of the two half-planes bounded by the real axis, including the real axis itself, and contains no interior point of the other half-plane. In this case, we call ζ_0 an essential singularity of the second kind.*

3. *One of the two functions $f(z)$ and $1/f(z)$ is regular at the point ζ_0, and the Schwarz Reflection Principle can be applied in a neighborhood of ζ_0.*

Examples (§ 426)

426. We shall now consider some actual examples to illustrate the various possibilities allowed by the last theorem. It may happen that each and every point of the arc AB is an essential singularity of the first kind. This is the case, for instance, if we choose for $f(z)$ the modular function $\Omega(z)$ of § 404. We have seen in § 420 that for this function, the radial limits exist only on a denumerable number of radii; on any radius not belonging to that denumerable set we can find sequences of points that converge to the periphery of the unit disc and on which $\Omega(z)$ assumes real values. Thus the conditions imposed on $f(z)$ in § 425 are satisfied here. Moreover, on each of the radii other than those of the denumerable set, there are sequences of points that yield boundary values of $\Omega(z)$ having a positive imaginary part, as well as sequences that yield boundary values having a negative imaginary part. Therefore, every point ζ_0 of $|z| = 1$ is an essential singularity of the first kind.

It is almost as easy to find examples of functions for which all points ζ_0 of a boundary arc AB are essential singularities of the second kind. To this end, let us consider a Schwarz circular-arc triangle lying in the upper half-plane of the w-plane and having the angles $\pi/2$, $\pi/4$, $\pi/6$, say. We map this triangle conformally onto a modular triangle of the z-plane whose three cusps lie on the circle $|z| = 1$ and which lies otherwise in the interior of this circle. The analytic continuation $\mu(z)$ of the mapping function represents the conformal mapping of the disc $|z| < 1$ onto a simply-connected regular (canonically branched) Riemann surface over the w-plane (*cf.* § 404), a surface that has logarithmic branch points at all of the points corresponding to the vertices of the original triangle as well as to the vertices of all the additional triangles obtainable by successive reflections in sides of triangles.

The circle $|z| = 1$ constitutes a natural boundary for the function $\mu(z)$. All the values assumed by $\mu(z)$ have a positive imaginary part. Every point of the unit circle is an essential singularity of the second kind, a fact that can also be proved directly without difficulty.

To show that $\mu(z)$ satisfies the conditions of § 425, we note that almost all radii of the disc $|z| < 1$ are mapped by the function $w = \mu(z)$ onto curves of the w-plane that converge to some well-determined end point. Such an end point must coincide either with the point $w = 0$ or with a point of the real axis or with a point that corresponds to a vertex of the net of triangles. The last, however, is possible only if the corresponding radius of the disc $|z| < 1$ passes through no more than a finite number of triangles of the net. There are no more than denumerably many radii having this property, which shows that $\mu(z)$ satisfies the requirements of § 425.

The functions that serve as illustrations for the theorem of § 425 may also have isolated essential singularities. Thus, for example, the function

$$w = e^{i\frac{1+z}{1-z}}$$

has an essential singularity of the first kind at the point $z = 1$, and the function

$$w = i\,\frac{1+u}{1-u}, \quad u = e^{\frac{1+z}{1-z}}$$

has at the same point an essential singularity of the second kind. At all other points of the circle $|z| = 1$, the first of these functions is regular while the second has poles at points of the circle for which $z = 1$ is a point of accumulation.

It may also happen that all the points of the circle but one are essential singularities of the second kind, while the exceptional (isolated) point is an essential singularity of the first kind. To construct an example for this, we norm the above function $\mu(z)$ in such a way that it converges to a finite real value as z approaches the point $z = 1$ within a sector. Then the function

$$w = e^{i\frac{1+z}{1-z}} + \mu(z)$$

has at $z = 1$ boundary values with positive imaginary parts as well as boundary values with negative imaginary parts; thus the point $z = 1$ is an essential singularity of the first kind. At all other points of the unit circle there are boundary values with positive imaginary part but none with negative imaginary part; these points are therefore essential singularities of the second kind.

An Application to Measurable Real Functions (§§ 427-428)

427. We consider once more a mapping function $\mu(z)$ like the one of § 426, except that we assume it to give a mapping this time of a modular triangle of the Poincaré half-plane $z = x + iy$, $y > 0$ onto a Schwarz triangle of the w-plane. Then by Fatou's theorem, the limit

$$\lim_{y=0} \mu(x + i\,y) = \varphi(x) \qquad (427.\,1)$$

exists for all points x of the x-axis except for those in a certain set e' of linear measure zero. Moreover, there exists on the x-axis a denumerable and everywhere-dense set e'' having the property that for $x \in e''$ we have $\Im\varphi(x) > 0$.

Now let $\delta_x : a < x < b$ and $\delta_u : \alpha < u < \beta$ be arbitrary intervals on the x-axis and the μ-axis respectively. We denote by $e(\alpha, \beta)$ the subset of δ_x on which $\alpha < \varphi(x) < \beta$ holds. We shall prove that the linear measure $m\,e(\alpha, \beta)$ is > 0, by showing that the assumption $m\,e(\alpha, \beta) = 0$ leads to a contradiction.

To prove this, let K_ν be a disc of a normal covering sequence of the w-plane (cf. § 422) that has a chord lying within the interval $\alpha < u < \beta$. We assign to this disc the point set A_ν introduced in § 422, which in the present case is a subset of the x-axis. The intersection of A_ν and δ_x is contained in the set $e' + e'' + e(\alpha, \beta)$, which is of measure zero by the assumption we wish to disprove. Hence if we apply the theorem of § 424 to any point ζ of δ_x, we find that the point set H (cf. §§ 423-424) is here a subset of the μ-axis that excludes at least a subinterval of δ_u. Furthermore, no point of the half-plane $\Im w < 0$ is a boundary value of $\mu(z)$ at the point ζ. Therefore by the theorem of §425, $\mu(z)$ is analytic at ζ and hence is real, except possibly for poles, at every point of δ_x. But this contradicts the fact that the function $\varphi(x)$ has a positive imaginary part at every point of the everywhere-dense set e'', and the above statement is proved.

428. We now denote by $f(x)$ the real function which is equal to zero on the set $e' + e''$ of measure zero and equal to $\varphi(x)$ at all other points of the x-axis. The function $f(x)$ is measurable, because on the complement of $e' + e''$ it is the limit function of a sequence of functions that are everywhere continuous. We have thus obtained the following result:

There exist measurable real functions $f(x)$ which are such that for any and every given interval $\alpha < \mu < \beta$, the set of points x at which $f(x)$ assumes values belonging to the given interval intersects every interval of the x-axis in a set of positive (non-zero) measure.

Remark. The above function should not be confused with a famous example of Lebesgue[1] that lies on an entirely different plane. In Lebesgue's case, the problem is to construct a function $\lambda(x)$ that *assumes every* value at least once in *every* interval. But this function $\lambda(x)$ is not required to be measurable; also, a solution $\lambda(x)$ would be considered acceptable in this problem even if the set of all points at which $\lambda(x) \neq 0$, say, should be of measure zero. Our above $f(x)$, on the other hand, must first of all be measurable, and we also require that the pre-image on the x-axis under $u = f(x)$ of any interval of the u-axis should not intersect any interval of the x-axis in a set of measure zero. Again, $f(x)$—as opposed to $\lambda(x)$—may omit all values belonging to some set that is everywhere dense on the u-axis; this set of omitted values may even be such that it intersects no interval of the u-axis in a set of measure zero.

---

[1] C. Carathéodory, *Vorlesungen über reelle Funktionen*, 2nd ed. (Chelsea Publishing Co., New York 1948), § 227, p. 228.

INDEX

INDEX